Tectonics and Seismic Sequence Stratigraphy

Geological Society Special Publications

Series Editor J. BROOKS

GEOLOGICAL SOCIETY SPECIAL PUBLICATION NO 71

Tectonics and Seismic Sequence Stratigraphy

EDITED BY

G. D. WILLIAMS
University of Keele

A. DOBB
Mobil North Sea Limited, Aberdeen

1993

Published by

The Geological Society

London

THE GEOLOGICAL SOCIETY

The Society was founded in 1807 as the Geological Society of London and is the oldest geological society in the world. It received its Royal Charter in 1825 for the purpose of 'investigating the mineral structure of the Earth'. The Society is Britain's national learned society for geology with a Fellowship of 6965 (1991). It has countrywide coverage and approximately 1000 members reside overseas. The Society is responsible for all aspects of the geological sciences including professional matters. The Society has its own publishing house which produces the Society's international journals, books and maps, and which acts as the European distributor for publications of the American Association of Petroleum Geologists.

Fellowship is open to those holding a recognized honours degree in geology or cognate subject and who have at least two years relevant postgraduate experience, or have not less than six years relevant experience in geology or a cognate subject. A Fellow who has not less than five years relevant postgraduate experience in the practice of geology may apply for validation and, subject to approval, may be able to use the designatory letters C. Geol (Chartered Geologist).

Further information about the Society is available from the Membership Manager, The Geological Society, Burlington House, Piccadilly, London W1V 0JU, UK.

Published by The Geological Society from:
The Geological Society Publishing House
Unit 7
Brassmill Enterprise Centre
Brassmill Lane
Bath
Avon BA1 3JN
UK
(*Orders*: Tel. 0225 445046
        Fax 0225 442836)

First published 1993

British Library Cataloguing in Publication Data

A catalogue record for this book is available from the British Library

ISBN 0-903317-87-7

Distributors

USA
  AAPG Bookstore
  PO Box 979
  Tulsa
  Oklahoma 74101-0979
  USA
(*Orders*: Tel: (918)584-2555
        Fax (918)584-0469)

Australia
  Australian Mineral Foundation
  63 Conyngham Street
  Glenside
  South Australia 5065
  Australia
(*Orders*: Tel: (08)379-0444
        Fax (08)379-4634)

India
  Affiliated East–West Press PVT Ltd
  G-1/16 Ansari Road
  New Delhi 110 002
  India
(*Orders*: Tel: (11)327-9113
        Fax (11)331-2830)

Japan
  Kanda Book Trading Co.
  Tanikawa Building
  3-2 Kanda Surugadai
  Chiyoda-Ku
  Tokyo 101
  Japan
(*Orders*: Tel: (03) 3255-3497
        Fax (03) 3255-3495)

Typeset by Bath Typesetting Ltd., Bath, Avon

Printed and bound by
The Cromwell Press Limited,
Broughton Gifford, Melksham, Wiltshire

Contents

From WILLIAMS, G. D. & DOBB, A. (eds), 1993, *Tectonics and Seismic Sequence Stratigraphy*.
Geological Society Special Publication No. 71, 1–13.

Tectonics and seismic sequence stratigraphy: an introduction

G. D. Williams

Geology Department, University of Keele, Keele, Staffordshire ST5 5BG, UK

Abstract: The application of sequence stratigraphic models to seismic data is restricted by the vertical and spatial resolution of the data. The fundamental stratigraphic unit of the sequence stratigraphic technique is the seismically distinguished 'sequence' although the concept of tectonically related 'mega-sequences' is useful. Basin stratigraphy is controlled to varying degrees by eustatic sea-level change (or base level in lakes), subsidence/uplift (tectonics) and sediment supply. Three main basin types, rift-, wrench-, and thrust-related basins, have distinctive gross stratigraphic architectures. Localized, tectonically controlled subsidence and uplift has a significant control on three-dimensional stratigraphic patterns.

Stratigraphy is the partial record of basin evolution resulting from the interaction of a number of factors such as regional and local subsidence/uplift, sediment supply, eustacy and climatic change (Fig. 1). Basins that have a marine connection will show significant stratigraphic variations, especially in coastal deposits, that result from eustatic sea-level fluctuations. Other key factors will include the availability of sediment and the role of tectonically induced subsidence and uplift. Alternatively, land-locked or intermontane basins whose fluvial systems drain ultimately into a lake will preserve a stratigraphy dominated by local relative uplift and subsidence (local tectonics), by climatic controls and the rate of sediment supply. Tectonic activity is an important factor in controlling stratigraphy in the majority of sedimentary basins. Tectonism generates accommodation space in basins, it alters base levels and it controls source areas. When mountain ranges are generated, tectonics may even influence local climatic patterns. It is difficult to separate the relative importance of tectonics versus other factors in controlling stratigraphic architecture in basins. In this introduction, basins formed on continental lithosphere and their associated stratigraphies will be considered.

Seismic resolution

Increasing resolution of seismic sections invites direct comparison with stratigraphic cross-sections. The geophysical limitations of seismic data should be appreciated before interpretation is attempted. Seismic sections represent the response of the Earth to seismic waves, and because most reflections are interference composites there is no direct correspondence between seismic events and interfaces in the Earth (Sheriff 1977). The stratigraphic significance of seismic data is apparent only when tied to well data.

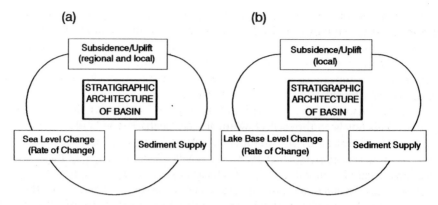

Fig. 1. Controls on the stratigraphic architecture of (**a**) basins with a marine connection; and (**b**) intermontane lacustrine basins.

Seismic resolution is the factor which limits the amount of stratigraphic and structural data that can be obtained from seismic sections. Resolution is the ability to tell that more than one feature is contributing to an observed effect (Sheriff 1985). The vertical resolvable limit in seismic data is equivalent to one-quarter of the dominant wavelength. A reflector with a velocity V and a wavelet with a dominant frequency f has a quarter wavelength of $V/4f$. For example, a poorly consolidated sand–shale section at *c.* 1500 m depth would have a vertical resolvable limit of *c.* 7.6 m. Deep reflectors are characterized by higher velocities and lower frequency and might show a quarter wavelength thickness of *c.* 76 m (Sheriff 1985). Many important stratigraphic observations must be made at sequences that are thinner than these values. Expanded stratigraphic packages in local depocentres may become condensed on to highs. Individual seismic reflectors in the expanded sequence may die out or interfere with other reflectors in the condensed sequence as the reflector separation reduces to less than the resolvable limit. Therefore, the resolvable limit is vitally important for stratigraphic interpretation.

Spatial or horizontal resolution on unmigrated sections is described in terms of the Fresnel zone. The first Fresnel zone is the area of a reflector from which the reflected energy reaches the detector within a half cycle so that interference is constructive. The dimension of the Fresnel zone depends on the seismic frequency, with higher frequencies generating smaller Fresnel zones for a given reflector. Spatial resolving power deteriorates with depth. A deep reflector must have larger areal extent than a shallower reflector to produce the same effect on a seismic section (Sheriff 1977).

With migrated seismic data, Fresnel zone size is not an important consideration. Migration works properly only on primary reflection and diffraction energy and it smears out noise to give migration 'smiles'. Migration of noise is one of the factors that limits spatial resolution on migrated sections.

Sequence stratigraphic concepts

Sloss (1950) first defined a 'sequence' as an unconformity-bounded stratal unit. This led to the recognition of six 'sequences' on the North American craton ranging in age from late Precambrian to Holocene (Sloss 1963). Mitchum *et al.* (1977) provided the present definition of a sequence as 'a stratigraphic unit composed of a relatively conformable succession of genetically related strata and bounded at its top and base by unconformities and their correlative conformities'. The 'sequence' of Mitchum *et al.* (1977) incorporates a much smaller time range than that of Sloss (1963) and, therefore, the six sequences of the North American craton could be multiply subdivided. Sloss' sequences were renamed 'super-sequences'. Vail *et al.* (1977*a,b*) proposed that eustacy is the predominant driving mechanism for the generation of sequences. This has been the subject of much recent debate (e.g. Galloway 1989) and the concept is addressed by the majority of authors in this volume.

Seismic sequence analysis introduced by AAPG Memoir 26 (Payton 1977) was further advanced via seminal articles by Jervey (1988) and Posamentier *et al.* (1988). A key element in such analysis is the recognition of seismically distinguished sequences bounded by chronostratigraphically significant surfaces of erosion, non-deposition or their correlative surfaces. A sequence boundary is a single widespread surface that separates all of the rocks above from all of the rocks below the boundary and it forms independently of sediment supply. A sequence boundary is commonly marked by significant erosional truncation beneath and onlap above. A major research effort by the Exxon Group during the 1970s and 1980s led to the publication of the Exxon Cycle Charts (Fig. 2), (Vail *et al.* 1977*b*; Haq *et al.* 1987, 1988) which record global sea-level fluctuations through Phanerozoic time.

The role of tectonics versus eustacy in the formation of sequence boundaries has been widely debated (e.g. Bally 1982; Thorne & Watts 1984; Cloetingh 1986; Hubbard 1988; Sloss 1988). Hubbard (1988) described 'megasequence boundaries' in the Santos, Grand Banks and Beaufort basins that related to folding and faulting of underlying strata at the various stages of basin evolution. Hubbard described stages of rift onset, syn-rift faulting and rift termination with reference to basin megasequences. Megasequence boundaries were shown to have an average cyclic frequency of *c.* 50 Ma in contrast to sequence boundaries which have a frequency range of 10–15 Ma.

Cloetingh (1986) proposed that temporal stress variations in the lithosphere of a few hundred bars can explain stratigraphic changes at passive margins and intra-cratonic basins. A stress change of 1 kbar would produce an apparent sea-level change of > 50 m and such stress changes could occur episodically over a few million years. Therefore, rapid sea-level changes on the Exxon Cycle Charts could represent plate tectonic reorganization of lithospheric stress fields (Bally 1982).

Factors controlling basin stratigraphy

Sea-level change

Evidence for the relative change in sea-level relies on the fact that regional cycles determined on different continental margins are synchronous and the magnitude of relative sea-level change is similar (Vail *et al.* 1977*a,b*). The global cycle charts of Vail *et al.* (1977*b*) show cycles of three orders of magnitude. Two first-order cycles in the Phanerozoic are present: the older from Precambrian to early Trias (300 Ma duration); and the younger from mid-Trias to the present (225 Ma duration). There are fourteen second-order cycles from 10–80 Ma duration and over eighty third-order cycles with durations of 1–10 Ma (Fig. 2). Van Wagoner *et al.* (1990) have

4

G. D. WILLIAMS

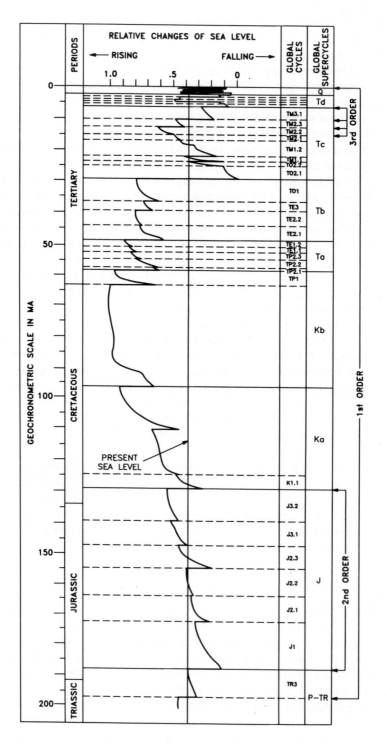

Fig. 2. Jurassic–Tertiary global cycle chart indicating three orders of cyclicity (after Vail *et al.* 1977*b*).

proposed that high-frequency sequences in siliciclastic deposits are formed in response to sea-level cycles of 100 000 to 150 000 years. Therefore, there may be fourth- and fifth-order cyclicity superposed on the third-order cycles proposed by Vail *et al.* (1977*b*) and Haq *et al.* (1988).

A eustatic sea-level change may result from a change in the volume of sea water such as during periods of glaciation and deglaciation, or from a change in the shape of ocean basins as a result of plate tectonic processes, or by a combination of both mechanisms. Plate tectonic mechanisms are of sufficient duration and magnitude to account for first- and second-order cycles. Glaciation and deglaciation may result in third-order cycles and some second-order cycles (Vail *et al.* 1977*b*). Climatic changes recorded from isotopic changes and faunal evidence correlate with sea-level high stands—climatically warm conditions, and low stands—climatically cool conditions.

A departure from the Vail *et al* (1977*b*) stratigraphic model has been presented by Pitman (1978) and Posamentier *et al.* (1988). Here, the rate of sea-level change is critical in determining the stratigraphic architecture of a basin, especially when coupled to the rate of regional subsidence. In this model, eustatic sea-level rise will be amplified by subsidence and sea-level fall will be damped by subsidence (Allen & Allen 1990). The rate of basin subsidence, if assumed to be constant, may be added to the rate of change of sea-level to give the rate of relative sea-level change. This leads to a curve that models the rate of addition of new accommodation space in the basin that is available to be infilled with sediment. A further parameter, the sediment supply, must be introduced to model the complete stratigraphic response (for a full discussion, see Allen & Allen 1990, p. 182–4). In this way, constant regional rates of subsidence coupled with rates of changing sea-level interact to generate accommodation space that may be filled with sediment depending on the rate of sediment supply.

Subsidence/uplift

Subsidence or uplift of the Earth's continental surface on a regional scale is controlled by:

1. increasing or decreasing the crustal/lithospheric thickness;
2. loading or unloading the lithosphere, thus upsetting its isostatic balance;
3. perturbing the thermal structure of the lithosphere—this is a natural consequence of points 1 and 2 above.

Basins generated as a result of tectonic processes may be classified into three broad types: thrust-related, rift-related and wrench-related basins depending on the dominant mode of basin forming tectonism. Each basin type develops a characteristic form of structural geometry during its evolution and each may develop a typical stratigraphic architecture. Basin stratigraphy will result from the interaction of several factors including tectonics, eustacy and sediment supply and it must be considered in terms of three-dimensional assemblages of depositional systems and contemporaneous systems tracts (Allen & Allen 1990).

Thrust-related basins Thrust-related basins or foreland basins are generated by subsidence due to the flexural response of the lithosphere during thrust-sheet loading.

The propagation of thrust sheets on to a foreland is accompanied by an equivalent propagation of the associated foreland basin system. Early formed foreland basin deposits become incorporated into thrust sheets at the mountain front; sediment is cannibalized and is redeposited in a subsequent stage of foreland basin development. At the developing mountain front, offlap, erosion and progressive unconformities are common features. In contrast, at the foreland margin of the basin, progressive onlap of the flexural bulge is usually recorded (Fig. 3). Significant departures to these patterns have been reported by Ricci-Lucchi (1986) in the Po Basin of northern Italy which shows piggy-back basin development. Tankard (1986) described offlapping sequences related to hinterland migration of the flexural bulge of the Appalachian foreland basin due to visco-elastic relaxation of the lithosphere following initial thrust-sheet loading.

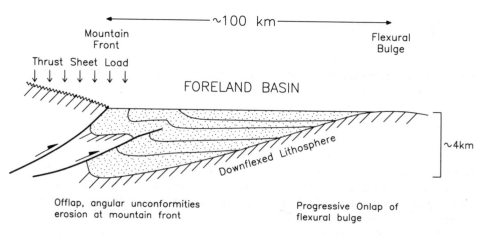

Fig. 3. Schematic diagram to indicate gross stratigraphic patterns and main structural controls in a thrust-related (foreland) basin.

Rift-related basins   Rift-related basins and passive margins exhibit a gross stratigraphy which, in its simplest form, may be subdivided into pre- syn- and post-rift megasequences (Hubbard 1988). These may be related to the model of McKenzie (1978) which involves extension within continental lithosphere that generates a rift system. If extension proceeds to rupture, then oceanic lithosphere is generated during oceanic spreading and a passive margin is formed. At the end of rifting, extensional faulting ceases and the passive margin or rift system begins to subside in response to cooling and thermal contraction of the lithosphere. This post-rift thermal phase is usually characterized by the basinward progradation of a clastic wedge and absence of tectonic deformation (Hubbard *et al.* 1985). Such a pattern of rifting, thermal subsidence and sediment loading yields a typical 'steer's head' geometry to rift-related basins (Fig. 4) (Dewey 1982).

Wrench-related basins   Basins associated with major wrench zones have a distinctive geometry and subsidence history. Such basins tend to be relatively small, are elongated parallel to the trend of major controlling faults and exhibit rapid rates of subsidence with substantial sedimentary accumulations. Structures associated with

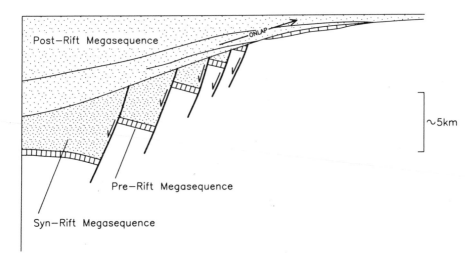

Fig. 4. Schematic diagram to indicate gross stratigraphic patterns and structural controls at a passive margin (after Dewey 1982).

individual wrench faults have been described by Wilcox *et al.* (1973) and Harding (1976). Crowell (1974), Rodgers (1980) and Woodcock & Fischer (1986) have discussed the effects of en échelon faults. Right-stepping dextral and left-stepping sinistral en échelon faults produce a zone of extension and subsidence termed a 'pull-apart basin' (Crowell 1974). Pull-apart basins are characterized by crustal thinning, high heat flow and potentially thick sedimentary accumulations that make the basins potential targets for hydrocarbon exploration.

Rodgers (1980) presented the results of a simple mathematical model for the development of pull-apart basins associated with overlapping en échelon wrench faults (Fig. 5). The model involves two major wrench faults that increase their length and overlap with time. Regions of dominantly normal faulting (basin depocentres) and wrench faulting are predicted. With increasing overlap of the master wrench faults, a single elongate depocentre controlled by extensional faulting develops into two separate depocentres with an intervening high characterized by wrench faulting. The progressive migration of depocentres and loci of dominantly extensional and dominantly wrench faulting generates a complex pattern of fault controlled stratigraphy.

Sediment supply

Eustatic sea-level rise coupled with subsidence generates accommodation space in basins. The rate of sediment supply will dictate to what degree the accommodation space will be filled. The thickness of sediment preserved in basins does not equate directly with basin subsidence nor with relative sea-level rise, as basins may remain underfilled for significant periods of time. This is the case if source areas are neither available nor active, and there may be a climatic control on sediment supply. Bertram & Milton (1989) have discussed the importance of palaeobathymetry in techniques of backstripping stratigraphic sequences from well data or seismic sections.

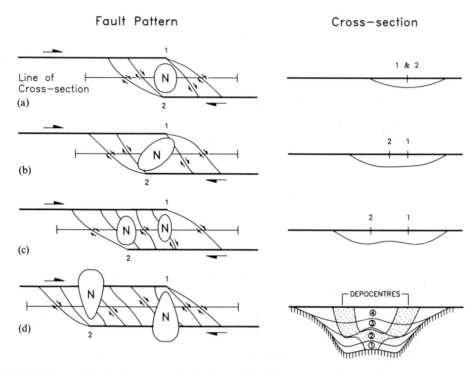

Fig. 5. Sequential development of a pull-apart basin related to progressively overlapping, dextral, right-stepping wrench faults (after Rodgers 1980). N indicates the areas of dominantly normal faults and basin depocentres. The cross-section in Fig. **5d** shows the result of stacking the four stages of basin fill.

An active source area is vitally important in generating a syn-rift megasequence in rift-related basins. Large extensional faults active in Jurassic times generated accommodation space in the Central, Viking and Witch Ground grabens of the North Sea (Sclater & Christie 1980; Barton & Wood 1984; Ziegler 1990). These deep marine graben and half-graben generated thin syn-rift megasequences and remained under-filled for a significant period of time. Starved and condensed sequences typify the so-called Apto-Albian hiatus (Bertram & Milton 1989). Barton & Wood (1984) contend that water was deep in the Central Graben at the end of the Cretaceous and that Palaeocene sediments infilled a considerable palaeobathymetry. Rapid Palaeocene sedimentation is due to the progradation of thick submarine clastics as a result of erosion of the Scottish mainland source which was uplifted at that time by igneous and tectonic processes (Bertram & Milton 1989). In the Central Graben of the North Sea, predicted palaeo-water depths increased rapidly during rifting to a maximum of *c.* 1 km then shallowed gradually to the present day. The thickness of post-rift units is controlled by depositional geometry, sediment supply and basin floor topography that results from extensional faulting.

Local tectonic control on stratigraphy

Stratigraphic sequences and megasequences may be controlled locally at scales of hundreds of metres to several kilometres by individual tectonic features. In such examples it is clear that eustacy has a minimal controlling effect on stratigraphy. The concept of localized tectonic control on stratigraphy is illustrated using an example of an extensional tilted fault block and an anticline generated during overthrusting at a mountain front.

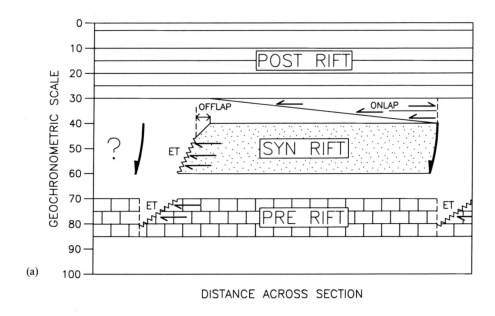

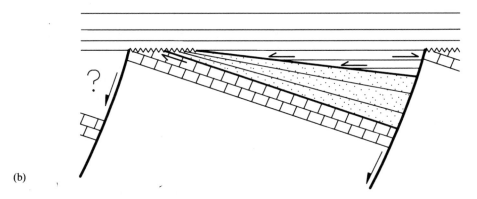

Fig. 6. (a) Chronostratigraphic chart and (b) schematic stratigraphic cross-section, showing localized tectonic control on stratigraphy in a tilted fault block setting. On the chronostratigraphic chart, ET indicates erosional truncation beneath the post-rift megasequence boundary, and onlap and offlap relationships are indicated. The large arrows indicate periods of extensional faulting coincident with the syn-rift megasequence.

Extensional tilt fault block

Tilt fault blocks are the controlling structural elements in the evolution of rift basins and passive margins. In the simplest form of tilt block development, three megasequences (Hubbard 1988) may be preserved; the pre-, syn- and post-rift mega-sequences (Fig. 6). The crests of tilted fault blocks are often exposed above sea-level and eroded during rifting. Erosional truncation of syn- and pre-rift sequences is a common feature in large-scale tilt block structures. With sufficient sediment supply during the period of rifting, a syn-rift megasequence may be preserved with an expanded thickness in the half-graben depocentre and condensation, perhaps beneath the scale of seismic resolution, on to the fault block crest. Offlapping relationships may be observed at the fault block crest although stratigraphical relationships at this position will be complex in detail. The availability of an active source area and the supply of sediment during rifting will dictate the thickness of the syn-rift megasequence.

Following rifting, if sediment supply has been too little to fill the half-graben to sea-level, accommodation space will remain in the depocentre. This will become infilled passively by the post-rift megasequence which will show onlap relationships above the top syn-rift megasequence boundary and will onlap the exposed fault surfaces. The post-rift megasequence will eventually bury the eroded fault block crests (Fig. 6).

Thrust anticline

Because of foreland-ward propagation of thrust mountain fronts, foreland basin sedimentary units are continuously modified by local tectonics. Continued uplifting of a mountain belt by thrusting ensures a constant supply of sediment from an active source area, especially in the late stages of basin evolution (Allen *et al.* 1986). Syn-thrusting sedimentary sequences within a foreland basin may be locally controlled by anticline growth above a thrust fault (e.g. Puigdefabregas *et al.* 1986). Progressive uplift and growth of an anticline will counteract flexural subsidence, and sequences will become condensed at the anticlinal crest. Progressive syn-thrusting unconformities with local erosional truncations may be generated by continued anticlinal growth (Fig. 7). During and following thrusting, a reduction in thrust-sheet and sediment load results from processes or erosion which lead to lithospheric readjustment in the form of uplift of the mountain belt and foreland basin. Post-thrusting erosion plays an important role at a late stage of foreland basin evolution.

Discussion

The increased resolution of modern seismic data has enabled the recognition of three orders of stratigraphic cyclicity that have been related solely to global sea-level change (Vail *et al.* 1977b). Fourth- and fifth-order sea-level cycles have been proposed by Van Wagoner *et al.* (1990) from studies of well and outcrop data. In the preceding discussion it has been suggested that other factors, especially tectonics and sediment supply, play an important part in the development of stratigraphic architecture in all basins. Global eustatic cycles were established initially using worldwide seismic data from passive margins (continental features which owe their existence to processes of rifting and thermal subsidence). It is becoming evident that many rift-related basins and passive margins preserve only a thin syn-rift megasequence due to the paucity of sediment supply during rifting. Therefore, global eustacy cannot be considered the dominant control on sequences observed at the scale of resolution of seismic data in rift-related basins. Similarly, in thrust- and wrench-related basins resulting from tectonically induced subsidence, stratigraphic architectures are heavily influenced by tectonic processes.

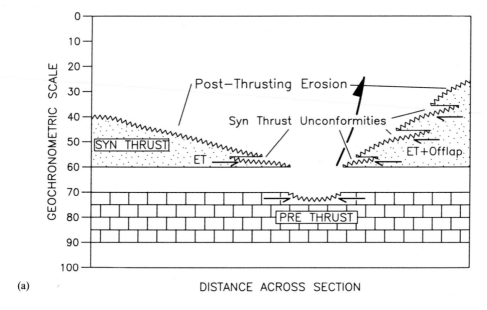

(a)

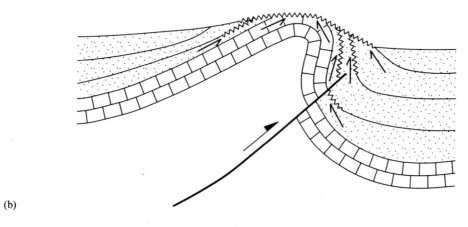

(b)

Fig. 7. (a) Chronostratigraphic chart and (b) schematic stratigraphic cross-section, showing localized tectonic control on stratigraphy in a thrust-related fold. On the chronostratigraphic chart, ET indicates erosional truncation at syn-tectonic unconformities. The large arrow indicates the period of thrust faulting coincident with the syn-thrust megasequence.

Local tectonic controls in rift-, wrench- and thrust-related basins are the dominant factors in controlling the three-dimensional geometry of syn-tectonic basin fill. Post-tectonic basin fill is controlled by basin floor topography (usually closely related to preserved local tectonic structures), the availability of sediment and sediment depositional geometries. The role of eustacy in the generation of stratigraphic architecture in basins is important but usually is not the dominant factor. It must be considered alongside other important factors such as tectonics, intra-plate stress changes and the availability of sediment. The relative importance of each of these interacting factors during basin filling is usually very difficult to determine.

I wish to thank Mr Terry Doyle for computer drafting all the figures in this contribution.

References

ALLEN, P. A. & ALLEN, J. R. 1990. *Basin Analysis*. Blackwell, Oxford.
——, HOMEWOOD, P. & WILLIAMS, G. D. 1986. Foreland Basins—an introduction. *In*: ALLEN, P. A. & HOMEWOOD, P. (eds) *Foreland Basins*. International Association of Sedimentologists Special Publication **8**, 3–12.
BALLY, A. W. 1982. Musings over sedimentary basin evolution. *Philosophical Transactions of the Royal Society of London*, **A305**, 325–338.
BARTON, P. & WOOD, R. 1984. Tectonic evolution of the North Sea Basin: crustal stretching and subsidence. *Geophysical Journal of the Royal Astronomical Society*, **79**, 987–1022.
BERTRAM, G. T. & MILTON, N. J. 1989. Reconstructing basin evolution from sedimentary thickness; the importance of palaeobathymetry control, with reference to the North Sea. *Basin Research*, **1**, 247–257.
CLOETINGH, S. 1986. Intraplate stresses: a new tectonic mechanism for fluctuations of sea level. *Geology*, **14**, 617–620.
CROWELL, J. C. 1974. Origin of late Cenozoic basins in southern California. *In*: DICKINSON, W. R. (ed.) *Tectonics and Sedimentation*. Society of Economic Paleontologists and Mineralogists, Special Publication, **22**, 190–204.
DEWEY, J. F. 1982. Plate tectonics and the evolution of the British Isles. *Journal of the Geological Society, London*, **139**, 371–414.
GALLOWAY, W. E. 1989. Genetic stratigraphic sequences in basin analysis 1—architecture and genesis of flooding surface bounded depositional units. *American Association of Petroleum Geologists Bulletin*, **73**, 125–142.
HAQ, B. U., HARDENBOL, J. & VAIL, P. R. 1987. Chronology of fluctuating sea levels since the Triassic. *Science*, **235**, 1156–1167.
——, —— & —— 1988. Mesozoic and Cenozoic chronostratigraphy and cycles of sea level change. *In*: WILGUS, C. K. (ed.) *Sea Level Change: An Integrated Approach*. Society of Economic Paleontologists and Mineralogists, Special Publication, **42**, 71–108.
HARDING, T. P. 1976. Predicting productive trends related to wrench faults. *World Oil*, **182**, 64–69.
HUBBARD, R. J. 1988. Age and significance of sequence boundaries on Jurassic and early Cretaceous rifted continental margins. *American Association of Petroleum Geologists Bulletin*, **72**, 49–72.
——, PAPE, J. & ROBERTS, D. G. 1985. Depositional sequence mapping as a technique to establish tectonic and stratigraphic framework and evaluate hydrocarbon potential on a passive continental margin. *In*: BERG, O. R. & WOOLVERTON, D. G. (eds) *Seismic Stratigraphy II*. American Association of Petroleum Geologists Memoir, **39**, 79–92.
JERVEY, M. T. 1988. Quantitative geological modelling of siliciclastic rock sequences and their seismic expression. *In*: WILGUS C. K. (ed.) *Sea Level Change: An Integrated Approach*. Society of Economic Paleontologists and Mineralogists, Special Publication, **42**, 47–69.
MCKENZIE, D. P. 1978. Some remarks on the development of sedimentary basins. *Earth and Planetary Science Letters*, **40**, 25–32.
MITCHUM, R. M. Jr, VAIL, P. E. & THOMPSON, S. III. 1977. The depositional sequence as a basic unit for stratigraphic analysis. *In*: PAYTON, C. E. (ed.) *Seismic Stratigraphy—Applications to Hydrocarbon Exploration*. American Association of Petroleum Geologists Memoir, **26**, 53–62.

PAYTON, C. E. 1977. *Seismic Stratigraphy—Applications to Hydrocarbon Exploration.* American Association of Petroleum Geologists Memoir, **26**.

PITMAN, W. C. 1978. Relationship between eustacy and stratigraphic sequences of passive margins. *Bulletin of the Geological Society of America,* **89**, 1389–1403.

POSAMENTIER, H. W., JERVEY, M. T. & VAIL, P. R. 1988. Eustatic controls on clastic deposition I—conceptual framework. *In*: PAYTON, C. E. (ed.) *Seismic Stratigraphy—Applications to Hydrocarbon Exploration.* American Association of Petroleum Geologists Memoir, **26**, 109–124.

PUIGDEFABREGAS, C., MUNOS, J. A. & MARZO, M. 1986. Thrust belt development in the eastern Pyrenees and related depositional sequences in the southern foreland basin. *In*: ALLEN, P.A. & HOMEWOOD, P. (eds) *Foreland Basins.* International Association of Sedimentologists, Special Publication, **8**, 247–258.

RICCI-LUCCHI, F. 1986. The Oligocene to Recent foreland basins of the Northern Apennines. *In*: ALLEN, P. A. & HOMEWOOD, P. (eds) *Foreland Basins.* International Association of Sedimentologists Special Publication, **8**, 105–140.

RODGERS, D. A. 1980. Analysis of pull-apart basin development produced by en échelon strike slip faults. *In*: BALLANCE, P. F. & READING, H. G. (eds) *Sedimentation in Oblique Slip Mobile Zones.* International Association of Sedimentologists Special Publication, **4**, 27–41.

SCLATER, J. G. & CHRISTIE, P. A. F. 1980. Continental stretching: an explanation of the post Mid Cretaceous subsidence in the central North Sea Basin. *Journal of Geophysical Research,* **85**, 3711–3739.

SHERIFF, R. E. 1977. Limits on resolution of seismic reflections and geological detail derivable from them. *In*: PAYTON, C. E. (ed.) *Seismic Stratigraphy–Applications to Hydrocarbon Exploration.* American Association of Petroleum Geologists Memoir, 26, 15–46.

—— 1985. Aspects of seismic resolution. *In*: BERG, O. R. & WOOLVERTON, D. G. (eds) *Seismic Stratigraphy II.* American Association of Petroleum Geologists, Memoir, **39**, 1–12.

SLOSS, L. L. 1950. Paleozoic stratigraphy in the Montana area. *American Association of Petroleum Geologists Bulletin,* **34**, 423–451.

—— 1963. Sequences in the cratonic interior of North America. *Bulletin of the Geological Society of America,* **74**, 93–114.

—— 1988. Forty years of sequence stratigraphy. *American Association of Petroleum Geologists Bulletin,* **100**, 1661–1665.

TANKARD, A. J. 1986. On the depositional response to thrusting and lithospheric flexure. *In*: ALLEN, P. A. & HOMEWOOD, P. (eds) *Foreland Basins.* International Association of Sedimentologists Special Publication **8**, 369–394.

THORNE, J. R. & WATTS, A. B. 1984. Seismic reflectors and unconformities at passive continental margins. *Nature,* **311**, 365–368.

VAIL P. E., MITCHUM, R. M. & THOMPSON, S. III 1977a. Relative changes of sea level from coastal onlap. *In*: PAYTON, C. E. (ed.) *Seismic Stratigraphy–Applications to Hydrocarbon Exploration.* American Association of Petroleum Geologists Memoir, **26**, 63–82.

——, —— & —— 1977b. Seismic stratigraphy and global changes of sea level Part 4: Global cycles of relative changes of sea level. *In*: PAYTON, C. E. (ed.) *Seismic Stratigraphy—Applications to Hydrocarbon Exploration.* American Association of Petroleum Geologists Memoir, **26**, 83–97.

WILCOX, R. E., HARDING, T. P. & SEELY, D. R. 1973. Basic wrench tectonics. *American Association of Petroleum Geologists Bulletin,* **57**, 74–96.

WOODCOCK, N. & FISCHER, M. W. 1986. Strike slip duplexes. *Journal of Structural Geology,* **8**, 725–736.

VAN WAGONER, J. C., MITCHUM, R. M., CAMPION, K. M. & RAHMANIAN, V. D. 1990. *Siliciclastic Sequence Stratigraphy in Well Logs, Cores and Outcrops.* American Association of Petroleum Geologists Methods in Exploration Series 7.

ZIEGLER, P. A. 1990. *Geological Atlas of Western and Central Europe,* 2nd edition. Shell Internationale Petroleum, Maatschappij.

From WILLIAMS, G. D. & DOBB, A. (eds), 1993, *Tectonics and Seismic Sequence Stratigraphy.*
Geological Society Special Publication No. 71, 15–34.

The lateral extent of sequence boundaries

J. A. Cartwright, R. C. Haddock
& L. M. Pinheiro

Department of Geology, Royal School of Mines, Imperial College of Science, Technology and Medicine, London SW7 2BP, UK

Abstract: Sequence boundaries, as defined by the Exxon group, are regionally extensive surfaces (basin-wide scales) that are characterized in part by stratal discontinuity surfaces in the form of onlap, downlap and toplap (Mitchum *et al.* 1977). The idea that sequence boundaries are so areally extensive is closely connected to the ideology favoured by the Exxon Group that sequence boundaries are·eustatic in origin. This concept of sequence boundaries was initially based on seismic stratigraphic observations of stratal reflection geometry, but has now been extended to rock stratigraphic relationships in general. One of the important issues in sequence stratigraphy is to decide whether concepts based on the low resolution seismic method are applicable at much higher orders of resolution, such as in outcrop. This paper examines the stratigraphic conditions necessary for the development of regionally extensive and discrete surfaces of onlap, downlap and toplap. The main conclusions are that in order for onlap, downlap and toplap surfaces to develop as discrete surfaces there must be no contemporaneous sediment accumulation beyond the lap-out position. If this condition is not met, then discrete lap-out surfaces do not develop. Instead, closely-related families of surfaces that individually are of limited areal extent are more likely to form.
  It is argued that in most depositional environments some form of sedimentation is likely to occur beyond the lap-out position. This suggests that sequence boundaries should only develop over extremely limited areas, and should not be expected to form regionally correlatable stratigraphic surfaces. The apparent regional extent of some sequence boundaries and their genetic linkage with eustatic changes is in conflict with predictions based on simple stratigraphic principles. The regional correlatability of sequence boundaries probably owes more to the limited resolution of seismic data and the map-driven need to correlate over large areas than to any physical continuity of a single surface.

Sequence boundaries are portrayed by the Exxon group as discrete surfaces that are correlatable over large areas and which represent, over at least part of that area, surfaces of stratal discontinuity (Mitchum *et al.* 1977; Posamentier & Vail 1988). Sequence boundaries are defined on seismic data by delineating and correlating surfaces at which stratal discontinuity in the form of toplap, onlap, downlap and erosional truncation is evident (Mitchum *et al.* 1977). The importance of these stratal relationships, both for defining the sequence boundary as a discrete surface and for determining its chronostratigraphic significance, is illustrated in Fig. 1. Many types of local disconformity surface apparent on seismic sections can, however, exhibit the diagnostic stratal relationships of onlap, downlap, toplap and erosional truncation, and can, at least locally, be confused for true sequence boundaries. In order to differentiate between local stratal discontinuities and true sequence boundaries, Mitchum *et al.* (1977) recommended that the stratal discontinuity surface should be correlated through the seismic grid in order to establish the regional extent of a surface. The lateral correlatability of a surface that exhibits some form of stratal discontinuity over all or part of its total surface area is, thus, a prerequisite for their designation as a sequence boundary. Large-scale (tens of kilometres) regional correlation of a clearly-resolved stratal discontinuity surface is the only conclusive means of separating true sequence boundaries from local discontinuities.

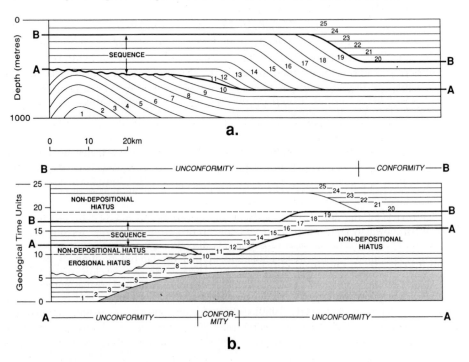

Fig. 1. Stratal relationships exhibited as sequence boundaries, and their chronostratigraphic significance, after Mitchum *et al.* (1977).

In recent publications developing the conceptual basis of sequence stratigraphy (Posamentier & Vail 1988; Posamentier *et al.* 1988; Van Wagoner *et al.* 1990), sequences are assumed to be deposited during one full cycle of eustatic sea-level change, and sequence boundaries (type 1 and type 2) are considered to form during specific times of accelerated fall in the absolute sea-level. Given this fundamental assumption, it is not surprising to find that sequence boundaries are viewed by these authors as being regional on the scale of basins. Mitchum *et al.* (1977) state that sequences may be 'bounded not only by interregional unconformities, but also by equivalent conformities, and are traceable over major areas of continents and basins.' If it is assumed that sequence boundaries are eustatic in origin, then there is a tacit expectation that they should be correlatable over large areas, i.e. on the scale of entire basins. The assumption that sequence boundaries have a eustatic origin, and hence a regional continuity, is thus a fundamental aspect of the conceptual framework and methodology of sequence stratigraphy as formulated by the Exxon group.

The geometrical properties and chronostratigraphic significance of sequence boundaries were formulated from seismic observations of stratal relationships. These observations were, however, subject to the limitations of the vertical resolution of the seismic data, a point that is consistently emphasized in Vail *et al.* (1977). In this respect, the conceptual framework was derived from a seismically-simplified representation of the true stratal relationships. As seismic stratigraphy has evolved into sequence stratigraphy, the sequence boundary has been transformed from a purely seismic concept into a more general stratigraphic concept, applied widely in field-based studies (Weimer 1984; Van Wagoner *et al.* 1990).

The move from the seismic domain to the outcrop domain is a translation from a medium which only allows a relatively crude imaging of detailed stratal relationships (Biddle *et al.* 1992) to one where that detail is readily observable, but with restrictions in continuity of exposure in three dimensions. This shift of domain has resulted in considerable refinements of the details of the sequence concept (Posamentier & Vail 1988), although the geometrical definition and regional extent of sequence boundaries has remained in much the same conceptual framework as that initially formulated a decade earlier.

The concept of basin-wide correlatability of sequence boundaries in a general stratigraphic context is thus rooted in the study of seismic data acquired in the 1970s. Seismic reflections are easier to correlate over considerable distances as apparently discrete surfaces if the frequency content is low. The low frequency, and consequently low vertical resolution, results in a 'smoothing' of subtle variations in the stratal configurations, and the interpreter is presented with an easier task of correlation than would be the case if the resolution was much greater. Modern reflection data have improved considerably over the last decade, and when recent sections with much higher resolution are compared with earlier low-resolution vintages, the different degrees of freedom in correlatability are often strikingly obvious (Fulthorpe & Carter, 1989). With this increased resolution, long-range seismic correlations of discrete stratal reflections or discrete interfaces such as unconformities, are in many cases more difficult to force through than they would have been on older vintages because the seismic data are now imaging a closer approximation to the true stratal complexity than under lower orders of vertical resolution.

The aim of this paper is to investigate whether the seismic–stratigraphic concept of regionally correlatable sequence boundaries is stratigraphically tenable when considered at the level of stratal resolution achievable at outcrop. The paper focuses on the stratigraphic conditions required for development of a laterally extensive discrete surface of onlap, downlap or toplap. The intention of the paper is to demonstrate that a surface of stratal discontinuity characterized by onlap, downlap or toplap can only be discrete and correlatable over an extremely limited area (scales much smaller than the dimensions of basins), except under specific and restricted conditions. The implication of this is that sequence boundaries defined from onlap, downlap or toplap should not be expected to be correlatable as discrete and valid stratigraphic surfaces over large distances.

The arguments presented in this paper are mostly concerned with absolute stratigraphic relationships in the sense that they are independent of scale or time. For this reason, some of the diagrams are deliberately presented without any spatial or temporal scales. Although considerations of spatial and chronostratigraphic resolution are extremely important in the application of seismic and sequence stratigraphy (Vail *et al.* 1977), the stratigraphic conditions necessary for the development of laterally extensive sequence boundaries are best discussed without any spatial or temporal limits. This avoids subjective assessments of whether a certain boundary is a correlatable surface when considered above some arbitrary level of seismic resolution. Our main objective is to stress the difference between a stratigraphic relationship that is apparently valid on seismic scales of resolution and a true stratigraphic relationship. Concepts that are formulated on the basis of seismic observations of stratal relationships do not necessarily hold when considered in an absolute stratigraphic sense.

Onlap onto discrete surfaces

In order for a discrete onlap surface to develop, there must be a slope for the onlap to develop onto, the slope must affect the depositional systems so that pinch-out occurs, and finally and most importantly, there must be no coeval deposition up-slope from the point of onlap.

Upper and lower threshold slope gradients for onlap

The basic requirement for onlap to occur is the presence of a depositional slope, i.e. a slope onto which onlapping units can successively pinch-out. In order to produce onlap onto a discrete surface, however, it can be argued that there will be some bounding limits to the gradient of the slope, outside which onlap will either not occur, or might be developed on more than one onlap surface.

Upper limit.   Some of the clearest seismic examples of onlap onto a discrete surface are where the onlap is onto steep slopes such as basement fault scarps or eroded edges of carbonate banks. The consolidated material from which the slope is built can sustain steep gradients without collapse, so that the slope remains intact throughout the duration of the onlap. Where slopes are inherently unstable, slope failure during the onlap will result in a disruption of the continuity of the onlap. Mass flow deposits derived from the slope will be interbedded with the onlap sequences, and the onlap surface will be continuously modified during the period of onlap (Fig. 2). It is unlikely that a single, sequence bounding onlap surface could develop in this situation. The upper limit for developing a discrete onlap surface is thus primarily a function of slope stability. An excellent example of the complex onlap relationships that result from intermittent slope failure during onlap can be seen on seismic data from the Cap Ferrat region of the Bay of Biscay (Ravenne *et al.* 1988).

Lower limit.   The concept of an upper slope threshold for onlap as a function of slope stability is straightforward. What is perhaps not so immediately apparent is the notion that there is a minimum angle below which onlap onto a discrete and laterally extensive surface is unlikely to occur. If the slope gradient is too gentle, then the angular relationships of onlap onto the discrete surface may be indecipherable from stratal relationships that are governed by lateral changes in depositional environment. The facies geometries would in many cases completely overprint the gross stratal relationship of onlap. This problem arises simply because bedding relationships developed locally will, in many cases, exhibit steeper angles than the gross angle of onlap (Fig. 3).

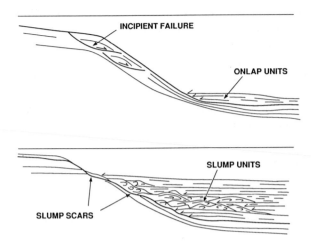

Fig. 2. Complex interrelationships between onlapping units and gravity flow deposits resulting from slope failure during the onlap of a slope. Note the shift in the position of onlap according to the concentration of gravity flow deposits.

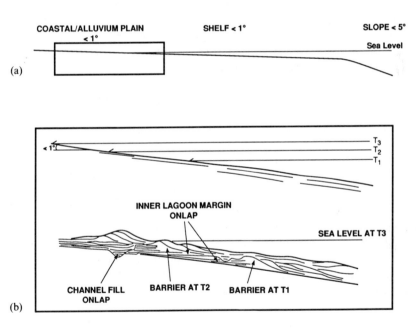

Fig. 3. Onlap onto slopes with gentle gradients. (**a**) Low angle onlap is to be expected on many basin margins. (**b**) Conjectural relationships developed on a barrier/lagoon system during a relative rise in a sea-level. Note that the regional onlap is indecipherable from the locally much steeper stratal relationships exhibited by the retreating barrier/lagoon.

Alluvial plain, coastal plain and shelf gradients of many continental margin settings are typically much less than one degree. If onlap onto a discrete and laterally extensive surface is to be recognizable in these settings, then the extremely low angular convergence subtended by the onlapping strata must be evident in the stratal organization at the scale of local facies transitions. This condition might be met, for example, in the juxtaposition of lagoonal muds against a former coastal-plain unit, but would this contact be laterally extensive on the scale of tens or hundreds of kilometres along the strike of a basin margin onlap succession? How would a one degree onlap be identified in alluvial plain facies, where the bedding relationships would be dominated by complex stratal interactions of channel migration, and overbank aggradation and progradation? Clearly, in many depositional environments, small angles of convergence are inseparable from facies-dependent angular stratal relationships. Such discrete onlap surfaces will be limited to the scale of those depositional or erosional features whose surfaces locally have slopes in excess of the ambient angle of onlap, such as channel or valley margins or lagoon margins or barrier foreslopes (Fig. 3).

The arguments above raise doubts over whether onlap onto a laterally extensive single surface could ever occur when the slope gradient is below this critical angle. We cannot specify a precise figure for this critical angle: it would be clearly dependent on a number of variables such as rate of onlap and depositional environment. It is argued, however, that coastal and alluvial onlap onto widely correlatable discrete surfaces is unlikely to occur on many basin margins because they have such low gradients (typically less than one degree). Even if, in a rare situation, low angle onlap onto a discrete surface was to occur, the limitations of vertical seismic resolution are such that this low angle onlap would be indistinguishable from apparent onlap due to progressive thinning beneath the resolution limit. Coastal and alluvial onlap is an important element in the sequence stratigraphic models of Posamentier et al. (1988). We do not question the occurrence of coastal and alluvial onlap, but the restrictions of the low gradient environments in which coastal and alluvial onlap often occur argue against any regional correlatability of onlap surfaces in these settings.

No contemporaneous up-slope deposition

Assuming that the conditions described above for slope gradient are met, what are the depositional requirements for developing onlap onto a laterally extensive discrete surface? The most obvious requirement is that the depositional system producing the onlapping sediments must be influenced by the presence of the slope in such a way as to produce a pinch-out at, or close to, the break of slope. Pinch-out is the sole geometrical requirement for onlap. Pinch-out can be depositional, as for example in the case of basin floor turbidites abutting against a topographic barrier, or it can be non-depositional, as in the case of pelagic ponding against a slope that is too steep to retain the pelagic drape. The net geometrical effect is the same in both cases: onlap at the position where the topographic feature alters the geometrical continuity of individual beds.

The critical condition for onlap onto a discrete surface is that there must be no contemporaneous deposition up-slope from the point of onlap during the development of the onlap fill. The implications of this condition are certainly more profound for marine environments where pelagic deposition has the potential to modify any incipient onlap surface, but it is emphasized that this condition applies irrespective of depositional environment or scale.

The condition of no contemporaneous up-slope deposition is illustrated by reference to a simple onlap relationship (Fig. 4). Figure 4(a) depicts the onlap of a depositional sequence containing three marker beds (T1, T2 and T3) onto a single, sloping boundary surface. The slope gradient lies at some notional value between upper and lower threshold values for the system. The basal surface is a discrete stratal discontinuity surface: it is a single surface that connects all the points of intersection of onlapping strata with underlying rock units. In order for the geometry depicted in Fig. 4(a) to be formed, the slope area not being onlapped must be totally devoid of any other form of sediment accumulation during the period that each increment of onlap is deposited against the slope (Fig. 4(b)). If any sediment accumulation does take place up-slope of the point of onlap, then the geometry produced during the burial of the slope is subtly different from the true onlap relationship depicted in Fig. 4(a). The two diagrams are superficially similar, but whereas the stratal surfaces of Fig. 4(a) terminate against the slope at a single surface (the onlap surface), the stratal surfaces of Fig. 4(c) continue from the onlapping sequences up into the contemporaneous sequences accumulating on the slope. As a result of the accumulation of a slope drape, therefore, no discrete onlap surface is produced. Pinch-out of the onlapping units would occur on stratal surfaces that would be progressively younger up the slope, reflecting the continued deposition of the slope drape units.

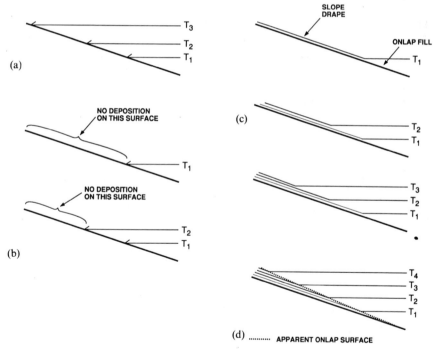

Fig. 4. Stratigraphic conditions necessary for the development of a discrete onlap surface. Onlap will develop onto a discrete surface (**a**) only if there is no up-slope sediment accumulation during the onlap (**b**). If sediment accumulation takes place beyond the limit of onlap, e.g. a slope drape, then onlap will occur on successively younger surfaces in an up-slope direction (**c**). This more complex form of onlap may be misinterpreted as a single onlap surface (dotted line) if the resolution is low (**d**). This apparent onlap surface is chronostratigraphically invalid, and violates the principle of superposition.

The stratal geometry depicted in Fig. 4(c) is grossly simplified; the relationships that would develop in reality would be more complex, and would depend on the relative rates and types of deposition in the onlapping units as compared to the slope drape units. The important point is simply that in order to develop a discrete onlap surface the slope has to be free of net sediment accumulation: the up-slope region may be either a site of non-deposition or erosion. However, if there is contemporaneous net accumulation up-slope, then the onlap will proceed up-slope onto successively younger onlap surfaces.

Onlap onto a discrete surface is commonly observable on seismic data. Onlap 'surfaces' are often picked and correlated as the starting point in a seismic–stratigraphic interpretation. Is seismic onlap invariably a genuinely discrete onlap of the type illustrated in Fig. 4(a)? Given the limitations of vertical seismic resolution, would we expect to be capable of distinguishing the different geometries shown in Figs 4(a) and 4(c)? If the thickness of the slope drape units is less than the vertical resolution, then the two contrasting geometries would appear almost identical on seismic data, i.e. they would both appear to onlap onto a single surface. Figure 4(d) shows an apparent onlap surface that might be constructed in the situation where the resolution was insufficient to show the more transitional nature of the stratal geometries. The single onlap surface would be picked by correlating the onlapping stratal terminations. The interpretation of this surface would seem perfectly reasonable in the absence of any evidence to the contrary, particularly if there is an expectation that onlap occurs normally onto discrete and correlatable surfaces. In this case, however, the interpreted onlap surface crosses time-lines, and so has no chronostratigraphic validity as a stratigraphic surface. The dotted line of Fig. 4(d) is not an unconformity, it is better considered a facies boundary. The inability to image the true stratal geometry thus leads to a chronostratigraphically invalid correlation. Age equivalent units would be divided and separated above and below the onlap surface.

The danger here is that if by virtue of having poor vertical resolution, we are unable to recognize the complex onlap onto multiple surfaces and instead simplify it to a single, more extensively correlatable surface, it is inevitable that the interpreted surface will cross time-lines. The severity of this violation of chronostratigraphy will depend on the resolution, sedimentation rates, slope gradient and the lateral extent of the correlation. In general, the longer the range of the correlation and the more condensed the slope drape, then the greater the error.

Seismic illustration of onlap onto multiple surfaces: Gulf of Taranto.

To illustrate the point made in the preceding section regarding the resolution limitations imposed upon the correct identification of multiple onlap surfaces, we have selected an example from a high resolution multichannel seismic reflection survey of the Gulf of Taranto, Italy, courtesy of Enterprise Oil plc, and Petrofina S.A. The example illustrates a near-parallel Neogene sequence of clastic turbidites onlapping a fairly steep slope. The slope was developed by erosion of a thrust complex involving Miocene and older sequences. The onlap took place in water depths in excess of 400 m.

To simulate the interpretational difficulties inherent with low resolution data, the section (Fig. 5) is reproduced at a much-reduced scale. The reduced scale emphasizes

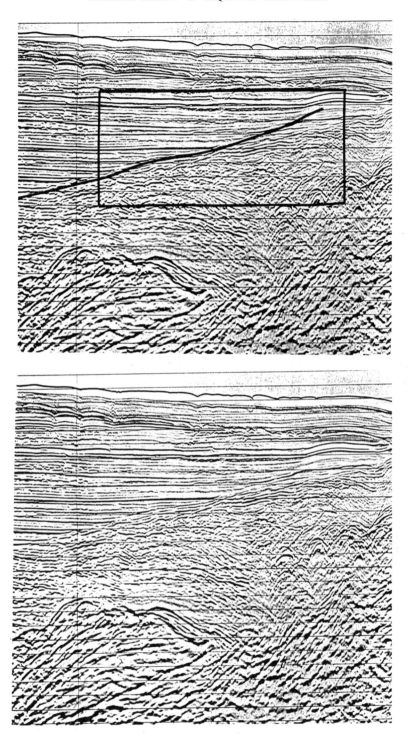

Fig. 5. Seismic section from the Gulf of Taranto, Italy. This small scale reproduction shows an apparently discrete onlap surface. Compare with the magnified (high resolution simulation) version in Fig. 6 (box indicates outline).

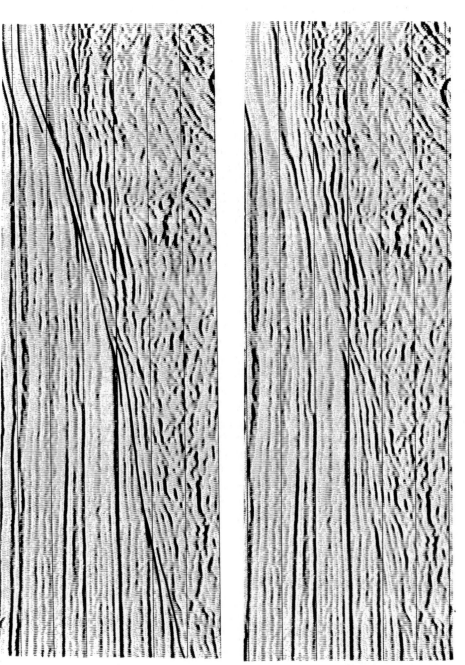

Fig. 6. Enlargement of box shown in Fig. 5. With the better resolution of this figure, the apparently single onlap surface of Fig. 5 can be seen to be composed of four or five separate onlap surfaces. Each individual surface can be traced from the slope into the onlapping fill. Data provided courtesy of

the onlap, and at this scale it appears to be a sharp surface marked by the abrupt pinch-out of the turbidites at the steep break of slope. The precise detail of the onlap geometry is not recognizable at this scale, so the obvious interpretation is to correlate a single onlap surface linking all the reflection terminations. The apparent geometry at this stage is identical to that shown in Fig. 4(a). The interpretational procedure for picking the onlap surface is largely governed by the interpreter looking for the typical angular relationships seen along the greater part of the contact. This geometrical pattern is then used as a correlation model that assists in making decisions where reflections split, or where the angular relationship is less obvious.

On the basis of this interpretation, it follows that all the onlapping turbidites would be regarded as being younger than the sequences that lie beneath the onlap surface at any position on the slope. Close inspection of an enlarged version of the same section (Fig. 6) shows that this is not the case. Reproduction of the section at a magnified scale is intended to simulate an improvement in the vertical resolution of the data. With this improved resolution, the details of the stratal geometries in the region of the slope are much easier to identify. From the higher resolution image it is possible to identify four or five separate surfaces of more localized onlap, corresponding to the interpretation on the smaller scale section of a single, more laterally extensive onlap surface. On Fig. 6, the turbidite units can be seen to onlap in relatively thin packages onto a small portion of the slope, but successively younger onlapping units terminate against surfaces that can themselves be traced out into the onlapping fill. The geometry of the onlap is thus a complex interaction of the onlapping units and the slope drape (Fig. 6). The result of this interplay is that instead of the onlap being onto a single, extensive surface, it is onto a suite of more areally limited surfaces that become younger as the slope is infilled. The geometry seen on Fig. 6 is very similar to the schematic illustration in Fig. 4(d).

Comparison of Figs 5 & 6 shows that the single onlap surface interpreted in Fig. 5 crosses depositional surfaces and time-lines. Without the benefit of the higher resolution image, therefore, our interpretation of the single onlap surface would have led to a correlation that was chronostratigraphically invalid, in that age-equivalent sequences would have been placed above and below the onlap surface. The simple conclusion derived from comparing Figs 5 & 6 is that because of the impossibility of accurately resolving absolute stratal relationships using seismic data, seismic correlations can often result in an over-simplification of stratal relationships to the point where the seismically apparent geometries are in conflict with the real chronostratigraphy. What appears as a discrete onlap surface on seismic, need not necessarily be so in reality. A distinction must, therefore, be drawn between an apparent seismic onlap and a true onlap.

In summary, it is concluded that:

(1) onlap surfaces that appear on seismic to be discrete and continuous over considerable distances may only be so because of poor resolution;
(2) the lateral extent of any discrete surface of onlap is limited to that portion of the slope on which there is no contemporaneous sediment accumulation
(3) seismically defined 'unconformities' based on onlap terminations will have no chronostratigraphic significance if deposition occurs up-slope from the point of onlap.

Laterally extensive onlap surfaces: do they exist?

Following on from the discussion of the conditions necessary for the development of discrete surfaces of onlap, we now consider if there are any geologically realistic situations where we can envisage progressive onlap over a large surface area such that in the time interval required to complete the onlap, no sedimentary accumulation takes place over any portion of the initial surface. This is the condition for the development of a discrete onlap surface (Fig. 4(a)).

Marine environments/marine onlap.   The condition of no contemporaneous up-slope sediment accumulation is extremely unlikely to pertain in any marine environment. Over all but the smallest of time increments, some form of sediment accumulation occurs over some parts of all marine shelves and slopes, and consequently intermittently transported onlap units must onlap successively younger surfaces. Possible exceptions might include (a) shelves where bedrock is exposed at the surface over large areas (e.g. English Channel) or where there are widespread hardground surfaces (e.g. Arabian Gulf), or (b) shelves or topographic features in deep water where current activity prevents any contemporaneous drape from accumulating.

Non-marine/coastal.   It might be envisaged that rapid flooding of an alluvial plain or coastal plain resulting from a relative rise of sea-level would be an ideal circumstance in which a regionally extensive discrete onlap surface could be formed. Indeed, this situation is the essence of the coastal onlap method for estimating the magnitude of relative rises of sea-level (Vail *et al.* 1977). Unless the flooding is truly instantaneous, however, and more importantly, the onlap accompanying the flooding is also instantaneous, discrete onlap surfaces are unlikely to be laterally extensive. Furthermore, if the alluvial plain/coastal plain does not have a gradient in excess of some minimum threshold value (see earlier discussion—'Upper and lower threshold gradients for onlap'), any onlap developed during the sedimentation accompanying the flooding is likely to be indecipherable from the overriding stratal relationships developed locally. Even if the gradient is sufficiently steep for onlap to be recognized, it is unlikely that in the finite time needed to develop a laterally extensive onlap that no sediment accumulation takes place beyond the position of onlap (see 'No contemporaneous up-slope deposition' discussed earlier).

   As an illustration of this point, consider the flooding of an old shelf that has earlier been subaerially exposed. The exposed shelf is part of the coastal plain, and sediment accumulation may occur in a variety of subaerial environments. Posamentier *et al.* (1988) consider that in this kind of situation the exposed shelf is a site of non-deposition or erosion (their lowstand systems tract), but what of overbank deposits, mangrove swamps, peats, dunes, lagoons and evaporite and biogenic deposits? Is it not unrealistic to suppose that the vast exposed shelf would be completely devoid of any sediment accumulation during the finite period required to inundate and bury the shelf under the incoming marine sediment? Irrespective of whether the drowning and sedimentary burial takes tens of years or ten thousand years to complete, it is virtually inconceivable that no subaerial sediment accumulation would be preserved. During the time taken for the encroachment of the onlap, successive marine units would then onlap onto partially preserved coastal plain aggradational sequences that were age-equivalents of downflank onlap units. If this was the case, then from Figure

4(c), the onlap surfaces would not be in the form of a single correlatable surface, but more realistically in the form of multiple and areally restricted onlap surfaces.

In conclusion, it is difficult to envisage how an areally extensive discrete onlap surface could form in any depositional setting. It is considered that onlap is more likely to develop in the form of a series of surfaces whose individual areal extent is limited by the degree of contemporaneous deposition up-slope from the region of onlap.

Downlap surfaces

Downlap surfaces are perhaps the easiest stratal discontinuity surfaces to recognize on seismic data, and as such they are often picked for regional correlation and mapping. They are not as important as onlap surfaces for defining sequence boundaries, but they can form part of a sequence boundary in some circumstances (Fig. 1). They are often easier to identify than onlap surfaces simply because the angular relationship of the slope clinoforms to the basin floor is often large enough so that resolution limitations are overcome. For low angle slope progradation into shallow bodies of water, however, it may be difficult or even impossible to recognize progradational configurations and a downlap surface (e.g. shelf deltas prograding with foreset gradients of 1:100). Much more easily recognizable are large-scale progradational systems building into deep water basins where the gradients are steeper. The average gradient of the continental slope on passive margins, for example, is of the order of 1:40 (Shepard 1973).

Conditions for laterally extensive discrete downlap surfaces

Figure 7 shows a series of prograding clinoforms advancing over a horizontal basin floor in such a way as to produce a discrete and correlatable downlap surface. In order for the downlap surface to be a discrete surface, at each stage in the advance of the prograding system there must be no sediment accumulation on the basin floor beyond the current point of downlap (Fig. 7(b)). If this condition is not satisfied and sediment aggradation on the basin floor accompanies the progradation, then each incremental clinoform advance will take place onto successively younger depositional surfaces (Fig. 7(c)). If the seismic resolution is not good enough to identify the true asymptotic relationship as depicted in Fig. 7(c), then the asymptotic relationship can easily be misinterpreted as a sharp downlap onto a discrete surface such as depicted in Fig. 7(a). This resolution problem is illustrated in Fig. 7(c) where the apparent discrete onlap surface is depicted as a dotted line. As was the case with the poorly resolved multiple onlap of Fig. 4(d), the inability of the seismic to portray accurately the true stratal relationships results in sequences in the condensed basin floor region being grouped stratigraphically beneath age-equivalent clinoform sequences.

The progradation of slopes is often represented in cartoon form in a manner similar to that depicted in Fig. 7(a). This graphical simplification is misleading in that it builds up an expectation derived from the model that the downlap is onto a discrete and laterally correlatable surface. Simple considerations of the depositional processes active at the toe of a slope suggest that the condition necessary for the development of a discrete downlap surface of the type illustrated in Fig.7(a) is only likely to occur in specific and restricted depositional settings.

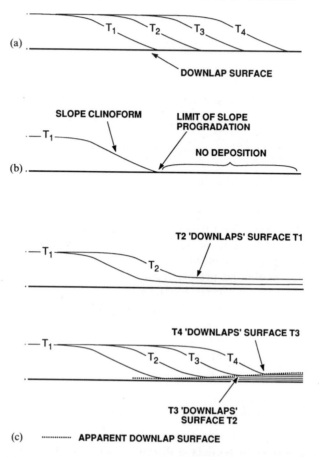

Fig. 7. Stratigraphic conditions necessary for developing a discrete downlap surface. **(a,b)** Discrete downlap can only occur if there is no sediment accumulation beyond the lap-out position during the progradation. **(c)** If sediment accumulates ahead of the prograding clinoforms, the resulting geometry is an asymptotic 'downlap', with clinoforms merging with successively younger stratal surfaces basinward. An apparent downlap surface might be observed under low resolution (dotted line), but this will cross the true stratal surfaces and time-lines.

The depositional components in the region of the toe of a prograding clinoform may comprise one or more of three types: a downslope component, a suspended component, and a pelagic component (Fig. 8). Volumetrically the most significant are sediments that could loosely be termed the downslope component. Included in this category are sediments deposited by all mass flow processes, traction currents and downslope creep, together with more catastrophic processes such as slumping and sliding. In Fig. 8(b) the notional thickness per time increment contributed by this component is shown as tapering downslope towards the toe, but in detail, the thickness relationships of individual sedimentary units comprising the total down-slope contribution will be more complex than those illustrated. The suspended load is divided into the background pelagic contribution, the volumetric distribution of which would most probably be unaffected by the depositional topography, and the suspended fines transported from the basin margin, the volumetric contribution of which would be slope dependent.

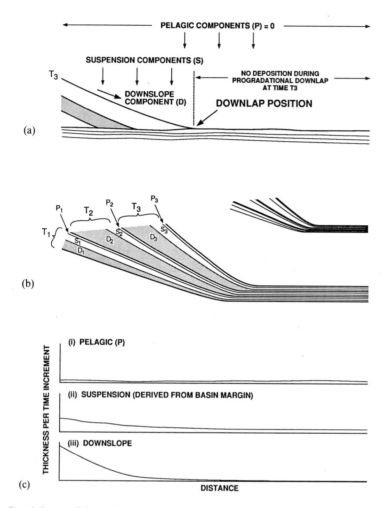

Fig. 8. Breakdown of depositional components at the foot of a prograding slope. In the toe region, the total sediment supply is composed of downslope, suspended and pelagic components. (**a**) For a discrete downlap surface to be produced, there must be no suspected or pelagic components beyond the break of slope. (**b**) The volumetric balance of these components is schematically represented as tapering asymptotically into the relatively condensed basin floor succession. This is considered to be the more realistic configuration. The inset shows the apparent downlap configuration of the asymptotic thinning under low resolution. (**c**) The three components of sediment supply.

From Fig. 8(a), it can be observed that in order to develop a discrete downlap surface, there must be no pelagic drape over the toe region during prograation, and there must be a sharp cut-off in the downslope and suspension components at the break of slope at the foot of the clinoform. If there is no abrupt pinch-out, successive clinoform units will downlap onto progressively younger surfaces (Fig. 8(b)). While it could be imagined that there may be situations where the downslope component would pinch-out fairly abruptly near the break of slope simply because the gravitational potential driving the sediment transport has ceased to apply, it is difficult to imagine a situation where the suspended load would also pinch-out abruptly at the break of slope. It is more probable that the suspended load would taper gradually basinward as indicated in Fig.8(b).

In what environmental settings would we expect to develop a discrete downlap surface? The simple answer is any progradational system where there is neither a background pelagic component nor a suspended component. Examples conforming to these conditions might include gravel deltas in glacial lakes, and carbonate ramps where slope clinoforms are composed of talus aprons. Mixed calibre siliciclastic systems should be expected to exhibit asymptotic geometries at the toe region as the rule rather than as the exception, and as such, discrete and areally extensive downlap surfaces should be extremely rare in these systems.

For the great majority of progradation systems, therefore, it is concluded that asymptotic geometries should be expected rather than an abrupt basal downlap. If there are downlap surfaces present within the asymptotic configuration at the foot of the slope, they are likely to be more local, rather than regional in extent.

In summary, it is concluded that discrete and areally extensive surfaces of downlap identified on seismic data are in most cases likely to be amalgamations of localized downlap surfaces or gradational facies boundaries, that are too closely spaced to be resolved individually. On a seismic section, we commonly observe discrete downlap surfaces that are apparently correlatable over large distances, but if we had the resolution to image bedding planes we would find that our seismic correlation crossed bedding planes and time-lines and that our downlap surface would, therefore, separate age-equivalent units. The progressive younging of successive local downlap surfaces developed during the progradation may not be visible on seismic, particularly if the rate of background pelagic deposition is much less than the rate of progradational deposition.

By correlating the closely spaced downlap surfaces as a single, sharply defined surface, it is likely that significant errors in the dating and regional correlation of surfaces will be incurred, particularly if correlated over any considerable distance. Seismic downlap is, more often than not, simply an apparent stratal geometry that arises from complex stratal thinning beneath the vertical seismic resolution (Biddle *et al.* 1992). Seismic downlap surfaces will, in many cases, not correspond to discrete geological surfaces and thus have no chronostratigraphic significance. The recognition of a seismic downlap should be used with extreme caution in constructing models to assist in log correlation. Discontinuity of bedding surfaces over short distances should be assumed unless there is overriding biostratigraphic or lithostratigraphic evidence to the contrary.

Toplap surfaces

Toplap is a geometrical relationship defined by Mitchum *et al.* (1977) as lap-out at the upper boundary of a depositional sequence (e.g. sequence boundary B of Fig. 1). The term is commonly used in a seismic–stratigraphic context, particularly in association with upper bounding surfaces to progradational systems, but the definition does not restrict the use of the term to seismic observations. Mitchum *et al.* (1977) make the important point that 'the lateral terminations updip may taper and approach the upper boundary asymptotically. On seismic sections, the resolution may be such that reflections appear to terminate against the upper surface at a high angle.' This comment stresses the ambiguity inherent in the geometrical relationships that are revealed by seismic data. It raises the question as to whether toplap is a geometrical relationship that actually occurs in prograding sequences, rather than a seismic simplification of more complex stratal relationships that do not strictly correspond to the geometrical definition of toplap.

The geometry of toplap illustrated in Fig. 1 can only be produced under the specific condition that during the progradation of clinoforms there is no sediment accumulation and preservation on the topset surface during the progradation (Fig. 9). Mitchum *et al.* (1977, p. 59) argue that this situation arises when the depositional base level is too low to permit the strata to extend updip. They envisage sedimentary bypassing and minor erosion above base level while sediment prograges below base level, and mention delta topsets and the tops of prograding submarine fans as typical environments in which toplap occurs.

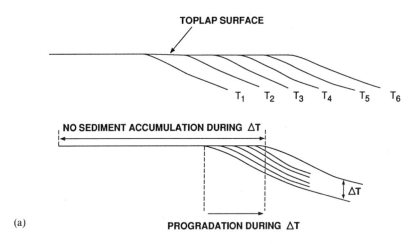

(a)

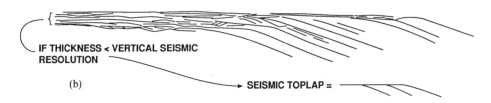

(b)

Fig. 9. Stratigraphic conditions necessary for development of a discrete toplap surface. (a) For a discrete toplap surface to develop, there must be no aggradation of the topset units during the progradation. (b) If aggradation occurs, but is not resolvable, an apparently discrete toplap geometry will be observed.

Do surfaces of discrete toplap exist over large areas of delta and submarine fan tops? The critical condition necessary for the development of an areally extensive toplap surface is sedimentary bypass over that area during the progradational advance. On a delta top, the only zones of sediment bypass are channels. The inter-fluves are sites of intermittent overbank deposition, swamp and lagoon development, where sediment aggradation would take place, albeit at extremely low rates, and where sediment preservation would be a function of near-surface compaction. The proportion of the total surface area of any given delta top which at any time is a locus of sediment bypass is likely to be subordinate to that over which some degree of sediment aggradation is taking place. The zones of sediment aggradation in the swamps, levees, lagoons and floodplains can be thought of as the equivalent to the condensed sequences of the basin floor at the foot of the advancing slope clinoforms. It is considered unlikely, that in the time taken for the delta to prograde over any significant distance, there would be no net sediment aggradation over some significant part of the delta topset surface, particularly in view of the rapidity of compaction in the near-surface sediments in deltaic systems. As such, it is suggested that it is unlikely that laterally extensive toplap surfaces could develop on delta tops. Deltaic toplap surfaces recognized on seismic data are more probably surfaces of marine planation, such as abandonment surfaces.

The upper surfaces of prograding submarine fans often display seismically defined toplap relationships, particularly in longitudinal sections along a prograding canyon fill system (Mitchum 1985). The sites of primary sediment bypass are restricted to channels. Sediment aggradation over the inter-channel regions of the fan may, however, be inhibited by secondary processes, i.e. current reworking, particularly if the fan is located on a slope which is swept by contour currents. Under these conditions large areas of the upper surface of the fan could be sites of net non-deposition. Any aggradational deposits such as pelagic drape, or channel overbank deposits, might be completely removed from the fan top, and an areally extensive toplap would be the result. True stratal toplap could develop, therefore, on fan tops but only where there is areally extensive and persistent reworking of the fan top. It is debatable whether current reworking would completely inhibit fan-top aggradation, particularly in a mixed calibre system with a high sediment supply, but this would depend on the relative reworking potential of the currents versus the sedimentation rates in the inter-channel areas.

In summary, while true stratal toplap cannot be ruled out as a possible stratigraphic feature of prograding systems, it seems unlikely that sediment bypass could be maintained over a large enough area of the upper surface of a prograding body for a long enough period to produce a regionally extensive toplap surface. Exceptions to this general statement no doubt exist, e.g. contour current reworked fan or storm-dominated carbonate platform, but these are viewed as being relatively rare cases where regional toplap surfaces could develop. Regionally correlatable seismic toplap is, therefore, considered in the same way as regionally correlatable seismic downlap, i.e. it is more often than not an apparent geometrical relationship resulting from limited vertical resolution. The true stratal complexity of the tops of prograding bodies is beyond the resolving power of the seismic (Fig. 9(b)), and condensed aggradational sequences are indistinguishable as multiple stratal surfaces.

It is concluded that stratal discontinuities defined by seismic toplap relations should not be expected to correlate as discrete surfaces for any considerable distance. Where toplap surfaces are correlated on seismic over large distances (kilometres), it is almost inevitable that the surface would cross bedding planes and time-lines and therefore have no absolute chronostratigraphic significance.

Conclusions

(1) In order to develop laterally extensive onlap, downlap or toplap surfaces, there must be no sediment accumulation contemporaneous with the onlapping, downlapping or toplapping units on the depositional surface beyond the point of lapout. Simple consideration of depositional processes suggests that this condition only applies in a very restricted range of environments.

(2) Onlap onto a discrete surface is only likely to develop where the slope gradient falls between an upper and lower threshold value. Coastal onlap is unlikely to occur on many basin margins, because of the typically gentle slope gradients of the depositional surface.

(3) Laterally extensive onlap, downlap, and toplap surfaces are probably extremely rare in the stratigraphic record. It is more common to find that a general onlap, downlap, or toplap of a sequence occurs on a number of closely related and spatially restricted discontinuity surfaces that overlap or merge in a zone of general stratal condensation. To a low resolution method, these multiple surfaces may be imaged as a single surface that is apparently correlatable over large distances.

(4) Areally extensive correlations of apparent discontinuity surfaces will in many cases cross time-lines and will thus be chronostratigraphically invalid. Unconformities defined solely from seismic relationships of onlap, downlap and toplap should not be assumed to be true unconformities, and may only rarely be so.

(5) A distinction should be drawn between seismically-apparent onlap, downlap and toplap, and true stratigraphic onlap, downlap, and toplap. Geometrical relationships of stratal discontinuity surfaces apparent on seismic do not translate directly into an absolute stratigraphic counterpart.

(6) A major assumption of the sequence stratigraphic models proposed by Vail *et al.* (1977) and Posamentier *et al.* (1988) is that sequence boundaries are regional in extent. This assumption is based on a further assumption that sequence boundaries form as a result of eustacy. From the arguments presented in this paper, it is concluded that sequence boundaries are unlikely to develop as regionally correlatable discrete surfaces. The apparent regional extent of some sequence boundaries probably owes more to the limited resolution of seismic data and to the map-driven need to correlate over large areas than to any absolute stratigraphic continuity of a single surface. Closely related families of surfaces may approximate to a single sequence boundary, but correlations based on grouping families of closely related surfaces into a regional framework should not be used as evidence in support of eustatic origins for sequence boundaries.

(7) Chronostratigraphic schemes that are based on regional correlation of sequence boundaries will in many cases violate the principle of superposition. Sequence stratigraphy is a method that relies on the regional correlation of surfaces that will, in the majority of cases, be uncorrelatable in an absolute sense, and that are intrinsically limited in lateral extent. If depositional sequences are to be used as a basis for regional basin analysis, it makes more sense to define the sequence boundaries on the criteria of maximum stratal continuity and extent (Galloway 1989) and not on those of stratal discontinuity with limited lateral extent.

Financial support from Fina UK Ltd (JAC), the Gulbenkian Foundation (LMP), and Shell UK Ltd (RCH) is gratefully acknowledged. Enterprise Oil plc and Petrofina SA kindly made available the Gulf of Taranto seismic data. Graham Evans, Mark Helman, and Aidan Joy are thanked for thorough reviews of the manuscript. Thanks also to Splott Stratigraphic Services for logistical support.

References

BIDDLE, K. T., SCHLAGER, W., RUDOLPH, K. W. & BUSH, T. L. 1992. Seismic model of a progradational carbonate platform, Picco di Vallandro, the Dolomites, Northern Italy. *American Association of Petroleum Geologists Bulletin*, **76**, 14–30.

FULTHORPE, C. S. & CARTER, R. M. 1989. Test of seismic sequence methodology on a southern hemisphere passive margin: the Canterbury Basin, New Zealand. *Marine and Petroleum Geology*, **6**, 348–359.

GALLOWAY, W. E. 1989. Genetic stratigraphic sequences in basin analysis 1: architecture and genesis of flooding-surface bounded depositional units. *Bulletin of the American Association of Petroleum Geologists*, **V73**, 125–142.

MITCHUM, R. M. 1985. The seismic expression of submarine fans. *In*: BERG, O. R. & WOOLVERTON, D. G. (eds) *Seismic Stratigraphy 2*, American Association of Petroleum Geologists, Memoir **39**.

——, VAIL, P. R. & THOMPSON, S. 1977. Seismic stratigraphy and global changes of sea-level, part 2: The depositional sequence as a basic unit for stratigraphic analysis. *In*: PAYTON, C. E. (ed.) *Seismic Stratigraphy—Applications to hydrocarbon exploration*, American Association of Petroleum Geologists, Memoir **26**, 53–62.

POSAMENTIER, H. W., JERVEY, M. T. & VAIL, P. R. 1988. Eustatic controls on deposition 1—Conceptual framework. *In*: WILGUS, C. K. *et al*. (eds) *Sea-level changes: an integrated approach*, Society of Economic Paleontologists and Mineralogists Special Publication **42**, 109–124.

—— & VAIL, P. R. 1988. Eustatic controls on clastic deposition 2—Sequence and system tract models. *In*: WILGUS, C. K. *et al*. (eds) *Sea-level changes: an integrated approach*, Society of Economic Paleontologists and Mineralogists Special Publication **42**, 125–154.

RAVENNE, C., CREMER, M., ORSOLINI, P. & RICHE, P. 1988. Mass slides and turbidite-type deposits recognised by offshore seismic prospecting. *In*: *Atlas of Seismic Stratigraphy, Volume 2*. American Association of Petroleum Geologists, Studies in Geology, **27**, 248–264.

SHEPARD, F. P. 1973. *Submarine Geology*, Harper and Row, New York, 551.

VAIL, P. R., MITCHUM, R. M. & THOMPSON, S. 1977. Seismic stratigraphy and global changes of sea-level, part 3: Relative changes of sea level from coastal onlap: *In*: PAYTON, C. E. (ed.) *Seismic Stratigraphy—Applications to hydrocarbon exploration*, American Association of Petroleum Geologists, Memoir **26**, 63–81.

VAN WAGONER, J. C., MITCHUM, R. M., CAMPION, K. M. & RAHMANIAN, V. D. 1990. *Siliciclastic sequence stratigraphy in well logs, cores and outcrops*. American Association of Petroleum Geologists, Methods in Exploration Series, **7**.

WEIMER, R. J. 1984. Relations of unconformities, tectonics, and sea-level changes, Cretaceous of western interior, U.S.A. *In*: SCHLEE, J. S. (ed.) *Interregional unconformities and hydrocarbon accumulation*, American Association of Petroleum Geologists, Memoir **36**, 7–35.

From WILLIAMS, G. D. & DOBB, A. (eds), 1993, *Tectonics and Seismic Sequence Stratigraphy*.
Geological Society Special Publication No. 71, 35–66.

Rift-related linked depositional systems and their seismic expression

Sarah Prosser

Geology Department, University of Keele, Keele, Staffordshire ST5 5BG, UK
Present address: Geology Department, Oxford Polytechnic, Gipsy Lane, Headington, Oxford OX3 0BP, UK

Abstract: The spatial distribution and temporal evolution of depositional systems in active-fault bounded basins are considered to be significantly influenced by tectonics. Fault movement and stage of basin development control the potential for erosion and the rate of sediment flux. Distinct stages of rift evolution can be recognized, each with characteristic linked depositional systems and distinctive expressions on seismic reflection profiles. A four-fold division relating to rift initiation, rift climax, immediate post-rift and late post-rift stages of basin evolution is proposed to characterize most basin infill stratigraphies. The three-dimensional linked depositional systems (systems tracts) associated with each of these stages will vary according to climate, source rock composition, position relative to sea-level, and eustatic fluctuations; however, a dominant tectonic signature can still be isolated if analysis is undertaken in an appropriate fashion. The general suitability of the application of this new method of describing rift basin stratigraphies in terminal half-graben type basins is demonstrated using case studies and published examples. The introduction of new terminology for use in tectonically active settings is justified on the basis that no other technique sufficiently emphasizes the fundamental link between tectonics and sedimentation.

The current techniques of basin analysis are intimately associated with the tools of seismic and sequence stratigraphy. Although the fundamental principles date back to the publication of AAPG Memoir 26 (Payton 1977), numerous additions, adaptations and criticisms have since been presented (e.g. Van Wagoner *et al.* 1990; Galloway 1989; Hubbard 1988; Wilgus *et al.* 1988; Brown & Fisher 1980). The original hypotheses, however, still stand up as the source of a valuable new method of basin analysis. Amongst other things, Memoir 26 contains definitions of depositional sequences (Mitchum *et al.* 1977) and outlines the fundamental techniques of seismic stratigraphy still used to describe and interpret seismic reflection profiles. One such technique is the definition and recognition of *systems tracts* which are defined by Brown & Fisher (1977) as 'a linkage of contemporaneous depositional systems'. They state that 'a basin will be filled (with these systems) as they change according to changes in tectonics and source area'. Since this original broad-based definition was coined, more specific implications have been given to systems tracts by Posamentier & Vail (1988). These authors describe the nature of idealized linked depositional systems that develop in response to a cyclical change in relative sea-level, controlled by fluctuations in eustacy, tectonics and sedimentation rates. The highstand, lowstand, transgressive and shelf margin systems tracts defined provide a method of basin analysis that integrates spatial and temporal approaches to interpretation, and offers a technique that has the potential to be applied to both field-based and seismic interpretations. These systems tract models of Posamentier & Vail were developed on passive continental margin settings where tectonic subsidence is variable over a much longer time scale than the eustatic sea-level changes (though see Watts 1989). The tectonic component of subsidence can, therefore, be considered as approximately linear, and quantifiable in the calculation of its contribution to relative sea-level changes (Posamentier & Vail 1988). Thus, while tectonics may affect the absolute point and time about which eustatic fluctuations occur, it is usually a subordinate effect in determining which systems tract develops at a particular stage of the passive margins' development. Eustacy is, therefore, inferred to be the dominant controlling influence on systems tract development.

But how are the characteristics of the systems tracts affected if tectonics, as opposed to eustacy, become the dominant factor in the control on sedimentation? In actively extending rift systems the strength of the tectonic signature is likely to be very important. In these settings it may not be possible to identify the eustatically controlled systems tracts of Posamentier & Vail (1988). Where sequences are recognized in settings that were obviously tectonically active during deposition (or immediately prior to deposition), such as fault-bounded asymmetric grabens, it may be that the reflector dispositions and internal facies characteristics are related to a dominantly tectonic control. In these cases the linked depositional systems would be tectonic in origin and might be defined as **tectonic systems tracts**. The possibility of such an adjective before the term that today carries so many prior implications (i.e. systems tract), and the method of possibly recognizing such elements in basin analysis, are the subject of examination and discussion through the rest of this paper.

For the purposes of description and discussion in this paper, rift-related three-dimensional linked depositional systems (the potential tectonic systems tracts) are considered on the scale of a seismic reflection profile, although the actual scale will vary according to resolution and medium of analysis (field studies, high-resolution seismics, low-resolution seismics). The (slightly) more predictable duration of global or regional eustatic fluctuations (the hierarchical system of different order of sequences as suggested by Vail *et al.* (1977)) cannot be applied in active tectonic settings, and suggesting a time interval for each stage of basin evolution and the associated depositional systems is almost impossible to undertake (though Hubbard (1988) does suggest some possible durations of tectonically controlled megasequence development). The duration of each rift-related linked depositional system, and the sequences they form part of, will depend on the rate of faulting and basin formation, which may be highly variable.

Previous publications of rift basin settings where systems tracts have been used in basin analysis include those of Vail (1987) and of Scholz *et al.* (1990). The example used by Vail (1987) is typical of a growth fault (*sensu stricto*) where the expansion of the stratigraphic succession across a normal fault is related not to extension of the crust but to gravity-driven listric faulting where detachment along near-horizontal planes is taken up in the sedimentary pile. Thus, extensional tectonic forces are not controlling the creation of new space, and regional sea-level changes are likely to be reflected in both the expanded and more condensed successions on either side of the fault, though there may be a variation in stratigraphical expression due to increased water depths on the hangingwall side. Thus, the use of eustatic, or regional sea-level variation, systems tract terminology may be consistent with the observed stratigraphic relationships, as accomplished by Vail (1987) who considers the fault break as equivalent to a shoreline break. Such an approach is harder to apply with meaningful results in typical rift basins (see below). The study in the East African Rift by Scholz *et al.* (1990), illustrates a lowstand systems tract and a highstand systems tract dependent on the level of the lake that occupies the centre of the half-graben. The level of such a lake is, however, more likely to be controlled by climatic fluctuations, and for this reason it is suggested that the different linked depositional systems might be termed **climatic systems tracts**.

In terminal asymmetric basins, bounded by crustal scale faults that move in response to extensional tectonic forces, facies relationships include features that may be related to influences that are solely local-tectonic in origin, and that could not be due to a more regional change in relative base level. It is demonstrated in the discussion below that in some cases it could be more informative and consistent to use tectonic systems tracts in the basin analysis of fault-bounded basin fills.

Prior to describing the characteristics of each of the tectonic systems tracts, and exploring their suitability for general application to basin analysis, it is necessary to emphasize the effects that tectonism can have on sedimentation, and to clarify some apparent misconceptions that occur in published examples regarding the interpretation of rift basin stratigraphies.

The potential for subsidence to outpace sedimentation

A crucial aspect of sedimentation in response to normal faulting and basin formation is the potential for subsidence to outpace sedimentation, which normally results in transgression and a reduction in sediment flux to the basin centre. Many interpretations of seismic reflection data appear to overestimate the proportion of basin fill that was deposited as fault movement occurred (e.g. Beach *et al.* 1987; Badley *et al.* 1984; and reviewed in Prosser (1991)) and in many cases the syn-rift sequence is found to be only a minor constituent of the basin fill (e.g. Mutter & Larsen 1989; Burrus 1989; the North Shetland Trough and Barents Sea half-grabens (see below)). This alters the results of basin analysis (e.g. duration and timing of rifting), and gives a different perspective on which characteristics are those distinctly associated with fault-controlled seismic sequences. Some of the contributing factors to potential basin starvation during active faulting are discussed below:

Individual fault growth

The characteristics of fault growth will determine the rate at which space is created in which sediment can be deposited, and also influence the resultant geometry of the infilling sedimentary bodies. Studies of individual fault growth suggest that displacement rates may increase through time due to the relationship between slip increment and fault length (Waterson 1986). This implies that *if* the rate of sediment supply remains constant through time, the potential for subsidence to outpace sedimentation will increase with the duration of fault movement. Hooke (1972) uses field observations to calculate an exponential increase in displacement through time on the basin-bounding fault of Death Valley, a conclusion consistent with the work of Scholz *et al.* (1986) on earthquake mechanisms.

Rift system development

The large-scale architecture of rift basins is often characterized by a major basin bounding fault with subsidiary synthetic and antithetic faults. The work of Crossley (1984) and Watson *et al.* (1987) demonstrates that early stages of rift development are characterized by numerous small, isolated, fault-bounded basins, with displacement switching to a dominant major basin-bounding fault during the rift climax. Schlische & Olsen (1990) develop a quantitative model for the filling of extensional basins that highlights some important results of the interaction of sedimentation and tectonics. They study the changes in the volume of sediment available for deposition in an extending basin and note that in a young basin the relatively small area and volume of the depocentre enables sedimentation to keep pace with subsidence. This contrasts with the larger volume of a more fully extended basin where deposition is spread over a greater area. This is expressed as the thinning of successive strata, and a consequent increase in bathymetry as a reduction in sediment accumulation rate occurs. The effects of sedimentation in a single asymmetric graben described by Schlische & Olsen (1990) could be extended to the scale of an entire rift system. Early small, isolated basins would be more likely to infill with sediment as subsidence occurred, than the larger volume of the basin during rift climax.

Drainage basin development

It is useful to consider two effects of the relative sizes of drainage basin and depositional basin when considering the possibility of basin starvation.

(1) The size of a drainage basin is critical in determining the rate of sediment input into the basin (Denny 1965; Hooke 1968). The climate, nature of the source rock and gradient of slope will all influence the rate at which the drainage basin expands and the erosion rate, and thus, the sediment supply rate. However, the drainage basin area during active rift development is likely to be strongly dependent on its duration of existence prior to basin formation initiation. The frequency of rainfall and, therefore, the potential for perennial or ephemeral stream flow, will depend not only on the climate, but also on the area of the drainage basin and the probability of precipitation occurring above it (Blair 1987, 1988). In an evolving rift the consequent (Leeder *et al.* 1988) drainage basins in the hangingwalls and footwalls will be smaller than the antecedent drainage basins of adjacent hinterland. Thus, the continuous flow in streams of depositional systems from these latter areas are likely to provide the major part of sediment supplied to the basin. The systems carrying this sediment load will most likely occupy longitudinal positions parallel to the axis of the rift, entering at the ends of the rift system and at relay and accommodation zones (Larsen 1988; Crossley 1984). The sediment deposited will be relatively fine grained and mature compared to the material derived from the local hangingwall and footwall crests. This latter material will consist of much coarser, proximal deposits, but will at this stage only form a minor constituent of the basin fill because of the nature of drainage basin development (see below).

(2) The typical size of a drainage basin is large compared to the area of the basin to which it is transporting sediment, but the relative rates of sediment supply and subsidence need to be compared to see if the basin will be kept 'topped up' as differential subsidence occurs. A study by Pitman & Andrews (1985) (developed for strike-slip basins, but with important implications for dip-slip basins also) indicates that the potential for starvation (resulting from rapid drowning as

subsidence outpaces sedimentation rates) is high, and that not until several million years after the end of active rifting is the basin likely to be infilled.

Spatial and temporal characteristics of sedimentation

Spatial

The pattern of sediment dispersal in rift basins is strongly related to the rift architecture, as clearly illustrated in the publication by Leeder & Gawthorpe (1987) for continental half-grabens, and also in various publications that discuss the sediment entry points into asymmetrical basins at points of fault overlap and interaction (Rosendahl 1987; Larsen 1988; Morely *et al.* 1990; Gawthorpe & Hurst in press). In a subaerial setting the low angle of the hangingwall dip-slope and the relay zones are more likely to be exploited by stream erosion than the steep footwall scarp, both because of the larger area across which incision may occur and the likely method of stream development: rapid stream incision on the low-angle hangingwall and relay zones compared to slower nick-point migration on the footwall scarp (Crossley 1984).

Temporal

The question of how sedimentation changes in response to active faulting is fundamental in determining the timing of rifting from field and well data. A commonly held view in published literature seems to be that the creation of a new source area along the footwall and hangingwall will be reflected immediately in the basin stratigraphy as a coarsening-upwards succession (Gloppen & Steel 1981; Heward 1978; Steel & Wilson 1975). Thus a gradual fining-upwards sequence is produced as the source becomes degraded. The work of Blair (1987, 1988) and Bilodeau & Blair (1986) suggests that on the contrary the onset of rifting should more correctly be correlated with the onset of deposition of finer-grained sediment. The small consequent drainage basins in the new source areas are not able to expand and incise as long as differential subsidence across the fault is occurring. Erosion may be confined to canyon cutting in an attempt to remove the differential relief and over-steepened stream profiles across the fault scarp. Only when fault movement ceases can the drainage basin expand and incise into the new source area; the larger area will then be affected by more precipitation events. The rate of erosion and sediment supply will, therefore, according to this theory of Blair (1987, 1988), increase after rifting has ended (during post-rift times), when the stratigraphy will record an increase in coarse-grained proximal deposits. Thus, active rifting will be associated with sediment that is generally finer grained, and although degradation of the source areas will occur it will only be at some time after the cessation of active rifting that large volumes of coarser sediments are introduced into the basin. The duration of this introduction of coarser sediments into the basin, will depend on source rock composition, climate (including potential for submersion) and topographic gradient.

Seismic reflection profiles provide an ideal data medium for examining the changing response of depositional systems to active faulting because they show a complete temporal view. Consideration and incorporation of the more detailed depositional systems that are likely to occur in rift basins can enhance interpretation considerably. In this way, a new method for the description and interpretation involved in extensional basin analysis can be developed that is applicable to many basins. Modifications for local settings will need to be applied as appropriate, and these important variations on the basic models presented below are essential to remember.

Rift-related linked depositional systems and their seismic expression

Detailed analyses of reflector configurations reveals a consistent pattern of basin development that can be recognized in half-grabens in widely different geographical and geological settings (reviewed in Prosser 1991). Two case studies are considered in this paper, one from a half-graben on the Ringvassøy-Loppa Fault Terrace in the Barents Sea (Faleide *et al.* 1984), and the other from the Magnus Basin in the northern North Sea (Evans & Parkinson 1983). The seismic expression of the possible tectonic systems tracts are described below and illustrated in Figs 1 & 2. It should be noted that the Barents Sea half-graben is 5 km across, forming on a fault that may detach at depth above the basement, while the Magnus Basin is 40 km across, and is bounded by a major crustal fault. Despite the difference in scale, a single method of basin analysis is possible when a tectonic systems tract approach is applied.

Four stages of basin evolution (approximately equivalent to S2 to S5 in Figs 1 & 2), each with their own idealized systems tract, are described below. Each stage has a distinct linkage of depositional systems and a seismic expression that enables its recognition on reflection profiles. Although the case studies are used as examples, it is important to realize that these are just two of the possible expressions of the stages of evolution and associated systems tracts. Other seismic sections and field studies will undoubtedly reveal alternative linked depositional systems that might also be identified as systems tracts that indicate sedimentation occurred in environments where tectonics were the dominant control on deposition.

The definition of a tectonic systems tract can be established after examination of seismic reflection configurations with support from seismic facies analysis and/or well data, or else from bedding relationships with support from lithofacies analysis in outcrop studies. Thus, the definition conforms with that of Mitchum & Van Wagoner (1990) whereby

'Each systems tract is interpreted to have been deposited during a specific phase or portion of one complete cycle of relative fall and rise of sea level.'

The hypotheses behind this definition strongly imply global eustacy (or at best regional tectonic) is the dominant component of the relative sea-level change; the relevant phrase could perhaps be re-read with 'phase or portion of tectonic development' substituted for the purpose of active fault-bounded basins. Continuing the above definition Mitchum & Van Wagoner go on to state:

'The sequences and systems tract are, however, defined on the basis of stratal and physical relationships, using objective stratal and facies criteria that do not depend on frequency of occurrence, size, or interpreted depositional mechanism.'

which still holds when dealing with tectonic systems tracts.

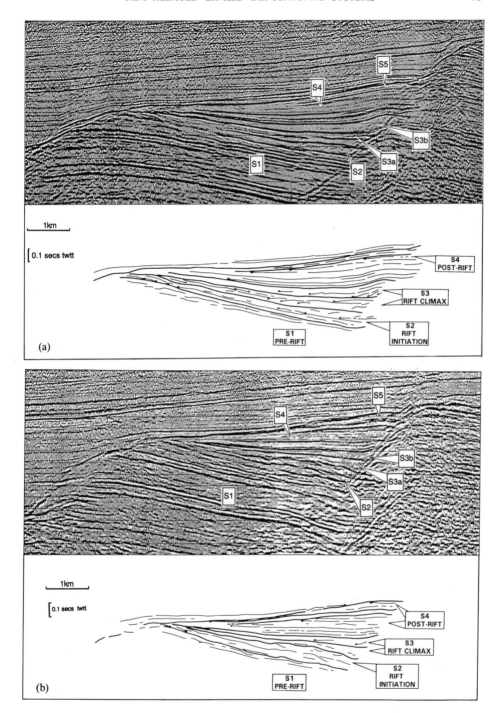

Fig. 1. Barents Sea half-graben. The seismic section in (**a**) is located 5 km north of that in (**b**) Note the early stages of divergence followed by passive infill. The interpretation of these sections is discussed more fully in the text. S1 is the pre-rift stage. S2 is the rift initiation stage, with wedge-shaped reflector packages and hummocky internal seismic facies. S3 is the rift climax, and S4 the post-rift stages of evolution and associated systems tracts.

Rift initiation (S2)

The first increment of movement on a fault causes a depression in the crust's surface to which gravity-driven sedimentary systems will respond. For the purposes of tectonic systems tract description the basin is presumed at this stage to be subaerial, with enough water supply to maintain perennial fluvial systems, and the surrounding source areas to be composed of consolidated, competent rock. Variations from this highly assumed situation will result in vastly different depositional mechanisms and type of facies that accumulate; thus, the physical relationships of the strata should be concentrated on to establish the presence of this systems tract. A summary diagram of this systems tract in the situation described above is given in Fig. 3; the modifications that can be applied for variations in climatic, eustatic, and source rock composition are discussed later.

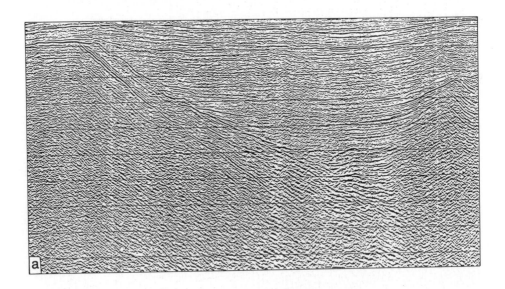

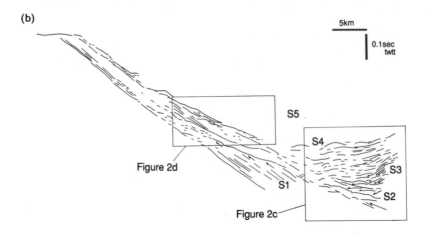

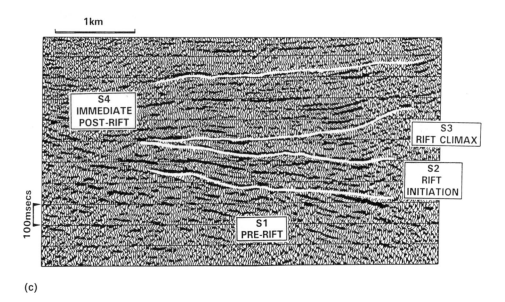

(c)

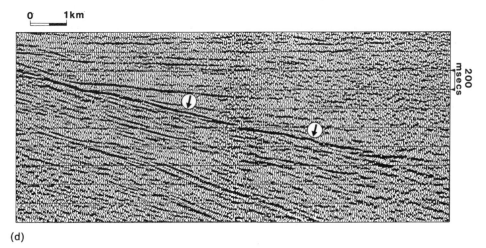

(d)

Fig. 2. Magnus Basin. (**a**) Seismic section and (**b**) interpretative line drawing of the Magnus Basin, with location of (c) and (d) indicated. Note the sub-parallel nature and strong onlap onto the hangingwall dip-slope of most of the reflectors that constitute the basin infill, with geometries modified only by compaction at the basin margins. (**c**) Detail close to the fault plane, at the base of the basin fill, illustrating change from prograding (S2) to aggrading (S3) reflector packages, interpreted as the change from rift initiation to rift climax systems tract. S4 is the immediate post-rift systems tract characterized by sub-parallel reflectors onlapping onto the hangingwall slope. (**d**) Detail of hangingwall dip-slope, illustrating lozenge-shaped reflector geometries possibly corresponding to alluvial or submarine fan-type deposits. See text for further details.

44 S. PROSSER

Key points: subsidence = sedimentation
no established drainage basins in newly created topographic locations
dominantly axial input from antecedent mature drainage basins
small isolated sub-basins, small area for deposition

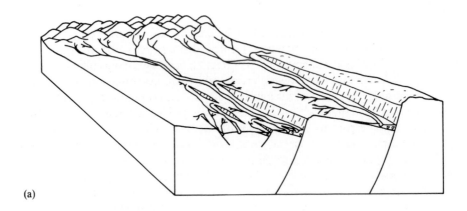

(a)

Fluvial channels axially positioned,
relatively fine grained sediments   small fault scarps

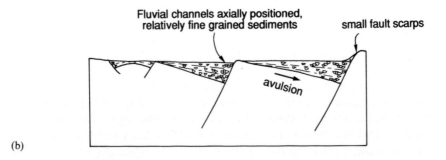

avulsion

(b)

Fig. 3. Rift initiation systems tract: (**a**) generalized block diagram; (**b**) schematic cross-section. Note the small localized nature of the fault-bounded basins, the longitudinal position of the major depositional system, and the small relief on the new fault scarps. See text for details and alternative depositional systems.

Seismic expression. The reflection geometries in the Barents Sea and Magnus Basin case studies illustrate some of the main characteristics of rift-initiation systems tracts on seismic sections. The sequence labelled S2 in the sections illustrated in Fig. 1 shows an overall wedge-shaped geometry. The thin end of the wedge lies high on the hangingwall dip-slope, and the internal reflector characteristics are generally hummocky and discontinuous. The interpretation of these reflector packages involves a system where sedimentation kept pace with subsidence, thus explaining the wedge-shaped geometries that are superimposed upon one another, rather than formed through onlapping reflectors infilling an earlier-formed depression. The hummocky discontinuous reflectors suggest a channellized system lying in a longitudinal position (Brown & Fisher 1980). There is no evidence of major transverse-derived depositional systems. The Magnus Basin (Fig. 2) displays evidence of prograding reflector geometries in the very lowest parts of the basin, implying sedimentation was able to infill the space created through subsidence. These observations are consistent with the models of Schlische & Olsen (1990) and other aspects of sedimentary response to early stages of rift formation discussed above.

Characteristic linked depositional systems. The creation of a depression in the pre-rift landscape has the following effects: (1) a new depocentre is formed into which gravity-driven depositional systems may be directed; (2) new topographic highs are formed at the footwall and hangingwall crests, which are potential source areas for sediment. The discussion above of the controls on sedimentation during active rifting suggests that these local highs with consequent drainage basins will not be those that are important with respect to source potential for basin filling. The streams from more distant source areas with larger, established drainage basins and continuous stream flow are rapidly redirected to lie in longitudinal positions in the new basin axis. These older source areas will provide relatively fine, mature, sediment to the basin. Thus, the depositional elements that constitute this systems tract are (1) a longitudinal river system with channels and inter-channel-type deposition; (2) small coarse-grained talus cones from the low relief fault scarps.

Rift climax (S3)

The time of maximum rate of displacement on a fault can be termed the rift climax. At this stage sedimentation is likely to be outpaced by subsidence and differential relief will be created across the fault scarp. A summary block diagram is illustrated in Fig. 4, with a schematic drawing of the cross-section. The systems tract of Fig. 4 represents a time when most of the basin has drowned, perhaps corresponding to a fairly late stage in development. Prior to this the topographic highs of the fault block crests may have been in a subaerial environment while the lows were simultaneously submerged (assuming a subaerial setting at the end of the rift initiation stage). It is, therefore, possible to erect a number of scenarios each leading towards the model of almost total basin submergence, illustrated in Fig. 5. Again the facies and depositional systems are variable depending on a number of factors such as climate, source rock composition and position relative to sea-level; it is the geometries and relationships of the reflections emanating from stratal horizons, or of the strata themselves, that reveal the presence of rift climax systems tracts.

Three stages, each a separate systems tract can be described. The possibility of each occurring depends on the time elapsed before subsidence below sea-level occurs. This, in turn, will depend on the position of sea-level relative to the basin floor at the start of rifting. Each expresses characteristics of rift climax control and, therefore, are all rift climax systems tracts; the position of base level in the basin may vary through time influencing the changes in the systems tracts in an order described below.

Seismic expression. On a seismic section the rift climax systems tract is characterized by an increase in the amount of aggradation, together with the development of divergent forms related to continued tilting of the hangingwall during deposition. Seismic noise generated by the fault plane may obscure detailed reflector geometries close to the fault scarp (Fig. 2(c)) and mounded forms associated with footwall-

Key points: subsidence > sedimentation
              minor sediment accumulation due to increase in rate of
              subsidence (related to fault growth), increase in area for
              deposition, hydrological control (small drainage basins,
              canyon cutting, nick point migration mechanism)
              Unlikely to record minor eustatic changes

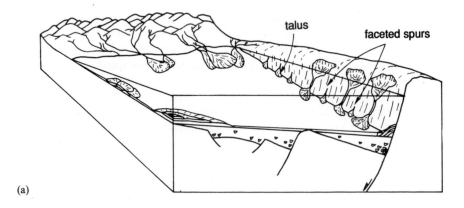

(a)

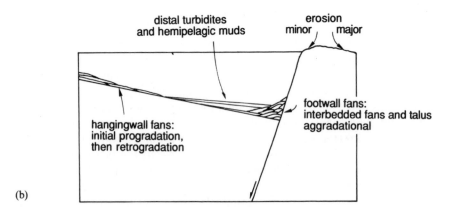

(b)

Fig. 4. Rift climax systems tract: (**a**) generalized block diagram; (**b**) schematic cross-section. Note the large amount of relief on a single dominant fault plane, the small size of the consequent drainage basins and the increase in the area for deposition. This diagram represents a late stage in the climax of rifting when the hangingwall has been transgressed and submerged. Earlier stages may show systems tracts with a lacustrine or marine gulf environment in the basin axis, with alluvial fans or fan deltas at the margins. See text and Fig. 6 for further details.

derived fans and talus may, therefore, be hard to identify except on high quality data (Fig. 1(a)). Chaotic zones close to the footwall may represent coarse-grained rock falls and talus which have no ordered bedding and no chance of generating reflections. In more basinward positions, the contrast in lithology between fans and lacustrine/marine deposits means that inter-bedding of horizons with strongly contrasting lithologies is likely to occur and reflections should be generated. The soft sedimentary features triggered by seismic energy will commonly be below the level of seismic resolution. Large-scale slide blocks may be recognized, but a faulting-induced origin is hard to confirm.

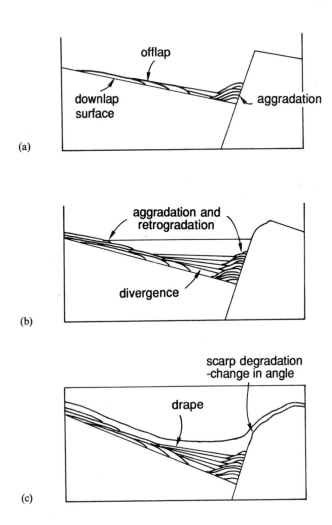

Fig. 5. The possible reflector configurations of the early, mid and late stages of rift climax systems tracts. Tilting and divergence are common to each stage, though seismic resolution may not pick this up. (**a**) Early rift climax: aggradation of the footwall-derived sequences, offlap and progradation of the hangingwall-derived sequences. (**b**) Mid-rift climax: retrogradation and aggradation of the hangingwall sequences, continued aggradation of the footwall sequences. (**c**) Late rift climax: blanketing of the topography with a drape of constant thickness.

  It is proposed that cyclicity or repetitive reflection stacking, if discernible, is probably the result of successive faulting increments. Any eustatic or regional change in relative sea-level may be masked by this higher frequency tectonic signal, though in areas close to the margin of the rift system, or at points close to hinge lines where local tectonics have little effect on subsidence the signature of regional sea-level fluctuations are more likely to be recorded (though not necessarily preserved). Association of seismic facies analysis with the sedimentological attributes discussed below may allow an estimation of the relative timing and duration of rifting with respect to total duration of basin infill to be made.

Characteristic reflector geometries will be generated that mark the onset and termination of the three different rift climax systems tracts. These are illustrated in Fig. 5, and described below.

(1) The early rift climax systems tract is ideally distinguished from the rift initiation systems tract below by a downlap surface. This is associated with aggrading reflectors close to the footwall and progradation and offlap from the hangingwall (Fig. 5(a)). The lozenge-shaped reflector packages on the hangingwall of the Magnus Basin (Fig. 2(d)) may represent lobe-type deposits (e.g. alluvial fans or deltas), and likewise there is some evidence of downlapping footwall-derived systems in Fig. 1(a) of the Barents Sea half-grabens. Generally, however, the potential for preservation of sedimentary bodies in this setting is low and, therefore, the importance of the sediment component derived from the hangingwall slope may not be resolved on seismic data. The preservation of faceted spurs will depend on the rate of burial by younger sediments and on the rate of scarp degradation; continued fault movement will juxtapose unexposed fault plane against the reflector packages that constitute the rift climax systems tracts.

(2) The onset of the mid-rift climax systems tract is characterized by a change to retrogradational geometries of the reflectors on the hangingwall dip-slope, and possibly also on the footwall-derived systems. The rate of transgression will determine the amount of associated aggradation with progradation on the hangingwall dip-slope where the low angle of dip may mean that retrogradation and drowning is rapid. The linear (along strike) facies belts suggested above as being characteristic of the systems tract may be almost impossible to resolve on seismic reflection data, and may be represented only in a slight change in reflector characteristic. Basinal deposits will be more continuous reflectors that will display divergence towards the fault plane, only if sufficient thickness of sediment accumulated between faulting events is resolved on the seismic section.

(3) The late rift climax systems tract is recorded on the seismic section as a draping reflector that can be traced across the basin onto the adjacent footwall and hangingwall crests. This may be an extremely continuous reflector, especially over the highest areas where lithology contrasts and, therefore, acoustic impedance contrasts will be greatest. Sediment accumulation rates are likely to be so reduced at this stage of evolution that no divergence of reflectors towards the fault plane is recorded.

Characteristic linked depositional systems.   A general feature of all the stages in the rift-climax systems tracts is the presence of soft sediment deformation structures that indicate seismic triggering. These may range from rock falls and debris flows to dewatering features and slumping, the cause of seismites and large-scale slide block displacement and seiche initiation (though these features may also be found in other palaeoenvironmental scenarios).

EARLY RIFT CLIMAX SYSTEMS TRACT. The discussion above suggested that differential topography across the fault scarp is likely to develop during the rift climax because of the nature of individual fault growth, the change to a single dominant fault, the increase in volume for deposition, the low potential for erosion and high sediment supply, and the relative rates of erosion and deposition relative to subsidence. Starvation of the basin is, therefore, likely to be characteristic of the rift climax stage.

The fault scarp will display signs of recent exposure such as triangular-faceted spurs and immature drainage patterns (in the subaerial setting of this model). The early rift climax systems tract is characteristically composed of a lacustrine or marine gulf in the basin, as close to the fault plane as fans and talus cones derived from the fault plane permit. The sediment deposited in these standing bodies of water will be relatively fine grained in nature, compared to the coarse-grained talus and fans from the footwall and also fan or delta deposits from the hangingwall. Both these latter sources have low source potential at this stage of development as discussed above (though the hangingwall will be areally the more important of the two). The hangingwall-derived deposits are likely to be from depositional systems strongly influenced by gravity and are likely to be lobe-shaped in geometry: alluvial fans in subaerial environments and shoal-type deltas in subaqueous settings. Successive tilting increments will lead to offlap in a basinward direction (Hunt & Mabey 1966; Hooke 1972; Leeder & Gawthorpe 1987) and forced shoreline regressions (Udall & Nolan 1964). The potential for important sediment volumes to be derived from the hangingwall is unlikely to be represented in the stratigraphical expression of a rift basin, due to the low potential for preservation.

MID-RIFT CLIMAX SYSTEMS TRACT. The onset of the mid-rift climax systems tract is associated with the point at which transgression of the hangingwall dip-slope occurs, with the drowning of earlier lobe-type deposits. This will be expressed as retrograding systems up the hangingwall until the feeder drainage basins are themselves submerged. At this point there will be a fundamental change in sediment transport direction: from gravity-driven downslope to along-slope current-driven trends. This will be expressed as a change from lobe-shaped facies accumulations to linear facies belts such as long-shore bars and beach barrier systems. The hangingwall drainage basin is likely to be submerged before the footwall drainage basin due to a component of non-rotational normal fault movement during tilting of the fault block. Thus, although the hangingwall slope has a greater potential for sediment supply it is often the footwall sources that become more important during later stages of development. In summary, footwall systems will be characteristically small submarine fans, basinal systems will involve suspension fall-out as hemipelagic muds and silts, and the hangingwall systems will be linear facies belts of regressional shallow marine deposits, though variations of each will occur according to the unique setting of each basin.

LATE RIFT CLIMAX SYSTEMS TRACT. The late rift climax systems tract is taken to consist of the depositional systems that predominate in a totally submerged environment. Rates of sediment supply to the basin are low: local source areas are subject to submarine erosion processes, while the products from more distal source areas will be deposited at the rift margins. Sedimentation of fine-grained siliciclastics from pelagic fall-out and distal turbidite flows is likely to occur over most of the area. This will be seen as a blanket of sediment of relatively uniform thickness draping the asymmetric basin topography. Shoreline facies may develop at the rift margins, and emergent footwall crests may provide small amounts of coarse-grained material in the form of submarine fans and talus.

Key points: subsidence < sedimentation
increase in general grain size due to expansion of footwall
drainage basins, increase in progradation, filled to spill
point. More likely to record minor eustatic changes.

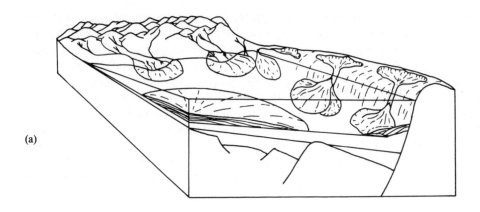

(a)

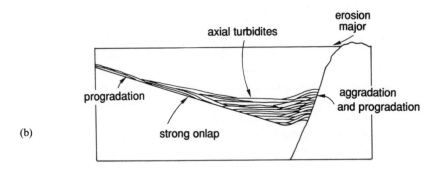

(b)

Fig. 6. Immediate post-rift systems tract: (**a**) generalized block diagram; (**b**) schematic cross-section. Note the expansion and down-cutting of the drainage basins, the aggradation of facies through infilling rather than differential subsidence, the prominent onlap surface and progradation of sediment into the basin from transverse as well as longitudinal systems. While the lowest sequence boundary is tectonically generated, eustatic fluctuations will be more important within and at the margins of the succession.

Immediate post-rift (S4)

The end of active tectonism and displacement on the basin-bounding fault has two main implications for the systems tract characteristics: (a) tilting of the hangingwall and differential subsidence across the fault plane ceases; and (b) the rate of regional subsidence will decrease, although subsidence will continue due to the lithospheric thermal cooling effects. The change in tectonic regime at the base of this stage of basin evolution produces a tectonically-generated onlap surface, but the probability of eustatic variations controlling the smaller-scale features and packages identified by reflection terminations within the basin succession and at the rift margins, is greatly increased since faulting is no longer active. Figure 6 shows the schematic block diagram and cross-section that summarize the main characteristics of the immediate post-rift systems tracts. This is based on the setting of the model developed above; variations in sea-level and climate are discussed below.

Seismic expression.   The end of a fault displacement and the replacement of the rift climax systems tracts by the immediate post-rift systems tracts is marked by the end of both tilting and the creation of divergent reflector packages. The succeeding reflectors may show a continuation of the preceding aggradation initially as they infill the depression, but may show a greater proportion of associated progradation also. The lower boundary that marks this systems tract may, therefore, be a downlap surface in the centre of the basin, and a strong onlap surface updip on the hangingwall dip slope and the footwall scarp slope. The continuity of reflectors may indicate the energy of deposition, which may, in turn, be dependent on the magnitude of the differential relief across the inactive fault scarp. This is seen in Fig. 2 of the Magnus Basin where the discontinuous nature of the reflectors in the immediate post-rift systems tract package may reflect the 2 km fault scarp relief interpreted to have existed at the end of rifting.

Any variations from a simple parallel infill can be explained by depositional processes and by later compactional deformation (Prosser 1991), and possibly eustatic fluctuations. The infilling reflector package that constitutes the immediate post-rift systems tract will assume the wedge-shaped geometry of the remnant rift topography, but the internal architecture will be witness to the quiescent nature of the basin-bounding fault. The accumulation of parallel reflectors as a result of non-rotational planar faulting (Cartwright 1987) is ruled out in cases where there is an absence of drag against the fault plane, a similarity in height of the hangingwall and footwall crest, and not thickening towards the fault plane (expected even on planar non-rotational faulting due to isostatic and elastic strain constraints).

Ignoring the importance of infilling remnant topography in the creation of overall wedge-shaped geometries and the possibility of divergent reflector configurations induced by compaction, can lead to overestimations in the duration of active faulting (discussed in detail in Prosser, 1991).

Characteristic linked depositional systems.   The features associated with deposition in this environment are those associated with the infilling of a hole, though regional subsidence may prevent development of the depositional systems described below and instead induce further drowning and reduction of sediment supply. If local drainage basins are in subaerial positions at this point of development they will now expand rapidly and the rate of sediment supply to the basin will increase. The coarse-grained material derived from these proximal sources will encroach across the basin and a coarsening-upwards succession will be generated. Together with the decrease in subsidence rate, there is a greater chance of infilling the basin and gradually shallowing and possibly eliminating the marine or lacustrine environment of the basin centre. This will only occur if the drainage basins in question are available for exploitation, that is, if they are now in a submarine environment the rate of erosion will be low and the coarsening-upwards sequence may not be generated. In this situation, a slow infill of the basin will occur by sediment deposited by local marine erosion and distal turbidite systems.

Late post-rift (S5)

The final response to the creation and infilling of a rift basin will be the gradual and slow peneplanation of the topography created through faulting. This may take many millions of years but is still a sedimentary response to a rifting event that once occurred. The late post-rift systems tract may be masked by subsequent tectonic events, but in some cases characteristic linked depositional systems may develop that can be recognized, and are summarized in Fig. 7.

Seismic expression.   This late post-rift infill systems tract will be imaged on a seismic reflection profile as parallel reflectors that are of a more continuous nature than the early post-rift systems tract. They will continue to onlap the hangingwall dip slope and the degraded fault scarp. The boundary between the upper and lower systems tracts may be a surface with concordant reflectors on either side, but a change in reflector characteristics may indicate the warning influence of the tectonics on sedimentation. The effects of differential compaction above the asymmetrical base to the basin and resulting sediment thickness variations will cause upturn of reflectors, and possibly compaction induced faulting. Eustatic systems tracts are likely to be identifiable in the shallow/marginal parts of the basin.

Characteristic linked depositional systems.   The erosion and degradation of the local (fault block crest) source area will lead to a fining of the sediment grain size through time. The reduction of differential topography will concomitantly lead to a lowering of the energy conditions depositing sediment down the fault scarp slope. Fluctuations in base level due to eustatic variations may control sediment input rates and the depositional systems.

Variations in climate

Humid tectonic systems tracts

The nature of sedimentation in a humid environment will be affected by (a) the increase in chemical weathering of the local source areas, (b) the probable constant flow of large river systems through the basin and (c) the increase in vegetation. The stabilizing effects of vegetation are counterbalanced by the increase in weathering; the amount of rainfall is critical in determining the net result (Langbein & Schumm 1958). The rates of sediment supply are likely to be much greater than the basic model described above and the accumulation rates will be more likely to keep pace with subsidence. High rates of erosion and sediment supply from the footwall block crest to the basin will form large fans that reach out into the basin, forcing any longitudinal rivers to migrate away from the basin axis to a position higher up the hangingwall slope. The possibility of generating a divergent reflector package during the rift climax that can be resolved on a seismic section is enhanced because of the greater amounts of sediment accumulation between successive faulting increments.

Key points: subsidence ?= sedimentation
fine grained sedimentation due to degradation of fault scarp and continued thermal subsidence drowning major subaerial drainage basins.
Eustatic signature more likely to be recorded.

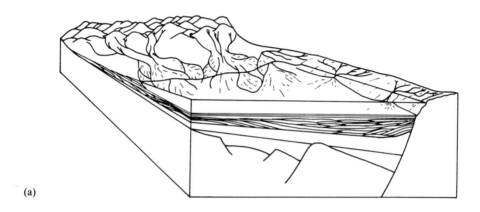

(a)

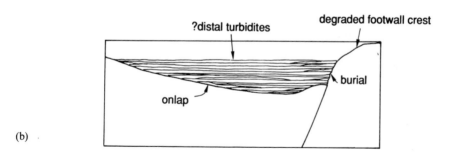

(b)

Fig. 7. Late post-rift systems tract: (**a**) generalized block diagram; (**b**) schematic cross-section. Note the degradation of the footwall scarp as stream profiles return to equilibrium. Bathymetry may be preserved through thermal subsidence but burial of the fault-related topography will occur, with associated onlap surfaces. Eustatic and climatic fluctuations may be important in determining the internal characteristics.

Arid tectonic systems tracts

In an arid rift environment the amount of water will be limited both for sediment transport and for accumulation as standing bodies of water in the basin axis. The flash floods and ephemeral streams that characterize this setting may not keep pace with subsidence and will rather infill in more sporadic events. Wedge-shaped geometries may still be generated, though their internal reflector configurations may be chaotic or transparent. The arid rift climax systems tracts may be composed of an evaporite-dominated basin centre with large alluvial fans on the hangingwall slope and smaller footwall fans and talus cones against the footwall slope (e.g. Death Valley, where the hangingwall fans reach 8 km long and up to 7 km wide at their bases, compared to the 1 km diameter of the concentric footwall fans). Even if the immediate basin setting is arid, the environment of the longitudinally positioned systems may be more likely to receive a constant rainfall in higher altitudes. Thus, a constant supply of water to the basin may be maintained. Evaporites formed through the evaporation of standing bodies of water can accumulate at extremely high rates (e.g. Scott & Govean, 1985), often exceeding their clastic equivalents in rift basins. This may be due to the independence from the tectonic influences on drainage basins discussed above.

Sand dune development may also occur. Rift basins are important sites for this type of deposition where linear topographies channel the winds that may then abut steep slopes of sharp changes in rift width that lead to fall-out and sand deposition as dunes (e.g. Death Valley). The immediate post-rift systems tract will be characterized by progradation of coarse-grained deposits across the basin, either as debris and mass flow deposits or alluvial fans in less arid environments.

Variations in sea-level

The effects of sea-level on tectonic systems tracts can be considered in two ways: (1) the position of sea-level relative to the basin centre and fault block crests during basin formation; and (2) the effects of sea-level fluctuations during the development of a tectonic systems tract.

Sea-level position

The position of sea-level relative to the basin determines whether continental or marine conditions prevailed during each stage of basin evolution (except in cases like Death Valley where the basin floor is below sea-level but no connection with the sea has been made). Whether the rift basin remains in a continental environment throughout the duration of its formation and infill (and is, therefore, dominated by alluvial fluvial, lacustrine, evaporitic-type deposits, such as in Death Valley), or if the basin began to form in a submarine environment and never had any subaerial topographic expression (and is, therefore, dominated by turbidites, etc., such as the Mesozoic rift system of the American Margin (Montadert *et al.* 1979)) it should still be possible to establish a particular set of linked depositional systems for any stage of basin development. Each of these may, in turn, be related to a particular stage of rift development, and tectonic systems tracts should be observed. The totally submarine tectonic systems tracts may dominate many rift basin stratigraphies, where a connection with the sea was established soon after rifting began (e.g. the Jurassic of the Italian Alps, (Winterer & Bosellini 1981)).

Sea-level fluctuations

Eustatic fluctuations that occur during basin formation will have profound effects on the depositional systems and their seismic expression, but will not necessarily dominate or mask the tectonic effects, especially in the areas most affected by local tectonic effects close to the active faults. The position of the source area relative to sea-level will determine the potential for subaerial or submarine erosion, thus, influencing the rate of sediment supply. The duration of rifting will control how many global eustatic fluctuations are contained within the seismic and stratigraphic signature of the basin. While aggradation, progradation, and retrogradation are the result of relative sea-level changes and, therefore, the result of tectonic, eustatic and sedimentary variations, it is not the case that eustacy is always the dominant control with the greatest potential for variation. In an actively rifting half-graben this is unlikely to be the case: published syn-rift subsidence rates reach 500 cm/1000 yr, averaged over the whole life of the basin (Hegarty *et al.* 1988; Collier (pers. comm.)). However, faster rates are likely to have persisted through the main rift climax stage, especially considering the episodic nature of faulting. Other published rates of subsidence during the syn-rift phase of basin development (e.g. Bessis 1986; Moretti & Colletta 1988) are always greater than rates of sea-level changes induced through non-glacial mechanisms. The maximum rate of sea-level change through glacial mechanisms is 1 m/1000 yr (Pitman & Golovchenko 1983), with only much lower figures (e.g. 4 mm/1000 yr through ocean ridge volume changes (Pitman 1979) or 1–10 cm/1000 yr through tectonic membrane stresses (Cloetingh 1988)) possible during interglacial times.

The discussion of rates of relative sea-level changes resulting from different causes are not, however, the only factor that will determine the merit of terming systems tracts 'tectonic'. The three-dimensional spatial distribution is also part of that definition, and in symmetric fault-bounded basins, the primary control on depositional system organization is usually clearly tectonic. Divergence of reflectors, part of the expression of stacked syn-rift depositional systems on seismic profiles, can only be attributed to tectonic tilting (or in some cases, later compactional deformation, (see Prosser 1991, for discussion on divergence resulting from compaction)) and, therefore, is a key tool in the first step of eliminating eustacy as the control on systems tract development.

Simultaneous fault block rotation and global sea-level changes may result in reflector configurations that could be interpreted as due to tectonic effects alone or due to a combination of the two effects, such as divergence with aggradation. If age econstraints are available, correlation with a standard sea-level chart (if these are to be believed) may help to isolate the tectonic component from eustacy. The Barents Sea half-graben (Fig. 1) was based in a setting where submarine conditions were probably established before fault movement began and, therefore, eustatic controls are unlikely to have a direct effect on reflector configurations (although distant control on sediment supply may still exist). The Magnus Basin (Fig. 2) is more likely than the Barents Sea to show evidence to eustatic fluctuation, but interpretation incorporating a control that is dominantly tectonic is also consistent with observation.

The effects of sea-level should, of course, be incorporated into any basin analysis that uses the technique of systems tract definition, but the possibility that they were not the most dominant influence must be considered when active rifting was obviously occurring (i.e. during the formation of the syn-rift sequence, composed of the rift initiation and rift climax systems tracts). Eustatic or regional sea-level changes should not be automatically invoked in order to account for changes in sequence and reflection geometries in half-grabens, though their influence is likely to be recognized in the immediate and late post-rift stages of basin evolution.

Application and analogues

The usefulness of a new method of describing and interpreting the sedimentary facies and seismic stratigraphy of extensional basins depends on its applicability to any basin, and the objectivity with which it can be applied. Only if these systems tracts can be seen to occur in published examples of basin analysis from different areas, using different analytical techniques, will they be suitable for widespread application. If this can be accomplished, a clearer method of determining the timing of rifting relative to sedimentation, of predicting facies relationships and interpreting seismic sections, will have been developed. So, how do the tectonic systems tracts defined above relate to other basin analyses? These can be looked at from the different subjects of specific consideration to illustrate how if any one aspect of basin evolution is examined it is consistent with the descriptions above. There is no other tool yet developed, however, that is equally applicable to seismic, field and downhole databases and that can be used in such an adaptable manner.

Whole rift basin development and infill

There have been relatively few attempts to develop generalistic models for the tectono–sedimentary development of rift basins (though see Rosendahl 1987). This may be due to the lack of constraint on the rates of erosion, subsidence and deposition over short time periods in ancient basins, or due to the danger of developing models for a system that is dependent on so many interacting variables and controls. The general models that have been suggested tend to concentrate on a single aspect or medium such as spatial distribution of sediment or temporal changes in vertical sections, or have been compiled using only field-based or seismic-based studies. These subject-specific studies can be divided into four main groups.

(1) *Spatial sedimentary models.*   These include such models as those of Leeder & Gawthorpe (1987) for four possible end-member depositional environments and the alluvial fans and fan deltas of Leeder *et al.* (1988). These studies present reasonable models for a single moment in time, with a single type of deposition. They do not, however, suggest in which stage of rift development these models might occur, nor how they might change with time, nor yet how they might appear on a seismic section.

(2) *Temporal sedimentary models.*   The models and hypotheses derived to explain vertical changes in facies occurring in rift basins include that of Blair (1987), discussed above. The alternative and contradictory interpretations of Steel & Wilson (1975) and Heward (1978) are not consistent with observation and reasoning. Though the facies/tectonic-activity relationship suggested by Blair (1987) may be a

valid and useful hypothesis it does little to integrate the spatial sedimentary aspects of sedimentation in rift basins nor their appearance on seismic sections.

(3) *Tectonic models.* The possible stages in evolution of a rift system are addressed by Rosendahl (1987) from the onset of fault displacement to the breakup of a continent into two passive margins. The scale of such a model does not integrate varying rates of movement on individual faults, the details of the sedimentary response, or the seismic expression. The observations of early isolated small grabens switching to a single basin dominated by a major fault strand were mentioned above.

(4) *Seismo–stratigraphic.* The possible seismic–stratigraphic signature of sediment deposited at the time of rifting is suggested by Cartwright (in press). There is, however, no integration of changing controls on sediment supply in terms of a predictive facies evolution.

Predictive models for facies evolution

This next scale of predictive modelling of the tectono–stratigraphic development is to take a particular depositional environment and extrapolate the results to produce a more generalistic model for that particular system type.

The studies of longitudinal systems (commonly fluvial) and their response to tilting events by Bridge & Leeder (1979) and by Alexander & Leeder (1987) are directly comparable to the rift initiation systems tract described above. The channels are shown to shift towards the fault-controlled depression with each tilt event, the degree of interconnectedness being dependent on the rate of subsidence (Alexander & Leeder 1987). Thus the rate of subsidence may determine the degree to which units of contrasting acoustic impedance are juxtaposed and, therefore, whether a seismic reflection is likely to be generated.

Syn-rift turbidite models of Surlyk (1989) can be correlated with the rift-climax systems tract defined above. He recognizes four stages of evolution of the turbidite systems from East Greenland, with progressively increasing importance of the drainage basins located in the footwall crests that are consistent with the discussion above. Surlyk uses his observations to develop predictive models of syn-rift turbidite facies with variable rates of sea-level change and rates of faulting. These models are similar to the tectonic systems tract method of basin analysis in their predictive capabilities of temporal evolution, but neither extend to other environments of deposition, explain the reasons for variations in sediment supply nor suggest possible equivalent seismic facies appearances.

Watson *et al.* (1987) use observations from the Chinese basins to develop a simple model of facies evolution in response to extension. They use a basin that subsides according to the simple pattern of basin evolution suggested by McKenzie (1978), with an initial rapid fault-controlled subsidence followed by slower subsidence associated with thermal cooling. The resultant facies association of Watson *et al.* (1987) fits the more complex model derived in this paper, enabling a direct correlation with the tectonic systems tracts defined above in the following way. A basal widespread alluvial/fluvial sequence is controlled by many minor faults; this is the rift initiation systems tract. An increased rate of fault movement allowed stable lake sites to be established adjacent to the half-graben bounding fault that were then only a few major features; this is the rift climax systems tract. The end of rift was marked by a return to deposition in a widespread fluvial system; this is the immediate post-rift systems tract. The climatic influences on lithologies are also demonstrated in the basins of eastern China: the Subei Basin developed much later, but displays a similar sequence to the Eren Basin except in the immediate post-rift systems tract, when a change in climate allowed the fluvial beds to become inter-bedded with lacustrine sediments. The Songliao Basin demonstrates another aspect of how tectonic system tracts can be modified to adapt to local settings: the immediate post-rift stage accumulated in deep water environments and is characterized by a progressive shallowing up.

Changming *et al.* (1984) also worked in the Chinese basins and divided the basin stratigraphy into facies sequences: (1) alluvial, lake-basin bog facies association; (2) evaporite facies association; and (3) fluvial facies association. They define an initial rifting stage, an advanced rifting stage, an intensive late rifting stage and a degeneration rifting stage. These correlate in terms of facies associations with the four systems tracts defined above, though modification of whether active faulting was actually occurring is required to modify the correlation of terminology.

Field-based studies of basin fills

Such studies in a particular geographical location often reveal a stratigraphy that can be reinterpreted in terms of tectonic systems tracts. Evidence for an increase in the depth of water in which deposition occurs is evident in a number of basins as a change from early continental clastic sediments to deeper water facies higher in the infill succession. Examples include the Miocene of the Gulf of Suez (Sellwood & Netherwood 1984; Scott & Govean 1985) and the Jurassic/Cretaceous of East Greenland (Surlyk 1984). The presence of deeper water facies is not enough in itself to define a rift climax systems tract; it is the relationship with other sedimentary sequences above, below and laterally that will be diagnostic. The Devonian sequence of Orkney (Astin 1990) is another possible candidate where stacked fluvial sequences are superseded by deeper water facies and capped by extensive alluvial plain deposits. These can be regarded in terms of the rift initiation, climax and immediate post-rift systems tracts, though more information may be required to define the transition from one to the other.

The rift climax systems tract can be associated with observations in Death Valley, where over 350 m of lacustrine sediments have been reported (Hunt & Mabey 1966) to stack close to the fault plane. Death Valley is a classic example of an arid rift climax systems tract (Prosser 1991), demonstrating alluvial fans, an evaporitic basin fill, rock falls and talus cones, and a longitudinal river system.

Other examples with evidence of tectonism being the dominant control on facies evolution include the Late Carboniferous to Triassic succession in Madagascar (Nichols & Daly 1989), the Jurassic of nothern Italy (Winterer & Bosellini 1981) and the Ridge Basin in California (despite its strike-slip origin) (Nilsen & McLaughlin 1985).

Seismic and borehole studies

A basin analysis that is based on seismic–stratigraphic techniques alone relies on the interpretation of reflector geometries and seismic facies analysis. These techniques were applied to the case studies from the Barents Sea and the Magnus Basin presented above. Published accounts of the seismic expression of basin fill sequences are commonly vague, with little consideration for the information contained between individual reflectors. Syn-rift sequences are too often defined as wedge-shaped reflector packages, which could be further broken down into their constituent systems tract components.

Occasional studies do contain information suggesting these stages could have been defined. These include sections across the Turkana Rift (Dunkelman *et al.* 1988), where transparent basal reflector packages are thought to be grits (possible rift initiation deposits). These pass up into more continuous stronger reflectors relating to fine-grained silts and tuffs (possible rift climax deposits). Ebinger *et al.* (1987) describe data also from East Africa. They relate a strongly divergent seismic reflector package below the Nkhata Basin in the Malawi Rift with field observations that include exposed lake beds, abandoned shorelines, drowned river valleys, faceted spurs and little modification of the fault scarp by waves. These seismic and land observations correlate perfectly with the early rift climax systems tract defined above.

Other published seismic-based studies where tectonic systems tracts could have aided in interpretations, and clarified the presentation of the basin analysis, include those of Anderson *et al.* (1983) from Dixie Valley, Nevada, and that of Boote & Kirk (1989) from western Australia (discussed in Prosser 1991).

The analysis of well data from the Moray Firth by Frostick *et al.* (1988) led to an interpretation of the Triassic deposits as early rift deposits. Their interpretative diagram of a cross-section illustrating the facies distributions are more consistent with a rift climax systems tract. This also explains the lack of coarse-grained influxes into the basin which Frostick *et al.* (1988) incorrectly use as evidence for the early stage of evolution.

Summary and discussion

The results of detailed seismic interpretation and consideration of the tectonic influences on sedimentation has led to the recognition of a fundamental pattern in the type and architecture of the depositional systems that accumulate in a fault-bounded basin. These patterns are large-scale features that will show different expressions on a small scale depending on climate, source rock composition, and possibly eustatic fluctuations. The type of sediment that will accumulate in any given basin is difficult to predict given the complexity of controls on deposition, however, it is suggested here that there may be a common expression of tectonic control behind many rift basin stratigraphies. To distinguish these from the signature of other variables it may be helpful to look for characteristic linked depositional systems, to correlate them with a particular tectonic systems tract, and thus determine the stage of basin development. The definition of stages of basin evolution, and the associated tectonic systems tracts and seismic expression, introduces new terminology into an area of the subject already over-saturated with complicated jargon. However, it is argued that this has led to a situation where tightly defined terms are used that have implications that are not consistent with all the settings in which they are applied. The eustatic systems tracts of Posamentier & Vail (1988) are ideal for describing processes that affect passive continental margins, because they force the interpreter to consider all aspects affecting sediment accumulation in both space and time. However, the models are less appropriate when describing sediment packages that accumulated in active fault-bounded basins, where local tectonics intoduce important additional controls that are not incorporated into the above systems tracts, and towards which the interpreter is not led. If a tectonic signature is identified and basin analysis is approached from this standpoint, emphasis will be on the likely sedimentary facies that may develop in rifts in both temporal and spatial senses, and may thus elucidate the potential presence of source, seal and reservoir relationships.

An ideal rift basin might show each tectonic systems tract clearly in its stratigraphy, though in practice it may not be possible to define each systems tract if it is an extremely thin component of the basin fill, or if local influences prevented its formation or preservation (e.g. the total infill and burial of the small Barents Sea half-grabens, where no differentiation between an early and a late post-rift systems tract can be recognized). An ideal basin that did show each stage of evolution might appear similar to that illustrated in Fig. 8. A graphic sedimentary log through a position indicated by the arrow on Fig. 8, might appear like that of Fig. 9. The interpretation of the systems tract and its significance for basin analysis is indicated beside the theoretical log.

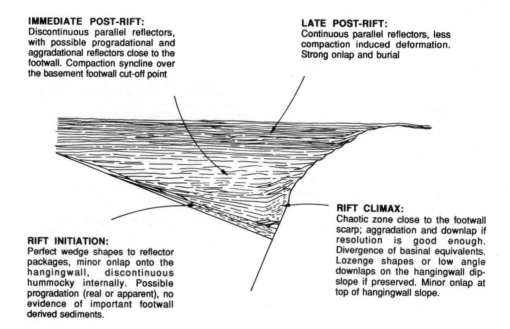

IMMEDIATE POST-RIFT:
Discontinuous parallel reflectors, with possible progradational and aggradational reflectors close to the footwall. Compaction syncline over the basement footwall cut-off point

LATE POST-RIFT:
Continuous parallel reflectors, less compaction induced deformation. Strong onlap and burial

RIFT INITIATION:
Perfect wedge shapes to reflector packages, minor onlap onto the hangingwall, discontinuous hummocky internally. Possible progradation (real or apparent), no evidence of important footwall derived sediments.

RIFT CLIMAX:
Chaotic zone close to the footwall scarp; aggradation and downlap if resolution is good enough. Divergence of basinal equivalents. Lozenge shapes or low angle downlaps on the hangingwall dip-slope if preserved. Minor onlap at top of hangingwall slope.

Fig. 8. An idealized section of a line drawing of a seismic section through an ideal basin, where each tectonic systems tract can be identified. The characteristic seismic expression of each is summarized in the annotation. This will not always be possible.

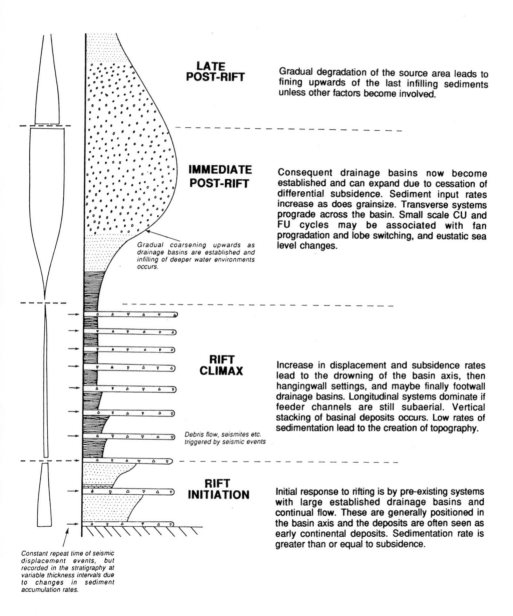

LATE POST-RIFT

Gradual degradation of the source area leads to fining upwards of the last infilling sediments unless other factors become involved.

IMMEDIATE POST-RIFT

Consequent drainage basins now become established and can expand due to cessation of differential subsidence. Sediment input rates increase as does grainsize. Transverse systems prograde across the basin. Small scale CU and FU cycles may be associated with fan progradation and lobe switching, and eustatic sea level changes.

Gradual coarsening upwards as drainage basins are established and infilling of deeper water environments occurs.

RIFT CLIMAX

Increase in displacement and subsidence rates lead to the drowning of the basin axis, then hangingwall settings, and maybe finally footwall drainage basins. Longitudinal systems dominate if feeder channels are still subaerial. Vertical stacking of basinal deposits occurs. Low rates of sedimentation lead to the creation of topography.

Debris flow, seismites etc. triggered by seismic events

RIFT INITIATION

Initial response to rifting is by pre-existing systems with large established drainage basins and continual flow. These are generally positioned in the basin axis and the deposits are often seen as early continental deposits. Sedimentation rate is greater than or equal to subsidence.

Constant repeat time of seismic displacement events, but recorded in the stratigraphy at variable thickness intervals due to changes in sediment accumulation rates.

Fig. 9. An idealized log of the vertical lithostratigraphy through the basin centre, interpreted as the expression of a changing tectonic control on the depositional system.

Conclusions

The discussions presented in this paper illustrate the suitability and practicality of using the concept of tectonic systems tracts in basin analysis. While hard evidence is somewhat circumstantial because of the lack of drilling through syn-rift wedges, integration of evidence from different sources adds together to form a consistent model of the pattern of sediment accumulation in asymmetric grabens bounded by active faults. Tectonic systems tracts are defined on the basis of stratal geometries, and integrated with facies interpretations to construct a detailed basin evolution. They can be recognized in field and seismic-based studies, and help the geologist to consider all the important aspects which should be taken into account when a rift basin development is described and interpreted. The descriptions are comparable and predictive, both spatially and temporally. They provide a method that is complementary to the eustatic systems tracts of Posamentier & Vail (1988), one that is suitable for the study of rift basin fills where tectonic controls may be the dominant influence on sedimentation. The approach to basin analysis from a tectonic stand can only be applied in fault-controlled basins, and is not meant to suggest these features can be seen in other settings. Van Wagoner et al. (1990) suggest that 'tectonism is the dominant control in determining the shape of the basin, the rate of sediment supply and possibly the second order arrangement of sequences, and that eustacy controls the timing and distribution of higher-frequency third- and fourth-order sequences'. That tectonics determine the shape and sediment flux of a fault-bounded basin, there can be no doubt, but if active faulting can also control the timing and distribution of the linked depositional sequences that stack to fill each basin, then the concept of tectonic systems tracts may be more useful than eustatic systems tracts in these settings.

The work involved in this paper was undertaken while completing a PhD at the University of Keele, funded by a NERC (BP case) studentship. BP are thanked for providing seismic data and allowing publication, as well as financial support for fieldwork and for computer facilities for compaction studies. Nick Milton, Rob Gawthorpe, Bernard Besly and an anonymous reviewer are thanked for helpful comments and contributions to the text.

References

ALEXANDER, J. & LEEDER, M. R. 1987. Active tectonic control on alluvial architecture. In: ETHERIDGE, F. G., FLORES, R. M. & HARVEY, M. D. (eds) Recent Developments in Fluvial Sedimentology, Society of Economic Paleontologists and Mineralogists, Special Publication, 39, 243–252.

ANDERSON, R. E., ZOBACK, M. L. & THOMPSON, G. A. 1983. Implications of selected subsurface data on the structural form and evolution of some basins in the northern Basin and Range Province. Geological Society of America Bulletin, 94, 1055–1072.

ASTIN, T. R. 1990. The Devonian lacustrine sediments of Orkney, Scotland; implications for climatic cyclicity, basin structure and maturation history. Journal of the Geological Society, London, 147, 141–152.

BADLEY, M. E., EGEBERG, T. & NIPEN, O. 1984. Development of rift basins illustrated by the structural evolution of the Oseberg Feature, Block 30/6, offshore Norway. Journal of the Geological Society, London, 141, 639–649.

BEACH, A., BIRD, T. & GIBBS, A. 1987. Extensional tectonics and crustal structure: deep seismic reflection data from the northern North Sea Viking Graben. In: Coward, M. P. & HANCOCK, J. (eds) Continental Extensional Tectonics. Geological Society, London, Special Publication, 28, 467–476.

BESSIS, F. 1986. Some remarks on the study of subsidence of sedimentary basins. *Marine and Petroleum Geology*, **3**, 37–63.

BILODEAU, W. L. & BLAIR, T. C. 1986. Tectonics and sedimentation: Timing of tectonic events using sedimentary rocks and facies. Geological Society of America Abstract Programs, **18**, 542.

BLAIR, T. C. 1987. Tectonic and hydrologic controls on cyclic alluvial fan, fluvial and lacustrine rift-basin sedimentation, Jurassic–Lowermost Cretaceous Todos Santos Formation, Chiapas, Mexico. *Journal of Sedimentary Petrology*, **57**, 845–862.

—— 1988. Development of tectonic cyclothems in rift, pull-apart and foreland basins: Sedimentary response to episodic tectonism. *Geology*, **16**, 517–520.

BOOTE, D. R. D. & KIRK, R. B. 1989. Depositional wedge cycles on an evolving plate margin, western and northwestern Australia. *American Association of Petroleum Geologists Bulletin*, **73**, 216–243.

BRIDGE, J. S. & LEEDER, M. R. 1979. A simulation model of alluvial stratigraphy. *Sedimentology*, **26**, 617–644.

BROWN, L. F. & FISHER, W. L. 1977. Seismic stratigraphic interpretations of depositional systems: examples from Brazilian rift and pull-apart basins. *In*: PAYTON, C. E. (ed.) *Seismic Stratigraphy—Applications to Hydrocarbon Exploration*. American Association of Petroleum Geologists Memoir, **26**, Tulsa, Oklahoma, 213–248.

—— & —— 1980. Seismic stratigraphic interpretation and petroleum exploration. *American Association of Petroleum Geologists Continuing Education Course Note Series*, **16**.

BURRUS, J. 1989. Review of geodynamic models for extensional basins; The paradox of stretching in the Gulf of Lions (Northwest Mediterranean). *Bulletin de la Société Géologique de la France*, **8**, 377–393.

CARTWRIGHT, J. 1987. Transverse structural zones in continental rifts—an example from the Danish Sector of the North Sea. *In*: BROOKS, J. & GLENNIE, K. (eds) *Petroleum Geology of North West Europe*, Graham & Trotman, London, 441–452.

—— 1991. The kinematic evolution of the Coffee Soil Fault. *In*: ROBERTS, A. M., YIELDING, G. & FREEMAN, B. (eds) *The Geometry of Normal Faults*. Geological Society, London, Special Publication, **56**, 29–40.

CHANGMING, C., JIAKUAN, H., JINGSANG, C. & XINGYOU, T. 1984. Depositional models of Tertiary rift basins, Eastern China and their application to petroleum prediction. *Sedimentary Geology*, **40**, 33–50.

CLOETINGH, S. 1988. Intraplate stresses: A new element in basin analysis. *In*: KLEINSPHEN, K. I. & PAOLA, C. (eds) *New Perspectives in Basin Analysis*, Springer-Verlag, 205–230.

CROSSLEY, R., 1984. Controls on sedimentation in the Malawi Rift, Central Africa. *Sedimentary Geology*, **40**, 73–88.

DENNY, C. S. 1965. Alluvial fans in the Death Valley region, California and Nevada. *US Geological Society Professional Paper*, **466**.

DUNKELMAN, T. J., KARSON, J. A. & ROSENDAHL, B. R. 1988. Structural style of the Turkana Rift, Kenya. *Geology*, **16**, 258–261.

EBINGER, C. J., ROSENDAHL, B. R. & REYNOLDS, D. J. 1987. Tectonic model of the Malawi Rift Africa. *Tectonophysics*, **141**, 215–235.

EVANS, A. C. & PARKINSON, D. N. 1983. A half-graben and tilted fault block structure in the northern North Sea. *In*: BALLEY, A. W. (ed.) *Seismic Expression of Structural Styles*. American Association of Petroleum Geologists, Studies in Geology, **15**, 7–9.

FALEIDE, J. I., GUDLAUGSSON, S. T. & JACQUART, G. 1984. Evolution of the Western Barents Sea. *Marine and Petroleum Geology*, **1**, 123–148.

FROSTICK, L. E., REID, I., JARVIS, J. & EARDLY, H. 1988. Triassic sediments of the Inner Moray Firth, Scotland: early rift deposits. *Journal of the Geological Society, London*, **146**, 235–248.

GALLOWAY, W. E. 1989. Genetic stratigraphic sequences in basin analysis I: architecture and genesis of flooding-surface bounded depositional units. *American Association of Petroleum Geologists Bulletin*, **73**, 125–142.

GAWTHORPE, R. L. & HURST, J. P. (in press). Transfer zones in extensional basins: their structural style and influence on drainage development and stratigraphy. *Journal of the Geological Society, London*.

GLOPPEN, T. G. & STEEL, R. J. 1981. The deposits, internal structure and geometry in six alluvial fan–fan delta lobes (Devonian Norway): a study in the significance of bedding sequence in conglomerates. *In*: ETHERIDGE, F. G. *et al.* (eds) *Recent and Ancient Nonmarine Depositional Environments; Models for Exploration.* Society of Economic Paleontologists and Mineralogists, Special Publication, **31**, 49–69.

HEGARTY, K. A., WEISSEL, J. K. & MUTTER, J. C. 1988. Subsidence history of Australia's southern margin: constraints on basin margins. *American Association of Petroleum Geologists Bulletin*, **5**, 615–633.

HEWARD, A. P. 1978. Alluvial fan sequence and megasequence models: with examples from Westphalian D–Stephanian B coalfields, Northern Spain. *In: Fluvial Sedimentology*, Canadian Society of Petroleum Geologists, Special Publication, 669–702.

HOOKE, R. LE B. 1968. Steady-state relationships on arid-region alluvial fans in closed basins. *American Journal of Science*, **266**, 609–629.

—— 1972. Geomorphic evidence for Late Winsconsin and Holocene tectonic deformation, Death Valley, California. *Geological Society of America Bulletin*, **83**, 2073–2098.

HUBBARD, R. J. 1988. Age and significance of sequence boundaries on Jurassic and early Cretaceous rifted continental boundaries. *American Association of Petroleum Geologists Bulletin*, **72**, 49–72.

HUNT, C. B. & MABEY, D. R. 1966. *Stratigraphy and structure, Death Valley, California.* US Geological Survey, Professional Paper, **494-B**.

LANGBEIN, W. B. & SCHUMM, S. A. 1958. Yield of sediment in relation to mean annual precipitation. *In*: KING, C. A. M. (ed.). *Landforms and Geomorphology*, Benchmarks Papers in Geology, **28**, 366–374.

LARSEN, P. H. 1988. Relay structure in a lower Permian basement-involved extension system, east Greenland. *Journal of Structural Geology*, **10**, 3–8.

LEEDER, M. R. & GAWTHORPE, R. L. 1987. Sedimentary models for extensional tilt-block/half-graben basins. *In*: COWARD, M. & HANCOCK, J. (eds) *Continental Extensional Tectonics. Geological Society, London, Special Publication*, **28**, 139–152.

——, ORD, D. M. & COLLIER, R. L. I. 1988. Development of alluvial fans and fan deltas in neotectonic extensional settings: implications for the interpretation of basin fills. *In*: NEMEC, W. & STEEL, R. J. (eds) *Fan Deltas: Sedimentology and Tectonic Settings*, 173–185.

MCKENZIE, D. 1978. Some remarks on the development of sedimentary basins. *Earth and Planetary Science Letters*, **40**, 25–32.

MITCHUM, R. M., VAIL, P. R. & THOMPSON, S. 1977. Seismic stratigraphy and global changes in sea level, Part 2: the depositional sequence as a basic unit for stratigraphic analysis. *In*: PAYTON, C. E. (ed.) *Seismic Stratigraphy—Applications to Hydrocarbon Exploration. American Association of Petroleum Geologists Memoir*, **26**, Tulsa, Oklahoma, 53–62.

—— & VAN WAGONER, J. C. 1990. High frequency sequences and their stacking patterns: sequence–stratigraphic evidence of high-frequency eustatic cycles. *Sedimentary Geology*, **70**, 131–160.

MONTADERT, L., ROBERTS, D. G., DE CHARPEL, O. & GUENNOC, P. 1979. Rifting and subsidence of the Northern continental margin in the Bay of Biscay. *In: Initial Reports of the Deep Sea Drilling Project*, **48**, Washington, US Government Printing Office, 1025–1060.

MORELY, C. K., NELSON, R. A., PATTON, T. L. & MUNN, S. G. 1990. Transfer zones in the East African Rift System and their relevance to hydrocarbon exploration in rifts. *American Association of Petroleum Geologists Bulletin*, **74**, 1234–1253.

MORETTI, I. & COLLETTA, B. 1988. Fault block tilting: the Gebel Zeit example, Gulf of Suez. *Journal of Structural Geology*, **10**, 9–19.

MUTTER, J. C. & LARSEN, R. L. 1989. Extension of the Exmouth Plateau, offshore north-western Australia: Deep seismic reflection/refraction evidence for simple and pure shear mechanisms. *Geology*, **17**, 15–18.

NICHOLS, G. J. & DALY, M. C. 1989. Sedimentation in an intracratonic extensional basin: the Karoo of the Central Morondava Basin, Madagascar. *Geological Magazine*, **126**, 339–354.

NILSEN, T. H. & MCLAUGHLIN, R. J. 1985. Comparison of tectonic framework and depositio-
    nal patterns of the Hornelan strike-slip basin of Norway and the Ridge Basin and Little
    Sulphur Creek strike-slip basins of California. *In*: BIDDLE, K. T. & CHRISTIE-BLICK, N.
    (eds) *Strike-slip Deformation, Basin Formation and Sedimentation*. Society of Economic
    Paleontologists and Mineralogists, Special Publication, **37**, 79–103.
PAYTON, C. E. 1977. Seismic stratigraphy: applications to hydrocarbon exploration. *American
    Association of Petroleum Geologists Memoir*, **26**.
PITMAN, W. C. 1979. The effect of eustatic sea level changes on stratigraphic sequences at
    Atlantic margins. *In*: Geological and Geophysical Investigations of Continental Margins.
    American Association of Petroleum Geologists Memoir, **29**, 453–460.
—— & ANDREWS, J. A. 1985. Subsidence and thermal history of small pull-apart basins. *In*:
    BIDDLE, K. T. & CHRISTIE-BLICK, N. (eds) *Strike-slip Deformation, Basin Formation and
    Sedimentation*. Society of Economic Paleontologists and Mineralogists, Special Publi-
    cation, **37**, 45–49.
—— & GOLOVCHENKO, X. 1983. The effect of sea-level change on the shelf edge and slope of
    passive margins. *In*: Society of Economic Paleontologists and Mineralogists, Special
    Publication, **33**, 41–58.
POSAMENTIER, H. W. & VAIL, P. R. 1988. Eustatic controls on clastic deposition. II—sequence
    and systems tract models. *In*: *Sea-level changes—An integrated approach*. Society of
    Economic Paleontologists and Mineralogists, Special Publication, **42**, 125–154.
PROSSER, S. D. 1991. *Syn-rift Sequences: their Recognition and Significance in Basin Analysis*.
    PhD Thesis, University of Keele.
ROSENDAHL, B. R. 1987. Architecture of continental rifts with special reference to East Africa,
    Annual Review of Earth and Planetary Sciences, **15**, 445–503.
SCHLISCHE, R. W. & OLSEN, P. E. 1990. Quantitative filling model for continental extensional
    basins with applications to early Mesozoic Rifts of eastern North America. *Journal of
    Geology*, **98**, 135–155.
SCHOLZ, C. H., AVILES, C. A. & WESNOUSKY, S. G. 1986. Scaling differences between large
    interplate and intraplate earthquakes. *Bulletin of the Seismological Society of America*, **76**,
    65–70.
SCHOLZ, C. A., ROSENDAHL, B. R. & SCOTT, D. L. 1990. Development of coarse-grained facies
    in lacustrine rift basins: Examples from East Africa. *Geology*, **18**, 140–144.
SCOTT, R. W. & GOVEAN, F. M. 1985. Early depositional history of a rift basin: Miocene in
    Western Sinai. *Palaeogeography, Palaeoclimatology, Palaeoecology*, **52**, 143–158.
SELLWOOD, B. W. & NETHERWOOD, R. E. 1984. Facies evolution in the Gulf of Suez area:
    Sedimentation history as an indicator of rift initiation and development. *Modern Geology*,
    9, 43–69.
STEEL, R. J., MAEHLE, S., NILSEN, H., RØE, S. L. & SPINNANGR, Å. 1977. Coarsening-upward
    cycles in the alluvium of Hornelen Basin (Devonian) Norway: Sedimentary response to
    tectonic events. *Geological Society of America Bulletin*, **88**, 1124–1134.
—— & WILSON, A. C. 1975. Sedimentation and tectonism (? Permo-Triassic) on the margin of
    the North Minch Basin. *Journal of the Geological Society, London*, **131**, 183–202.
SURLYK, F. 1984. Fan delta to submarine fan conglomerates of the Volgian-Valanginian
    Wollaston Foreland Group, East Greenland. *In*: KOSTER, E. H. & STEEL, R. J. (eds)
    Sedimentology of Gravels and Conglomerates. Canadian Society of Petroleum Geologists
    Memoir, **10**, 359–382.
—— 1989. Mid-Mesozoic syn-rift turbidite systems: controls and predictions. *In*: COLLINSON,
    J. D. (ed.) *Correlation in Hydrocarbon Exploration*. Norwegian Petroleum Society,
    Graham & Trotman, 231–242.
UDALL, S. L. & NOLAN, T. B. 1964. *The Hebgen Lake earthquake of August 17, 1959*. US
    Geological Survey Professional Paper, **435**.
VAIL, P. R. 1987. Seismic stratigraphic interpretation using sequence stratigraphy, Part 1:
    Seismic stratigraphic interpretation procedure. *In*: BALLY, A. W. (ed.) *Atlas of Seismic
    Stratigraphy*. American Association of Petroleum Geologists Studies in Geology, **27**,
    Tulsa, Oklahoma, **1**, 1–10.

——, MITCHUM, R. M. & THOMPSON, S. 1977. Seismic Stratigraphy and Global Changes in Sea Level, Part 3; Relative Changes of Sea Level from Coastal Onlap. *In*: PAYTON, C. E. (ed.) *Seismic Stratigraphy—Applications to Hydrocarbon Exploration*. American Association of Petroleum Geologists Memoir, **26**, Tulsa, Oklahoma, 63–82.

VAN WAGONER, J. C., MITCHUM, R. M., CAMPION, K. M. & RAHMANIAN, V. D. 1990. *Siliciclastic Sequence Stratigraphy in Well Logs, Cores, and Outcrops: Concepts for High-Resolution Correlation of Time and Facies*. American Association of Petroleum Geologists in Exploration Series, **7**.

WALSH, J. J. & WATERSON, J. 1987. Distribution of cumulative displacement and of seismic slip on a single normal fault surface. *Journal of Structural Geology*, **9**, 1039–1046.

WATSON, M. P., HAYWARD, A. B., PARKINSON, D. N. & ZHANG, Zh. M. 1987. Plate tectonic history, basin development and petroleum source rock deposition inshore China. *Marine and Petroleum Geology*, **4**, 205–225.

WATERSON, J. 1986. Fault dimensions, displacement and growth. *PAGEOPH*, **124**, 365–373.

WATTS, A. B. 1989. Lithospheric flexure due to prograding sediment loads: implications for the origin of offlap/onlap patterns in sedimentary basins. *Basin Research*, **2**, 133–144.

WILGUS, C. K., HASTINGS, B. S., KENDALL, C. G. St. C., POSAMENTIER, H. W., ROSS, C. A. & VAN WAGONER, J. C. 1988. *Sea-level Changes: An Integrated Approach*. Society of Economic Paleontologists and Mineralogists, Special Publication, **42**.

WINTERER, E. L. & BOSELLINI, A. 1981. Subsidence and sedimentation on Jurassic passive continental margin, southern Alps, Italy. *American Association of Petroleum Geologists Bulletin*, **65**, 394–421.

From WILLIAMS, G. D. & DOBB, A. (eds), 1993, *Tectonics and Seismic Sequence Stratigraphy*.
Geological Society Special Publication No. 71, 67–85.

Sediment geometries and domino faulting

David Waltham, Stuart Hardy &
Abdulnaser Abousetta

*Department of Geology, Royal Holloway & Bedford New College, University of London,
Egham, Surrey TW20 0EX, UK.*

Abstract: A general forward modelling scheme is used to produce a model of
sediment geometry in half-grabens formed during extension of domino fault
blocks. The model includes the effects of erosion, sediment transport, sedimentation and isostasy and simulates both syn- and post-rift sedimentary sequences.
The geometries and relationships produced by the model are broadly similar to
natural examples seen on North Sea seismic sections. This similarity is emphasized by the generation of synthetic seismic data using the numerically modelled
geometry as a template. The unconformable nature of the boundary between syn-
and post-rift seismic sequences is clearly visible on the synthetic data in the region
of the fault block crest.

Domino fault blocks, and the evolution of their sedimentary fill during development,
have been the subject of much interest in the past ten years. In particular, numerical
and analogue forward modelling techniques have been used to examine the geometries of the pre-, syn- and post-rift strata (Barr 1987*a,b*; Vendeville *et al.* 1987;
Yielding 1990; Barr 1991).

Domino fault blocks are a common type of normal fault observed in many
extensional basins (Mascle & Martin 1990; Jackson *et al.* 1988; Montadert *et al.*
1979). During extension there is a net rotation of each fault block accommodating
regional extension. Fault blocks are assumed to rotate rigidly with a diffuse
accommodation zone at their base. All dominoes are required to move simultaneously. Other models allow for 'soft' dominoes which deform during extension
(Walsh & Watterson 1991) or allow compaction of a soft domino during extension
and rotation (Iliffe *et al.* 1990).

The domino model of fault block rotation has been used (Barr 1987*a,b*; Jackson *et
al.* 1988; Yielding 1990) as the mechanism of upper-crustal deformation in a model of
uniform lithospheric extension (McKenzie 1978). This work has shown the control
on footwall uplift and hangingwall subsidence of fault block width, initial fault dip,
amount of extension and sediment loading. Yielding (1990) has shown that this
combined model predicts well the amount of footwall uplift and hangingwall
subsidence for three fields in the Brent Province of the North Sea.

Barr (1991) combined the domino fault block model with overall tectonic subsidence curves for several locations in the central North Sea. He demonstrated the
importance of variable sedimentation rates and sea-floor topography in controlling
the depositional geometries of the syn- and post-rift sediments. He also showed the
effect of compaction on syn- and post-rift sediments.

However, in all these approaches there has been a lack of quantitative sedimentary
modelling of the internal structures of the syn- and post-rift sediments and their
sequence boundaries. This paper attempts to combine the uniform lithospheric

stretching model of McKenzie (1978), the domino fault block rotation model and a diffusion model of erosion/sedimentation in order to forward model the relationships between the domino fault blocks and syn- and post-rift sediments. The seismic stratigraphy of these forward models will then be examined by generating synthetic seismic sections using Kirchhoff integral techniques. This approach has previously been used to examine listric normal fault geometries (McClay *et al.* 1991).

Mathematical modelling of sediments and tectonics

The numerical models demonstrated in this paper use the general forward modelling equation developed by Waltham (1992). This approach is based upon the idea that a geological surface can be modified in four ways: (i) material can be added or subtracted from the surface; (ii) material can be moved from one part of the surface to another; (iii) the surface can be physically moved; (iv) the surface can be deformed. The first two mechanisms are sedimentary while the latter two are tectonic. Expressing these ideas mathematically and for a two-dimensional model, leads to

$$\partial z/\partial t = \underbrace{(p - \partial F/\partial x)}_{\text{Sedimentary processes}} + \underbrace{(v - u.\partial z/\partial x)}_{\text{Tectonic processes}}, \tag{1}$$

where $\partial z/\partial t$ is the rate of vertical movement at a point, F is sediment flux, p is additional sedimentary gains or losses, v is the uplift rate and u is the rate of horizontal movement. The vertical coordinate, z, is assumed to be positive upwards throughout this paper. Two of the terms (F and u) in Equation (1) require a little more explanation. The role of the remaining terms in Equation (1) should become clear as we develop the domino model in the succeeding sections.

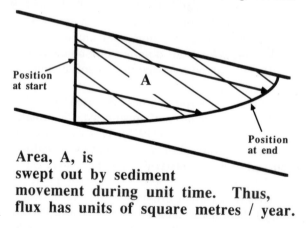

Position at start

A

Position at end

Area, A, is swept out by sediment movement during unit time. Thus, flux has units of square metres / year.

Fig. 1. Sedimentary flux, F, is defined as the area, A, swept out by mobile sediments in a period of 1 year.

Sediment flux, F, may be illustrated using Fig. 1 which shows movement of material along a surface due to sedimentary processes. The rate of movement may vary with depth below the surface and, in a period of say one year, the sediments at some fixed starting position sweep out an area as shown in the figure. This area is the sediment flux which, therefore, has dimensions of area per unit time. If the amount of flux entering a region is greater than the amount leaving then net sedimentation must be occurring. Similarly, if the amount entering is less than the amount leaving then net erosion is taking place. Thus, the change in surface height is controlled by the spatial rate of change in sediment flux, i.e. $\partial F/\partial x$.

It may seem puzzling that the rate of change in *height*, $\partial z/\partial t$, depends upon the rate of *horizontal* movement, u. The explanation for this is illustrated in Fig. 2, which demonstrates that the height at a fixed position varies due to horizontal movement of a non-horizontal topography.

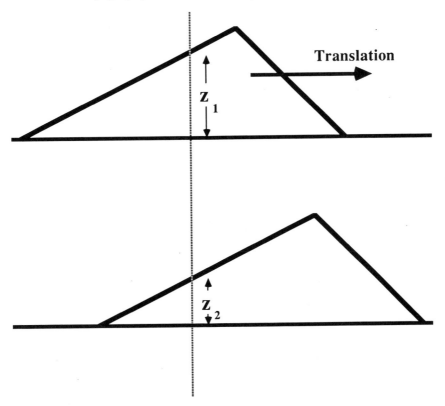

Fig. 2. Calculation of the rate of change of surface height requires knowledge of the horizontal rate of movement, since horizontal movement of a non-horizontal topography will lead to a change in height at a fixed point.

It is worth emphasizing that Equation (1) does not represent a conceptual model but is rather a method for implementing such a model. Equation (1) contains no geology or physics and is a purely geometric statement. The geology and physics are added when specific forms for the spatial and temporal variation of F, p, u and v are used. For example, the assumptions we make in the succeeding sections allow us to use Equation (1) for modelling sedimentation patterns on a set of extending domino fault blocks. However, Equation (1) has also been used, together with a rather different set of assumptions/concepts, to model carbonate platform evolution (Pomar *et al.* 1990). Conceptual models produced by other workers could also be implemented using this approach, e.g. the flexural cantilever model (Kuznir *et al.* 1991) or inclined simple shear above listric faults (White *et al.* 1986).

Using an approach based upon Equation (1) has three main benefits: (i) it greatly simplifies algorithm design and implementation; (ii) it clearly states the information required to model a given situation; (iii) it allows many apparently independent processes to be combined in a single modelling scheme.

Modelling erosion and sedimentation on extending domino fault blocks

In order to model the specific case of domino fault blocks, the velocities, u and v in Equation (1), need to be specified. A rigid block can only be rotated or translated and the horizontal and vertical velocities will, therefore, be of the form

$$u = -\omega z + u_0 \tag{2}$$

$$v = \omega x + v_0 \tag{3}$$

where ω is the rotation rate of the block and u_0 and v_0 are constants which control horizontal translation and subsidence, respectively. The overall uplift/subsidence rate of the block, as opposed to local uplift caused by rotation, is controlled by isostasy. We return to this later in the paper but, for now, we will set v_0 to zero.

The rotation rate, which depends upon extension rate and fault dip, is given by

$$\omega = (\partial\beta/\partial t)\sin(\theta)/\{\beta.\sqrt{(\beta^2 - \sin^2\theta)}\}, \tag{4}$$

where β is the stretch factor (McKenzie 1978) and θ is the initial fault dip.

Horizontal translation, u_0, is simply due to extension of the fault block system.

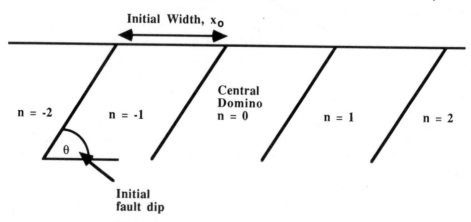

Fig. 3. The initial domino fault block geometry is defined by block width and fault dip. The dominoes are indexed according to their proximity to the central, stationary, domino.

Each block will move, relative to its neighbour, at a rate, U, given by

$$U = x_0 \partial\beta/\partial t \tag{5}$$

with x_0 equal to the initial block width. If the central block of the model is taken to be stationary, the other blocks will have translation velocities of

$$u_0 = n\,U \tag{6}$$

in which the index, n, runs from zero for the central block to $+1$, $+2$, ..., etc. for blocks to the right and -1, -2, ..., etc. for blocks to the left (see Fig. 3).

Equations (2) to (6), together with the initial geometry shown in Fig. 3, may be used in Equation (1) to model a set of rotating fault blocks. However, the results are not particularly interesting until the effects of erosion and sedimentation are also introduced. The simplest model of sediment transport which can be built into Equation (1) is the diffusion equation approach in which the flux, F, is assumed to be proportional to slope and directed down the slope, i.e.

$$F = -a\,\partial z/\partial x, \tag{7}$$

where a is the diffusion coefficient. This leads to the diffusion equation

$$\partial F/\partial x = -a\partial^2 z/\partial x^2, \tag{8}$$

provided a is assumed constant.

The above expressions could be used to model a set of, say, 3 or 4 dominoes. However, in practice, a width equal to the current model width βx_0 is modelled and cyclic boundary conditions are then employed. This means that any material transported off the left side of the model moves onto the right side, and vice versa. The effect is that calculations are performed for a single block width but give results for an infinite set of identical blocks placed side by side.

Figure 4(a) shows the results of applying Equations (1) to (8) to a domino block of initial width 15 km and initial fault dip of 60°. The blocks were stretched by a factor of $\beta = 1.4$ over a period of 25 Ma and this was followed by an additional 25 Ma of passive erosion and sedimentation. In all the following examples a stretching period of 25 Ma has been used together with a stretch factor of 1.4. These values were chosen as they correspond broadly to values suggested for the late Jurassic rifting in the northern North Sea (e.g. Barr 1991). A diffusion rate of 0.3 m²/a is assumed throughout this paper. The value of the diffusion constant is very difficult to assess since published estimates vary from 9×10^{-4} m²/a for arid fault scarps (Colman & Watson 1983) to 5.6×10^5 m²/a for a prograding delta (Kenyon & Turcotte 1985). Assuming that the domino model lies somewhere between these extremes suggests an intermediate value of approximately 1 m²/a might be appropriate. The value used in the examples in this paper is indeed approximately unity and has been chosen largely because it illustrates well the points we wish to make. The rate of diffusion in the model will be examined further in the discussion.

Several features of the result shown in Fig. 4(a) are worth noting. First, it can be seen that as the dominoes are rotated the uplifted areas are eroded, the eroded material is transported and deposited both to the left and to the right. Initial syn-rift sediment packages are wedge shaped with the greatest thickness adjacent to footwalls, but as rotation continues the syn-rift sediment packages become more symmetric. Syn-rift packages are seen to onlap both the footwall and the hangingwall

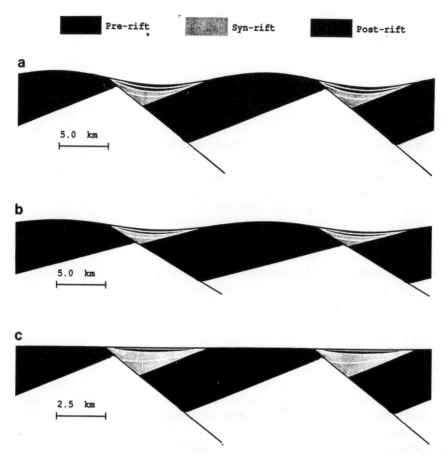

Fig. 4. The effect of altering the initial fault block geometry. (**a**) Domino block width = 15 km, fault dip = 60°, rifting takes 25 Ma, post-rift stage is an additional 25 Ma, diffusion coefficient = 0.3 m²/a, β = 1.4; (**b**) as for (a) except that initial fault dip is 45°; (**c**) as for (a) except domino block width is 7.5 km.

blocks. Post-rift sediments are also symmetric but are seen to offlap the older sediments. The post-rift sediment package is much smaller in volume than the syn-rift sediment package. An important feature of the diffusion model is that, within both the syn- and post-rift sediments, dip reversals are predicted. These dip reversals are a consequence of sediments being deposited non-horizontally. This contrasts with the work of other authors who assume that sediments are initially flat lying and that dip reversals are caused by later compaction (Barr 1991), compression (Frost 1989) or fault movement drag.

The effect of decreasing the initial domino fault dip is shown in Fig. 4(b). A decrease in the initial fault dip from 60° to 45° causes the syn-rift package to become less wedge shaped with gentler dip reversals. In addition the total amount of syn- and post-rift sediment is reduced. The relationships between pre-, syn- and post-rift are similar to the previous run. However, the overall topography at the end of the run is much smoother than that in Fig. 4(a).

The effect of decreasing the initial domino width by half is shown in Fig. 4(c). With a smaller domino the same stratal relationships are observed as before but, because the distances for sediment transport are smaller, erosion is able to flatten the topography completely in the same time. The proportion of syn-rift material is much greater than in the previous runs, most of the uplifted area being eroded during rotation with only very slight relief and erosion during the post-rift period.

The effect of additional background sedimentation

Comparing the geometry of Fig. 4(a) with those observed in the northern North Sea (Yielding 1990; Nipen 1987; Roberts et al. 1987; Bally 1988; Badley et al. 1984), it appears that the overall geometry of the domino block, with an eroded crest and a wedge-shaped syn-rift package, is correct. Dip reversals within the syn-rift sediments and onlap onto both hangingwalls and footwalls are also seen. However, in the northern North Sea, syn-rift sediments are often found in condensed sequences near the crests of the fault blocks. Furthermore, much of the syn-rift fill is not locally eroded material, which would be clastic, but contains mudstones and shales of the Humber group (Brown 1990) which must be distantly sourced. Post-rift sediments, which onlap and eventually drape the tilted fault block structures, are also externally sourced.

These observations suggest that the model could be improved by taking this background, non-local, sedimentation into account. This additional sediment input can be regarded, on this scale, as approximately constant across the domino system and may then be modelled by introducing a constant value for p in Equation (1). Figure 5(a) shows the results of running the model with parameters as for Fig. 4(a) but with the addition of a background sedimentation rate of 20 m/Ma. The figure of 20 m/Ma is at the lower end of the range of sedimentation rates derived by Barr (1991) from several northern North Sea wells. The addition of a background sedimentation rate causes some dramatic changes. First, the pre-rift layers do not suffer nearly as much erosion as before, leading to a fault block which only suffers limited crestal erosion. Second, the volume of syn-rift sediments is increased and the syn-rift sediments are found, thinned, far up the hangingwall block. Third, the volume of the post-rift sediments is increased and the post-rift sediments are seen to onlap the previously deposited sediments and the eroded fault block crest.

Isostasy

The background sedimentation described in the previous section must occur entirely below sea-level. However, the model run shown in Fig. 5(a) assumes that these sediments are deposited uniformly across the entire domino. A significant improvement can be obtained by setting a non-zero background sediment rate only for those points in the model which lie below sea-level. This requires that isostatic effects be incorporated into the scheme. The approach we have taken is to calculate, at each time step, a non-zero vertical velocity, v_o in Equation (3), which is dependent upon the mass imbalance, ΔM. This mass difference is defined as the difference in load between the current model and a model in perfect isostatic balance. The isostatic compensation velocity is then given by

$$v_o = \Delta M/(x\rho T_{iso}),$$

(9)

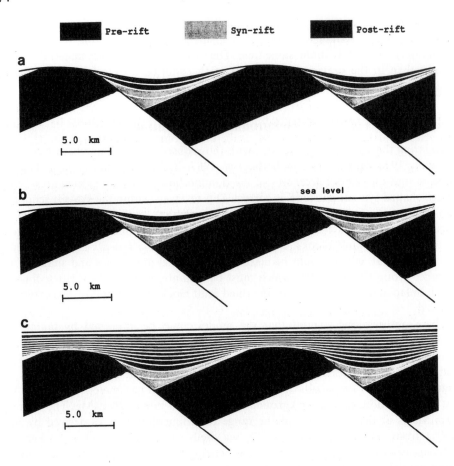

Fig. 5. The effect of background sedimentation and isostasy. (**a**) As for Fig. 4(a) except that an additional background sedimentation rate of 20 m/Ma is assumed; (**b**) as for Fig. 5(a) except that isostasy is included and background sedimentation occurs only below sea-level; (**c**) as for Fig. 5(b) except that there is an additional 100 Ma of post-rift subsidence (i.e. a total run time of 150 Ma).

where T_{iso} is the isostatic relaxation time (of the order of a few thousand years Cathless 1975)), x is the distance over which ΔM is calculated (see below) and ρ is a density which equals the difference between asthenosphere density and water density if isostatic compensation at the base of the lithosphere is assumed and the crust is completely flooded. The relaxation time is very small compared to run time so that the model is always very close to equilibrium. In fact, it is usually best to set T_{iso} equal to at least three time steps so that numerical stability is maintained. The mass imbalance is calculated using the following assumptions.

(i) Isostatic balance is only achieved over the entire domino width, i.e. $x = \beta x_o$, rather than point by point. This is because the domino is assumed to be internally rigid whereas point by point Airy isostasy would necessarily produce internal deformation.

(ii) Isostatic compensation occurs at a depth equal to the initial base of the lithosphere. Thus, the mass imbalance is calculated using

$$\Delta M = \beta M_o - M_w - M_{sed} - M_c - M_{sc} - M_a, \tag{10}$$

where M_o is the mass of unstretched lithosphere calculated using the initial domino width; M_w is the mass of water; M_{sed} is the load due to the additional background sediments; M_c is the mass of crust; M_{sc} is the mass of subcrustal lithosphere; M_a is the mass of upwelled asthenosphere.

(iii) Crust is conserved. Thus, the mass of crust contained within the initial domino width, x_o, is equal to the mass of crust contained within the stretched domino width of $x = \beta x_o$.

(iv) Thermal relaxation forces the depth of the base of the lithosphere to decay exponentially back to its initial depth as predicted by McKenzie (1978). Thus, the mass, M_{sc} of the subcrustal lithosphere must be recalculated at each time step using

$$\partial M_{sc}/\partial t = x\rho_{sc}\,\Delta z_{sc}/T_{th}, \tag{11}$$

where T_{th} is the thermal relaxation time (50 Ma) and Δz_{sc} is the distance of the current lithosphere base from its position at thermal equilibrium.

(v) The densities of the crust, sediment, sub-crustal lithosphere and asthenosphere are assumed to be constant. This is different to the classic McKenzie model (McKenzie 1978) in which the average densities of the crust and subcrustal lithosphere are slightly different before and after thermal relaxation ($\Delta\rho \ll 1\%$). In practice, intermediate values can be chosen and these will give subsidence which differs from the McKenzie model by around 5%. In fact, the range of parameters considered likely for this problem gives rise to differences of up to 20% in the initial and final values of subsidence (Barr 1987a). In addition, the simplifications (e.g. a linear temperature and, therefore, density profile, a horizontal base for the crust and lithosphere, etc.) will also cause significant deviations of the true subsidence from that predicted. Overall we consider that, for a simple model such as ours, constant density assumptions are sufficient and have the advantage of greatly simplifying the calculations. The densities that we have used are summarized in Table 1.

Table 1. *The densities used for calculating the isostatic response of the model*

	Densities (kg/m³)
Water	1000
Sediment	2200
Crust	2800
Subcrustal lithosphere	3245
Asthenosphere	3184

A model run which includes isostasy is shown in Fig. 5(b). The same general relationships as seen in Fig. 5(a) are shown. It can be seen that there is significant but variable bathymetry even after 25 Ma of thermal relaxation with 1.5 km of water in the deepest areas and 0.5 km in the shallowest areas. Although the fault block crests are below sea-level they are still not covered by sediment because the diffusion mechanism transports sediments away from these areas. The crests of the fault blocks have suffered slightly more erosion due to the lack of a protective cover of syn-rift sediments when they were above sea-level.

Allowing 125 Ma of thermal relaxation after the rifting event results in the development of a more complete sequence (see Fig. 5(c)). It can be seen that the post-rift sediments infill the topography created during rifting, initially onlapping and then draping the fault block crests. Significant thickness variations in the post-rift fill are still seen 50 Ma after the cessation of rifting. This result is similar to that predicted by Barr (1991) and that noted by Bertram & Milton (1989). The final post-rift sediments are essentially flat-lying with about 500 m of water present. The fault block crests are found more than 2 km below present sea-level and have suffered deep erosion of up to 2 km.

Although Fig. 5(c) was not an attempt to model a specific domino fault block geometry, the final result compares well with some northern North Sea profiles (e.g. Tampen Spur (Bally 1988), Statfjord (Kirk 1980) and Brent (Bowen 1975)). In these areas we see similar sized domino blocks which have suffered extension of around 40%. The overall relationships of pre-syn, and post-rift sediments are remarkably similar to those seen in Fig. 5(c)). Figure 6 is a line diagram, based upon a seismic line from Bally (1988), of the Tampen Spur. The syn-rift sequence is usually taken to lie between the Top Brent and Base Cretaceous. Figure 6 clearly shows the principal features of our model such as wedge-shaped syn-rift sequences and dip reversals.

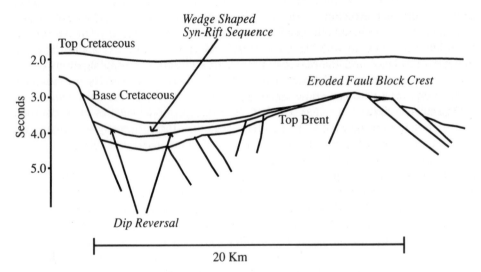

Fig. 6. Line diagram, based upon a seismic line in Bally (1988), from the Tampen Spur.

Bathymetry predictions

The modelling described in the preceding sections can be used to predict spatial and temporal changes in bathymetry. In this section we will use this to illustrate the effects of the various sedimentary parameters in the model and to predict typical bathymetric evolution for a North Sea domino structure using the same parameters as previously, where appropriate. Figure 7 shows the predicted water depth above the fault block crest and above the deepest part of the half-graben for a range of different sedimentary assumptions.

Figure 7(a) shows the effect of the linked upper-crustal domino and uniform lithospheric stretching models with no diffusion or background sedimentation. Thus, this shows the isostatic and tectonic effects on a set of dominoes which do not experience erosion or sedimentation. It can be seen that the 25 Ma rifting episode has the effect of elevating the crest to 1.6 km above the sea-level and subsiding the trough to 3.8 km below sea-level. Uplift and subsidence are most rapid in the initial stages of rifting when rotation rates are highest. The following 125 Ma of thermal relaxation result in gradual subsidence of the crest to 1 km above sea-level and further gradual subsidence of the trough to around 4.4 km.

Figure 7(b) shows the effect of the diffusion model of erosion and sedimentation with no background sedimentation. Thus, it shows the isostatic and tectonic effects seen by a set of dominoes which undergo local erosion and redeposition. It can be seen that the initial rifting still produces uplift and subsidence of the crest and trough, respectively. However, as rifting continues, the effect of erosion becomes apparent since the elevation of the crest decreases. At the end of rifting the crest is 340 m above sea-level, having previously reached a maximum of 460 m after 13 Ma of rifting. Similarly, the initial rifting produces a rapid increase in water depth of the trough which decreases as the trough fills with material eroded from the crest. The water depth at the end of the rifting event is 2.3 km. During the following 125 Ma of thermal relaxation, the diffusion model continues to act on the crest and trough causing a gradual reduction in relief. This results in the crest subsiding below sea-level due to the combined effects of erosion and thermal subsidence. The trough, on the other hand, fills up with the eroded material at a rate which is higher than the thermal subsidence and the maximum water depth reduces during thermal relaxation. At the end of the model run there is little contrast between crests and troughs, both being around 1.6 km below sea-level.

Figure 7(c) shows the effect of including background sedimentation with no diffusion acting on the model. Thus, it shows the isostatic and tectonic effects seen by a set of domino blocks which experience sediment loading but no erosion. As previously, it can be seen that there is initial uplift of the crest and subsidence of the trough during the rifting phase. The crest is elevated to a maximum of 1.5 km and the maximum water depth in the trough is 3.5 km. During the following 125 Ma of thermal relaxation, the effects of continuing sediment loading can be seen. The crest subsides back to sea-level due to sediment loading and a smaller component of thermal relaxation. In the trough, maximum water depth is reached immediately after rifting, during thermal relaxation the subsidence effects of sediment loading and thermal relaxation are overwhelmed by the decrease in water depth caused by sedimentary infilling. The water depth at the end of the model run is 2.6 km.

Figure 7(d) shows the results of including both diffusion and background sedimentation. Therefore, in this example, the graph shows the combined effects of erosion, sediment redistribution and additional sediment loading. The crest is elevated during the initial stages of rifting but this elevation is reduced by erosion during the latter half of rifting. The maximum amount of crest elevation is around 400 m. The trough subsides rapidly during rifting, then water depth decreases in the thermal relaxation

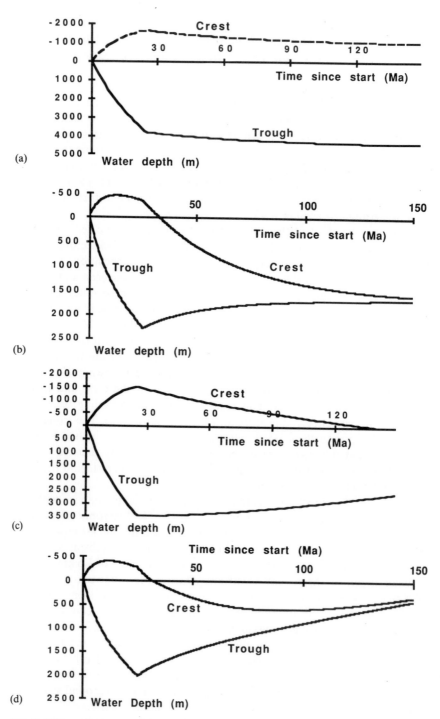

Fig. 7. Effect of various sedimentary assumptions on predicted maximum and minimum water depths. (**a**) Water depths for no diffusion or sedimentation; (**b**) water depths with diffusion but no sedimentation; (**c**) water depths with sedimentation but no diffusion; (**d**) water depths with both diffusion and sedimentation.

phase. The maximum water depth at the end of rifting is 2 km. During the following 125 Ma the combined effects of continued erosion, background sedimentation, sediment loading and thermal relaxation are active. This results in the crest subsiding below sea-level with water depth above the crest reaching a maximum of around 590 m at 90 Ma then decreasing as the effects of continued sediment infill become dominant over thermal subsidence and loading. The trough rapidly shallows as erosion and background sedimentation infill the topography. At the end of the model run there is still a 70 m bathymetric difference between the crest and trough with the water being 400 m at its greatest depth.

An important point arising from these graphs is the effect of position on subsidence history. The crest shows less initial subsidence than predicted by a pure shear stretching model, while the trough shows more. Sawyer (1986) has pointed out that this has serious effects upon subsidence history analysis.

Seismic expression of model

Domino fault blocks and their associated sedimentary cover have been modelled in this paper on a scale which is typical of the North Sea and, on the other hand, on a scale which is much larger than can generally be seen on outcrops. Thus, natural examples of these structures would invariably be investigated using reflection seismic surveys. In order to validate our modelling, and also to use the models as an interpretative tool, it is useful to predict the seismic appearance of our modelled structures. Recently, our research team has used this technique for similar reasons on analogue modelled structures (McClay *et al.* 1991).

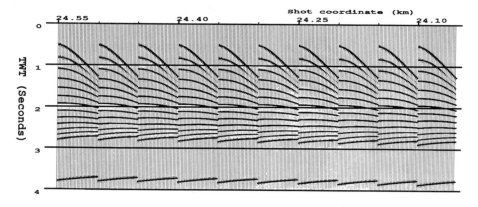

Fig. 8. Synthetic seismic shot records generated from the model of Fig. 5(c).

The method we have adopted is to produce synthetic shot record data and then to process these to produce a migrated seismic section. The modelling procedure consists of supplying a laterally invariant velocity model and a reflection coefficient for each boundary in the model. A Kirchhoff forward modelling algorithm (Hilterman 1970, 1975; Trorey 1970) is then used to generate the seismic traces. These traces contain all primary reflections and diffractions but do not contain multiples or mode converted events. Figure 8 shows ten out of the total of 600 shot records which result from using the velocity profile shown in Fig. 9 and the model geometry shown in Fig. 5(c). The pre-rift reflectors were assumed to have a reflection coefficient of 0.2 whilst the syn- and post-rift reflectors had coefficients of 0.05 and 0.1, respectively. Each shot record contains 30 traces and was produced using a 50 m shot and a 50 m receiver spacing. Note the non-hyperbolic moveout curves which result on shot records when reflectors dip.

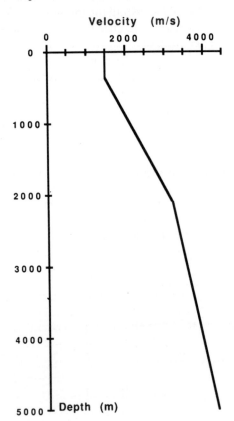

Fig. 9. Velocity profile used to generate the shot records.

The shot records were then muted, CMP sorted, NMO & DMO corrected and stacked using the known velocity model to produce the section shown in Fig. 10. Diffractions from bed terminations, loss of steep dip reflectors and velocity model induced distortions are all clearly visible on this section.

The stacked data were migrated using a Kirchhoff algorithm (Schneider 1978) to produce the section shown in Fig. 11 and the enlargement shown in Fig. 12. This procedure collapses the diffractions, moves reflectors to their correct horizontal locations, reduces the apparent dip of reflectors and unfolds synclines as expected. In addition, however, it has further attenuated steeper dipping events with neither the domino fault itself, nor steeper parts of the syn-rift sequence, visible in the final section.

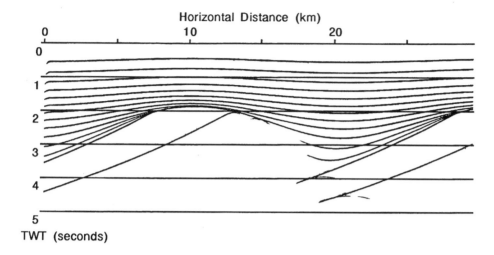

Fig. 10. Stacked section produced by applying CMP sorting, muting, NMO, DMO and stack to the shot records.

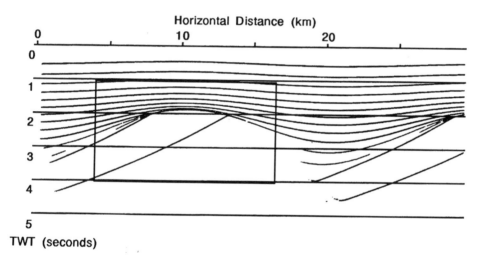

Fig. 11. Migration of the stacked data shown in Fig. 10. The box indicates the area that is shown enlarged in Fig. 12.

All main features seen in the final model run (Fig. 5(c)) are imaged on the section although these are obscured, in some cases, by acquisition and processing artifacts. For example, the pre-rift apparently thickens towards the crest of the fault block. This is a distortion induced by the velocity model which could lead the unwary interpreter to conclude that the pre-rift sequence thickened towards the right. The syn-rift sediments are quite distinct from both the pre- and post-rift sediments. The syn-rift sediments can be seen to thicken towards the footwall while the post-rift infill the half-graben and drape the fault block structure. Further, in the enlarged section showing the fault block crest, the base of the post-rift sequence is seen to be unconformable with respect to the syn-rift sequence. This unconformity is only apparent in the immediate area of the fault block crest since, in the trough, the syn- and post-rift sequences are conformable. Thus, the transition from active rifting to thermal subsidence is imaged on the seismic section as a sequence boundary which is clear only in the immediate vicinity of the fault block crest.

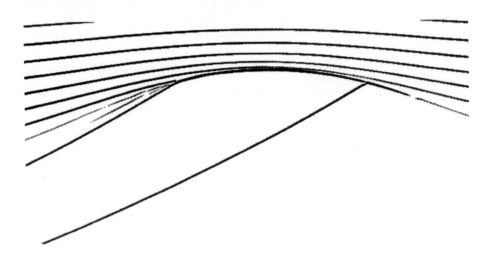

Fig. 12. Enlargement of the migrated section in the region of the fault block crest.

Conclusions

This paper is intended to demonstrate the power and flexibility of the forward modelling scheme given by Equation (1). We have used this approach to build up a sophisticated model of sediment geometry associated with extension of domino fault blocks. Each additional process considered has been incorporated into the existing algorithm in a simple manner which is only possible because of the very general nature of Equation (1). Thus, we have attempted to show that this approach allows simple, logical and consistent development of concepts and consequences. Additionally, very efficient computer programs can be written to implement Equation (1). The final domino model can be used, interactively, on a Macintosh computer with typical run times of a few minutes (or less) with a continuously updated screen showing the evolution of the system. A copy of this program can be obtained from the authors.

The resultant domino model produces geometries which are consistent with those seen on North Sea seismic data. The model reproduces the following features:

(a) syn-rift and post-rift dip reversals caused by non-horizontal deposition;
(b) wedge-shaped syn-rift sediments which thicken towards the footwall block but which are found, as a condensed sequence, far up the hangingwall block;
(c) fault block crests which are eroded deep into the pre-rift sequence and are unconformably overlain by post-rift strata;

(d) a post-rift sequence which is locally unconformable to both the syn- and pre-rift in the area of the fault block crest and which infills the half-graben and drapes the fault block structure. Significant thickness variations in the post-rift are seen across the fault block structure due to uneven bathymetry at the end of rifting.

Seismic modelling of the computer-generated geometry allows an evaluation to be made of which features can be seen and which cannot. In general, on the scale of modelling dealt with in this paper, the seismic method is capable of imaging all the important features. Thus, it illustrates the appearance of the seismic sequences associated with the extensional and thermal subsidence phases of basin development. Close examination of the seismic sections reveals the nature and location of the syn-rift/post-rift sequence boundary.

The model presented here is a very 'broad brush' model and it is still undergoing significant development. The most serious problem outstanding is that erosion, modelled using the diffusion equation approach, is assumed to be constant through-out the model. In practice, of course, there will be large variations caused by differing lithologies, water depth, subareal exposure, etc. The very different erosion mechanisms of gravitational slumping of soft sediments in a deep marine setting and, on the other hand, weathering of consolidated pre-rift blocks which have been uplifted above sea-level must produce widely varying rates of erosion and sediment transport. A solution to these problems can be achieved by allowing the diffusion coefficient, a, to be variable. Under these conditions the sediment flux term in Equation (1) becomes

$$\partial F/\partial x = -a(\partial^2 z/\partial x^2) - (\partial a/\partial x).(\partial z/\partial x) \tag{12}$$

which, comparing with Equation (8), has an extra term which depends upon the spatial variation in a. We are currently investigating the use of Equation (12) in our models but have not yet obtained publishable results. It is perhaps surprising that, despite the use of a constant diffusion coefficient, the results we have obtained match closely the results seen in natural examples. To a considerable extent this is due to the background sedimentation coating and protecting the submarine parts of the fault blocks while leaving the subarealy exposed block crests unprotected. The implication of this is that the weathering of the consolidated pre-rift may take place at a similar rate to the slumping of the soft syn-rift sediments after all!

Perhaps the next most significant omission in the current model is the absence of compaction effects. As indicated earlier, Barr (1991) has produced very similar geometries to ours by filling the half-grabens with horizontal sediments and then allowing them to compact vertically. We believe that both compaction and the effect of non-horizontal deposition are significant in this context and it is an open question as to which of these mechanisms is most important. Compaction could be incorporated into our modelling scheme by having an additional component in the tectonic velocities, u and v, for the syn- and post-rift sediments (Waltham 1992).

The early stages of rifting are frequently continental. Under these conditions, there is no background sedimentation in the sense used in this paper. Instead, there should be flat-lying, axial sediments forming at the base of the half-graben. These could be modelled by having a non-zero value for p at the lowest parts of the graben. Perhaps a more convincing approach would be to move to a full three-dimensional model.

This is, in principle, a small development of Equation (1) (Waltham 1992) but, in practice, will involve a considerable amount of further research.

Further developments, in addition to those indicated above, will be to model a group of fault blocks of different widths and to allow variable rates of sediment supply and extension with time. These will certainly lead to more complex stratal relationships. It should be possible to use factors such as palaeoslope and distance from block crest to indicate likely facies types within the half-graben. Finally, this paper has specifically investigated the effects of tectonics on stratigraphy. However, it would be a simple addition to allow the sea-level to vary eustatically.

Thanks to Derek Blundell for reading this manuscript and to Derek Powell for his constructive comments on the Macintosh program.

References

BADLEY, M. E., EGEBERG, T. & NIPEN, O. 1984. Development of rift basins illustrated by the structural evolution of the Øseberg feature, Block 30/6, offshore Norway. *Journal of the Geological Society, London*, **141**, 639–649.

BALLY, A. W. 1988. *Atlas of Seismic Stratigraphy. Vol. 2*. American Association of Petroleum Geologists Studies in Geology, **27**, Tulsa, Oklahoma.

BARR, D. 1987a. Lithosphere stretching, detached normal faulting and footwall uplift. *In*: COWARD, M. P., DEWEY, J. F. & HANCOCK, P. L. (eds) *Continental Extensional Tectonics*. Geological Society, London, Special Publication, **28**, 75–94.

—— 1987b. Structure/stratigraphic models for extensional basins of half graben type. *Journal of Structural Geology*, **9**, 491–500.

—— 1991. Subsidence and sedimentation in semi-starved half graben: a model based on North Sea data. *In*: ROBERTS, A. M., YIELDING, G. & FREEMAN, B. (eds) *The Geometry of Normal Faults*. Geological Society, London, Special Publication, **56**, 17–28.

BERTRAM, G. T. & MILTON, N. J. 1989. Reconstructing basin evolution from sedimentary thickness; the importance of palaeobathymetric control, with reference to the North Sea. *Basin Research*, **1**, 247–257.

BOWEN, J. M. 1975. The Brent Oil-field. *In*: WOODLAND, A. W. (ed.) *Petroleum and the Continental Shelf of Northwest Europe*, Applied Science, London, 353–360.

BROWN, S. 1990. Jurassic. *In*: GLENNIE, K. W. (ed.) *Introduction to the Petroleum Geology of the North Sea*, Blackwell Scientific, 219–254.

CATHLESS, M. L. III. 1975. *The Viscosity of the Earth's Mantle*. Princeton University Press.

COLMAN, S. M. & WATSON, K. 1983. Ages estimated from a diffusion equation model for scarp degradation. *Science*, **221**, 263–265.

FROST, R. E. 1989. Discussion on the structural evolution of the northern Viking Graben and its bearing upon extension modes of basin formation. *Journal of the Geological Society, London*, **146**, 1035–1040.

HILTERMAN, F. J. 1970. Three dimensional seismic modelling. *Geophysics*, **35**, 1020–1037.

—— 1975. Amplitudes of seismic waves—A quick look. *Geophysics*, **40**, 745–762.

ILIFFE, J. E., LERCHE, I. & NAKAYAMA, K. 1990. Structural implications of compactional strain caused by fault block rotation: evidence from two-dimensional numerical analogues. *In*: KNIPE, R. J. & RUTTER, E. H. (eds) *Deformation Mechanisms, Rheology and Tectonics*. Geological Society, London, Special Publication, **54**, 501–508.

JACKSON, J. A., WHITE, N. J., GARFUNKEL, Z. & ANDERSON, H. 1988. Relations between normal-fault geometry, tilting and vertical motions in extensional terrains: an example from the southern Gulf of Suez. *Journal of Structural Geology*, **10**, 155–170.

KENYON, P. M. & TURCOTTE, D. L. 1985. Morphology of a delta prograding by bulk sediment transport. *Geological Society of America Bulletin*, **96**, 1457–1465.

KIRK, R. H. 1980. Statfjord field—a North Sea giant. *In*: HALBOUTY, M. T. (ed.). *Giant Oil and Gas Fields of the Decade: 1968–1978*. American Association of Petroleum Geologists Memoir, **30**, Tulsa, Oklahoma, 95–116.

KUZNIR, N. J., MARSDEN, G. & EGAN, S. S. 1991. A flexural-cantilever simple-shear/pure-shear model of continental extension: applications to the Jeanne d'Arc Basin, Grand Banks and Viking Graben, North Sea. *In*: ROBERTS, A. M., YIELDING, G. & FREEMAN, B. (eds) *The Geometry of Normal Faults*. Geological Society, London, Special Publication, **56**, 41–60.

McCLAY, K. R., WALTHAM, D. A., SCOTT, A. D. & ABOUSETTA, A. 1991. Physical and seismic modelling of listric normal fault geometries. *In*: ROBERTS, A. M., YIELDING, G. & FREEMAN, B. (eds) *The Geometry of Normal Faults*. Geological Society, London, Special Publication, **56**, 231–239.

McKENZIE, D. 1978. Some remarks on the development of sedimentary basins. *Earth & Planetary Science Letters*, **40**, 25–32.

MASCLE, J. & MARTIN, L. 1990. Shallow structure and recent evolution of the Aegean Sea: A synthesis based on continuous reflection profiles. *Marine Geology*, **94**, 271–299.

MONTADERT, L., ROBERTS, D. G., DE CHARPEL, O. & GUENNOC, P. 1979. Rifting and subsidence of the northern continental margin of the Bay of Biscay. *In*: MONTADERT, L. & ROBERTS, D. G. (eds) *Initial Reports of D.S.D.P.*, **48**, 1025–1060.

NIPEN, O. 1987. Oseberg. *In*: SPENCER, A. M. *et al.* (eds) *Geology of the Norwegian Oil and Gas Fields*. Graham & Trotman, London, 379–387.

POMAR, L., BOSENCE, D. & WALTHAM, D. 1990. Computer modelling of a carbonate platform, Mallorca, Spain. Presented at 13th International Sedimentology Conference, Nottingham, England.

ROBERTS, J. D., MATHIESON, A. S. & HAMPSON, J. M. 1987. Statfjord. *In*: SPENCER, A. M. *et al.* (eds) *Geology of the Norwegian Oil and Gas Fields*. Graham & Trotman, London, 319–340.

SAWYER, D. S. 1986. Effects of basement topography on subsidence history analysis. *Earth & Planetary Science Letters*, **78**, 427–434.

SCHNEIDER, W. A. 1978. Integral formulations for migration in two-dimensions and three-dimensions. *Geophysics*, **43**, 49–76.

TROREY, A. W. 1970. A simple theory for seismic diffractions. *Geophysics*, **35**, 762–784.

VENDEVILLE, B., DAVY, P., BRUN, J. P. & CHOUKROUNE, P. 1987. Physical models of extensional tectonics at various scales. *In*: COWARD, M. P., DEWEY, J. F. & HANCOCK, P. L. (eds) *Continental Extensional Tectonics*. Geological Society, London, Special Publication, **28**, 95–107.

WALSH, J. J. & WATTERSON, J. 1991. Geometric and kinematic coherence and scale effects in normal fault systems. *In*: ROBERTS, A. M., YIELDING, G. & FREEMAN, B. (eds). *The Geometry of Normal Faults*. Geological Society, London, Special Publication, **56**, 193–203.

WALTHAM, D. A. 1992. Mathematical Modelling of Sedimentary Basin Processes. *Marine and Petroleum Geology*, **9**, 265–273.

WHITE, N., JACKSON, J. A. & McKENZIE, D. P. 1986. The relationship between the geometry of normal faults and that of the sedimentary layers in their hangingwalls. *Journal of Structural Geology*, **8**, 879–909.

YIELDING, G. 1990. Footwall uplift associated with Late Jurassic normal faulting in the northern North Sea. *Journal of the Geological Society, London*, **147**, 219–222.

From WILLIAMS, G. D. & DOBB, A. (eds), 1993, *Tectonics and Seismic Sequence Stratigraphy*.
Geological Society Special Publication No. 71, 87–121.

Tectonic and bathymetric controls on stratigraphic sequences within evolving half-graben

Alan M. Roberts, Graham Yielding & Michael E. Badley

Badley Earth Sciences Ltd, Winceby House, Winceby, Horncastle, Lincolnshire LN9 6PB, UK.

Abstract: A modification of the domino fault block model is presented, which can be used to evaluate possible tectonic controls on the development of stratigraphic sequences within an evolving half-graben. The model allows average half-graben load to vary with time and allows the rate of faulting to be varied relative to any background component of basin subsidence.

The basic domino model predicts only transgressive sequences at the crests of tilted fault blocks. It is found with the modified model that a decreasing average half-graben load (increasing bathymetry) or an increasing strain-rate may induce offlap and regression at the fault block crest. The model is used here successfully to model the syn-rift stratigraphy of a tilted fault block in the Viking Graben (North Sea). It is believed to have general implications for evaluating the syn-rift and early post-rift history of extensional basins.

The internal geometry of condensed and unconformable sequences at fault block crests may lie below the limit of seismic resolution. This calls into question the ability of the seismic stratigraphic technique to address successfully the full history of an evolving half-graben.

The domino fault block model

In two far-sighted papers, Barr (1987*a,b*) coupled together the McKenzie (1978) model for whole-lithosphere extension with a geometric model for upper-crustal normal faulting. Barr used the rotating-domino model of normal faulting (e.g. Morton & Black 1975; Wernicke & Burchfiel 1982; Mandl 1987; Davison 1989) to establish a new, predictive model, both for the magnitudes of uplift and subsidence associated with evolving half-graben and for the patterns of stratigraphic fill within the half-graben.

Assumptions and predictions of the domino model

In its basic form (Barr 1987*a,b*), the domino model makes a number of important assumptions about the state of the lithosphere and the sedimentary response to faulting. Of particular importance to the succeeding discussion are the following five points.

1. The lithosphere is assumed to be in thermal equilibrium prior to extension.
2. Airy-type isostatic compensation within the lithosphere is assumed, except in explicit cases where isostasy is ignored.
3. Lithospheric stretching is taken to be instantaneous and in accord with the McKenzie model.

4. The model half-graben are kept full to sea-level with sediment.
5. As a result of (4), the average density of the load within the half-graben remains
   constant or increases as extension proceeds.

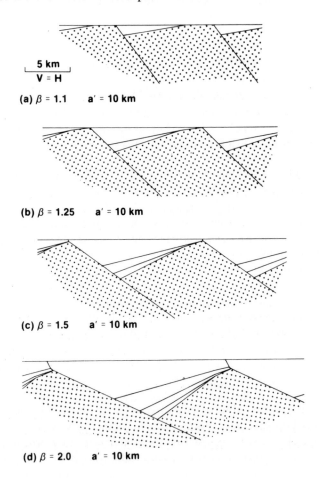

Fig. 1. Model set of half-graben and their stratigraphic fill, constructed by the domino model.
The fault blocks have an initial width of 10 km and the initial fault dip is 60°. The horizontal
line is sea-level, with older, rotated sea-level markers (≡ stratigraphy) below. Pre-rift basement
is stippled. Note initial uplift and erosion of fault block crests, followed by their burial below
the onlapping syn-rift sequence (from Barr 1987*b*).

On the basis of these assumptions the following structural and stratigraphic predictions may be made about evolving half-graben (e.g. Barr 1987*b*, Figs 8 & 9; Fig.1):

1. For a given fault dip and half-graben load, the footwall crests of fault blocks
   exceeding a threshold size will become emergent upon extension. The wider the
   fault block the higher is the predicted emergence.
2. As a result of footwall emergence an erosional unconformity may develop at the
   top of the pre-rift sequence. This unconformity is confined to the fault block
   crests.

3. As extension proceeds, progressive onlap will occur on the dip-slope of individual half-graben. Such onlap towards the fault block crest will bury the crestal unconformity. Progressively younger sediments should be found capping the unconformity higher on the structure.
4. Once the basal unconformity has been buried, stratigraphic conformity is observed within the syn-rift sequence. Stratigraphic condensing will occur towards the fault block crest, but there will be no missing section within the syn-rift fill.
5. No post-rift or 'break-up' unconformity develops above the syn-rift sequence. Post-rift sediments are deposited conformably upon the syn-rift.
6. As a result of the progressive onlap predicted by the model, the maximum width of emergent footwall island is observed upon the smallest increment of extension. It is the implications of this final prediction that we discuss in some detail below.

The structural predictions of the domino model, in terms of magnitude of footwall uplift versus hangingwall subsidence, have been tested against observations in a number of extensional basins (e.g. Barr 1987a, 1991; Jackson et al. 1988; White 1990; Yielding 1990; Yielding & Roberts 1991). Model predictions and geological observations have been found by these authors to be in close agreement. This has led Yielding & Roberts (1992) and Roberts & Yielding (1992) to suggest that in many cases the domino model provides a tractable simplification of the more-complete flexural solution to fault block geometry (e.g. Jackson & McKenzie 1983; Kusznir & Egan 1989; Kusznir et al. 1991); although the domino simplification will break down at basin margins (Sclater & Celerier 1989; Roberts & Yielding 1991).

While the structural predictions of the domino model are now well tested, the stratigraphic predictions have been less well investigated. With this in mind we aimed to test the stratigraphic predictions of the domino model on one of the best-documented structures in the Viking Graben of the North Sea basin, the Brent/Statfjord fault block (e.g. Bowen 1975; Kirk 1980; Roberts et al. 1987; Johnson & Eyssautier 1987; Livera & Gdula 1990; Struijk & Green 1991; Inglis & Gerard 1991) (Fig. 2). The structural geometry of this fault block has already been explained by the domino model (Yielding 1990; White 1990; Yielding & Roberts 1992); it is thus an ideal structure against which to test the stratigraphic predictions.

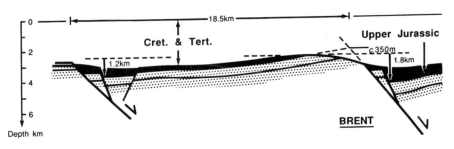

Fig. 2. Depth profile across the Brent fault block, northern North Sea. Fault-related uplift and subsidence during the Late Jurassic are estimated from the erosion profile of the present day crest. This paper is concerned with modelling the internal stratigraphy of the Upper Jurassic wedge (solid shade), on the dip-slope of the fault block, the details of which lie below seismic resolution (from Yielding 1990).

The Brent/Statfjord fault block

Publications cited above, released well data and our own previous work in the Viking Graben (e.g. Badley *et al.* 1984, 1988; Yielding 1990; Marsden *et al.* 1990; Roberts *et al.* 1990; Yielding *et al.* 1991; Yielding *et al.* 1992) allow us to synthesize a tectonostratigraphic picture of the Brent/Statfjord fault block (Table 1). In this paper, we are interested in the Late Jurassic extensional episode, rather than the earlier extension in the Triassic.

Table 1. *Summary of the intra-Middle Jurassic to intra-Early Cretaceous stratigraphy of the Brent/Statfjord fault block. A full time sequence is present downflank, but an erosional unconformity is identified within the syn-rift sequence at the fault block crest. Compiled from released well data and references cited in text*

Stage	Down-flank area	Crestal area	Tectonic setting
Valanginian	Cromer Knoll Group	Cromer Knoll Group	Post rift
Ryazanian			
Volgian	Kimmeridge Clay Fm	Kimmeridge Clay Fm	Syn-rift
Kimmeridgian			
Oxfordian			
Callovian	Heather Fm	Heather Fm	
Bathonian			
Bajocian	Brent Group	Brent Group	Pre-rift

The coastal-plain/shallow-marine Brent Group marks the top of the 'pre-rift' sequence to Late Jurassic extension, although a small extensional strain may have accumulated during Brent deposition (Yielding *et al.* 1992). The silts and shales of the Humber Group (Heather and Kimmeridge Clay Formations) are generally taken as the 'syn-rift' sequence, deposited as extension proceeded. Regional isochores show that the Brent Group is largely of uniform thickness on the Brent/Statfjord block, but the overlying Heather and Kimmeridge Clay Formations thicken westwards (away from the crestal area) with a wedge-shaped geometry (Brown *et al.* 1987; Johnson & Eyssautier 1987; Inglis & Gerard 1991). The deep-water marls of the Cromer Knoll Group mark the base of the 'post-rift' sequence.

In Barr's (1987*b*) stratigraphic models the downflank area of a domino fault block, i.e. away from the emergent crest, will contain a complete stratigraphic section from the pre-rift sequence upwards (Fig. 1). Such a sequence is indeed seen in the deeper, western part of the Brent/Statfjord structure. Released well 211/28-5 (UK), drilled in the deepest part of the fault block, contains an apparently complete Brent Group–Cromer Knoll Group succession (Table 1).

Barr's models also predict that any unconformity at the fault block crest should lie at the base of the syn-rift, i.e. at the base of the westwards-thickening Heather Formation (Table 1). Several authors have recorded, however, that, both on the Brent/Statfjord structure and on nearby fault blocks, the Heather Formation in crestal areas rests conformably on the underlying Brent, while the Kimmeridge Clay is separated from the underlying Heather by an unconformity (e.g. Livera & Gdula 1990; Roberts et al. 1987; Gradijan & Wiik 1987; Nyberg 1987; Johnson & Eyssautier 1987; Inglis & Gerard 1991) (Table 1). In structural terms this means that there is no unconformity at the base of the syn-rift wedge, but there is an unconformity within the syn-rift. Clearly this observation is at variance with the stratigraphic predictions of the basic domino model.

The syn-rift stratigraphy of the Brent/Statfjord fault block (Table 1) appears to record the following principal events.

1. At the onset of significant rotational faulting, during the Bathonian, the entire fault block was capped by marine siltstones of the Heather Formation.
2. Subsequent to deposition of the lower part of the Heather Formation, a regressive event of Callovian–Oxfordian age is recorded by an unconformity at the crest of the fault block. The unconformity does not extend to the downflank areas.
3. Renewed transgression in the late Oxfordian and Kimmeridgian flooded the unconformity at the fault block crest, resulting in capping by shales of the Kimmeridge Clay Formation.

The sequence of events recorded in the syn-rift stratigraphy is thus transgression–regression–transgression.

Causal mechanisms for intra-basinal unconformities

We have so far cited erosion at the uplifted crest of a tilted fault block as one possible mechanism by which to generate an unconformity within a stretched basin. The documented intra-syn-rift unconformity on the Brent/Statfjord structure does not, however, fit the prediction of the basic, domino fault block model.

Two alternative driving mechanisms are also commonly considered to contribute to the formation of unconformities and offlapping sequences within stretched basins. These are:

1. fluctuations in absolute sea-level (eustasy) (e.g. Haq et al. 1987). Vail & Todd (1981) have interpreted the stratigraphy of parts of the North Sea basin in terms of eustatic cycles;
2. fluctuating magnitudes of intra-plate stress (e.g. Cloetingh et al. 1985; Cloetingh & Kooi 1989; Embry 1989). Cloetingh et al. (1987) have applied this model also to the stratigraphic record of parts of the North Sea.

It is possible that the unconformity separating the Heather and Kimmeridge Clay Formations on the crest of the Brent/Statfjord structure might result from either of these mechanisms. The association of the unconformity with the crest of a contemporaneously-rotating fault block suggests to us, however, that despite the failure of basic domino model to predict the stratigraphic pattern, a causal mechanism resulting from fault block rotation remains more likely. Neither the eustatic model nor the intra-plate stress model has yet been developed to the stage where it can be quantitatively applied to actively-extending regions, in which the sea-floor is deforming. They remain as tools primarily for the stratigraphic analysis of the unfaulted, post-rift sequence within a stretched basin.

How then can we explain the Brent/Statfjord stratigraphy in terms of fault block rotation if the basic domino model does not make the required predictions? This question led us to consider whether the Viking Graben, and the Brent/Statfjord fault block within, truly fulfil the assumptions (listed above) built into the basic domino model.

The Viking Graben, deviations from the basic domino assumptions

The assumptions built into the basic domino model about lithosphere state before faulting and the sedimentary response to faulting were outlined above. We believe there are two aspects of the Viking Graben's geological history which would result in it not fulfilling these assumptions during the Late Jurassic.

1. In addition to extension in the Late Jurassic, the Viking Graben is believed to have undergone extension during the Triassic (e.g. Badley *et al.* 1984, 1988; Giltner 1987; Marsden *et al.* 1990; Steel & Ryseth 1990; Yielding *et al.* 1991; Yielding *et al.* 1992). It is assumed that this early extension perturbed the lithosphere temperature field. Given a thermal time-constant for the lithosphere of *c.* 60 Ma, it is likely that any thermal effects from extension early in the Triassic would not have relaxed completely by the onset of renewed extension in the Late Jurassic. Approximately 30% of the Triassic thermal anomaly is likely to have remained while significant extension began once again. It is, therefore, unlikely that the Viking Graben in the Late Jurassic fulfilled the assumption of the basic domino model that the lithosphere should be in thermal equilibrium prior to extension. The geological effect of the presence of a background thermal anomaly during extension would be to enhance subsidence of the basin floor.

2. The stratigraphic succession in Table 1 charts a transition in depositional environment from fluvial plain (Ness Fm, middle Brent) to shallow-marine sandstones (Tarbert Fm, upper Brent), to marine siltstones (Heather Fm), to marine shales (Kimmeridge Clay Fm), to deep-water marine limestones (lower Cromer Knoll). This transition is characterized by a reduction in the input of clastic sediment, followed by a reduction in the input of suspended sediment. At the same time an overall increase in bathymetry is indicated, from no bathymetry (Ness Fm) to several hundred metres (Cromer Knoll) (Bertram & Milton 1989; Barr 1991).

    Thus it is probable that the Viking Graben in the Late Jurassic fulfilled neither the assumption of the basic domino model that the evolving half-graben remained full to sea-level, nor that the average half-graben load (sediment plus water) remained constant or increased. An increase in bathymetry is likely to reduce the average half-graben load by reducing the ratio of sediment fill to water within the half-graben. The geological effect of decreasing the half-graben load with time would be to reduce subsidence to values less than the predictions of the fully-loaded domino model.

Quantitative basin-filling models

Progress has recently been made in the construction of quantitative models which aim to predict stratigraphic geometries in subsiding half-graben. Collier *et al.* (1990) and Collier (1990) have devised a basin-filling model incorporating basin-floor subsidence, eustasy and variable rates of sediment input, using the model to explain observations in the Corinth Basin (Greece) and in the Carboniferous of northern England. Schlische & Olsen (1990) have investigated a graben-filling model in which water depth may vary but sediment input-rate is held constant.

Both these models make quantitative predictions, but have some limitations in their applicability to evolving half-graben. In neither model is the basin floor allowed to rotate with time, nor is the basin-floor subsidence calculated isostatically. These filling models cannot thus be coupled with the isostatically-driven, rotating domino model.

Barr (1991) has refined the basic domino model to incorporate sediment starvation within the half-graben, but confined the detailed stratigraphic predictions of his revised model to sediment geometries observed in the post-rift sequence (see also Bertram & Milton 1989). Likewise Yielding (1990) acknowledged the likely presence of syn-rift bathymetry within the Late Jurassic Viking Graben, but confined his model predictions to structural effects rather than stratigraphic geometries.

It, therefore, appears that we cannot use either the basic domino model, or a published variant on this model, to investigate the complex syn-rift stratigraphy of the Brent/Statfjord fault block. Instead we have devised further modifications to the domino model which might allow us to investigate in more detail stratigraphic geometries within evolving half-graben.

The modified domino model

The parameters of the modified domino model are illustrated in Fig. 3. The modifications to the basic model address two points.

1. The first point is, perhaps, the more simple. As the half-graben evolves (by increments of tilt), specific increments of half-graben load are defined. If, for example, we believe that an increment of tilt was accompanied by no deposition, then the half-graben load for that increment is considered to be purely water, with a density of $1.0 \, \text{gcm}^{-3}$. If we believe that the space created by an increment of tilt was entirely taken up by sediment deposition, then the half-graben load for such an increment is approximated at $2.0 \, \text{gcm}^{-3}$ (porous sediment). Values between these limits may be used to represent partial sediment-starvation during extension. Compaction, i.e. density increase, is not forward-modelled. However, while incorporating compaction would be beneficial to the model, we are primarily interested in the proportion of sediment to water in the half-graben. The density contrast between water and porous sediment is much greater than the density contrast between porous sediment and partially-compacted sediment. We are, thus, using our model to tackle the first-order control on half-graben load; second-order refinements may be incorporated at a subsequent stage.

During model calculations the new load at each increment is combined with the pre-existing half-graben load and a new average load is derived. The new average load is then used, as in the McKenzie model and earlier domino models (Barr 1987a,b; Jackson *et al.* 1988; White 1990; Yielding 1990), to amplify the basin subsidence driven by lithospheric stretching.

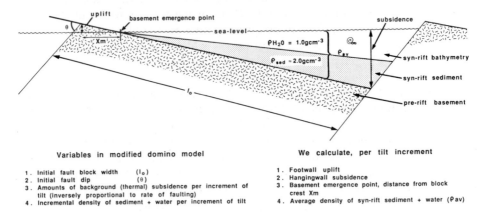

Variables in modified domino model

1. Initial fault block width   (l_o)
2. Initial fault dip   (θ)
3. Amounts of background (thermal) subsidence per increment of tilt (inversely proportional to rate of faulting)
4. Incremental density of sediment + water per increment of tilt

We calculate, per tilt increment

1. Footwall uplift
2. Hangingwall subsidence
3. Basement emergence point, distance from block crest Xm
4. Average density of syn-rift sediment + water (ρ_{av})

Fig. 3. Cartoon fault block illustrating the input parameters to, and calculated output from, the modified domino model. The position of the basement emergence point, on the dip-slope of the fault block, is thought likely to exert the principal control on the lateral extent of the syn-rift sediment wedge.

2. The second modification to the basic domino model attempts to incorporate the subsidence effects of thermally-unequilibrated lithosphere, i.e. an earlier (Triassic) stretching event. To do this we first calculate the likely amount of subsidence which would have occurred in the basin at the time of the second stretching event, had subsidence been driven solely by ongoing thermal-relaxation following the first stretch. This we refer to as the background, or inherited, subsidence. This calculated subsidence is then converted to an average background-subsidence rate (mMa^{-1}) for the duration of the second stretching event. Provided we are investigating a stretching event of duration $<c.\,60$ Ma (the thermal time-constant of the lithosphere) a linear background-subsidence interpolation will not deviate significantly from the true exponential rate.

The background subsidence rate is now used as the time framework for the second stretching event. Specifying a particular increment of background subsidence defines a particular interval of time. We are now free to define our second stretching event in terms of a rate of tilting relative to background subsidence. Fault block tilting is in turn related to the rate of faulting, which is in turn controlled by the rate of stretching. In our model, if we wish to specify a slow tilt we allow considerable background subsidence to accrue per increment of tilt. If we wish to specify a fast tilt we allow only a very small background subsidence to accrue per increment of tilt.

In the calculations, the accrued background subsidence is added to the instantaneous (McKenzie) tectonic subsidence induced by stretching (both compensated for half-graben loading), and a total subsidence is derived. This subsidence is then superimposed on the domino fault block topography (cf. Barr 1987*a,b*; Yielding 1990), to yield an uplift/subsidence geometry for the fault block relative to sea-level. Strictly speaking, the second stretching event should be treated with a time-dependent subsidence model, as we are treating the background subsidence as time-dependent. Provided, however, that the second stretching event was of magnitude $< 60/\beta^2$ (Jarvis & McKenzie 1980), an instantaneous approximation will allow us to investigate the first-order effects of a variable rate of faulting when superimposed on an already-subsiding basin floor.

Background subsidence in the Viking Graben

The stratigraphic successions in UK wells 211/24-1 (Statfjord) and 211/29-3 (Brent) have been used to calculate the likely magnitude of post-Triassic-stretching, background subsidence, on the Brent/Statfjord fault block, during the Late Jurassic.

The Statfjord Formation (basal Jurassic) and the Ness Formation of the Brent Group (Middle Jurassic) provide two stratigraphic sea-level markers, being of fluvial and fluvial-plain facies, respectively. Thus, the subsidence in the Viking Graben which allowed the Statfjord Formation–Brent Group succession to accumulate can be confidently interpreted as amplified by full sediment loading.

Using the shaly-sand decompaction parameters of Sclater & Christie (1980) the Statfjord–Brent sequence in 211/24-1 decompacts to 1043 m. The same sequence in 211/29-3 decompacts to 910 m. As an approximation, we can therefore say that *c*. 1000 m of sediment-loaded subsidence accrued on the Brent fault block during the first *c*. 45 Ma of the Jurassic. This converts to an average subsidence rate of *c*. 22 m Ma^{-1}. During this interval the Statfjord–Brent sequence was deposited.

The Humber Group (Heather and Kimmeridge Clay Fms, Table 1) was deposited during the succeeding *c*. 30 Ma (intra-Bathonian to intra-Ryazanian) and is generally considered to be the syn-rift sequence to Late Jurassic extension. Given a lithosphere thermal-time-constant of 60 Ma, the average rate of thermal subsidence during this period would have been approximately half the average rate in the preceding 45 Ma, given similar loading conditions. Thus we can estimate that the average sediment-loaded, background-subsidence rate during the Humber Group time interval would have been *c*. 11 m Ma^{-1}, or a total subsidence of *c*. 330 m.

This estimate of 330 m subsidence is the Bathonian–Ryazanian subsidence which would have occurred at the Brent/Statfjord fault block had there been no Late Jurassic stretching, and had the basin remained full to sea-level. This value would reduce to *c*. 200 m of subsidence for a basin partially-starved of sediment (i.e. Humber Group conditions) and to *c*. 100 m for an air-loaded basin. An air-loaded estimate is required for the forward-modelling because this subsidence is added to the tectonic subsidence induced by stretching, and then both together are amplified by the half-graben load. Thus, given an air-loaded subsidence estimate of *c*. 100 m, we can use an average air-loaded, background-subsidence rate of 3.5 m Ma^{-1} to incorporate into a forward model of the Brent/Statfjord fault block.

Results of the modified domino model

Before attempting to model the Brent/Statfjord stratigraphy some generalized results of the modified domino model are presented, in order to illustrate what we believe the independent effects of variable half-graben loading and variable rate of faulting might be for the general case of half-graben evolution. Although our model is aimed at one particular case study, we believe that the implications of the model may be used to reinvestigate stratigraphic relationships within the syn-rift sequence of any half-graben.

In order to vary the rate of faulting relative to background subsidence, a rate of background subsidence must first be specified. In our general models, therefore, use the value of 3.5 mMa^{-1} of air-loaded subsidence, which was derived above.

When investigating the results of the model we are particularly interested in two parameters (Fig. 3). These are (1) the uplift of the fault block crest above the sea-level; (2) the distance from the fault block crest (on the dip-slope) at which the pre-rift basement becomes emergent. It is this second parameter, i.e. the strand-line on the fault block (Xm in Fig. 3), which will control the maximum up-dip extent of any deposition within the half-graben. It is, thus, assumed that the position of this basement emergence point will ultimately control the limit of onlap (or offlap) within the half-graben. In the succeeding discussion we present a series of graphs in which the magnitude of footwall uplift and the position of the basement emergence point are calibrated against fault block tilt. We also present true-aspect-ratio cross-sections of the fault block crest at 1° and 7° of tilt, illustrating the geometry of the fault block crest relative to sea-level. The current, average dip of the Brent/Statfjord structure is 7°.

In all the succeeding models the initial width of the domino fault block is 15 km and the initial angle of fault dip is 60°. Again, these values are considered consistent with the geometry of the Brent/Statfjord structure (Fig. 2).

Basic domino model (Figs 4 & 5)

The first and most simple model is an illustration of the basic domino model (cf. Barr 1987a,b; Yielding 1990). A constant density of half-graben fill (1.5 g cm^{-3}) and no background (thermal) subsidence have been used in these calculations.

The results of this model are largely as anticipated. Throughout the 7° of tilt, the fault block crest undergoes continuous uplift, at an approximately constant rate. After 7° of tilt, the crest is elevated above sea-level by 495 m (Fig. 4). The basement emergence point in the model, defining the width of the emergent island, lies 4270 m from the fault block crest after 0.5° of rotation, and migrates towards the fault block crest (onlap) throughout the 7° of tilting. At 7° the emergence point lies 4030 m from the fault block crest (Fig. 4). On the assumption that stratigraphic relationships in the half-graben are ultimately controlled by the position of the emergence point, a gently onlapping stratigraphic sequence is predicted by this model.

Perhaps the surprise of this simple model, however, is the narrowness of the zone of onlap (240 m for 7° of tilt) (Fig. 5). This spacing of 240 m is considerably less than that found between rows of development wells on either the Brent or the Statfjord Field (Livera & Gdula 1990; Roberts et al. 1987), which are typically spaced at 500–1000 m. Thus, if the stratigraphy on the Brent/Statfjord structure was controlled by the domino model in its simplest form we should expect to see a very sharp divide, c. 4 km from the block crest, between wells containing no syn-rift sequence and wells containing a complete but much-condensed sequence. Even allowing for the compli-cating effects of gravitational collapse at the fault block crest (Livera & Gdula 1990;

Roberts *et al.* 1987; Struijk & Green 1991), the stratigraphic relationships on the fault block are more complex than can be accounted for by this model.

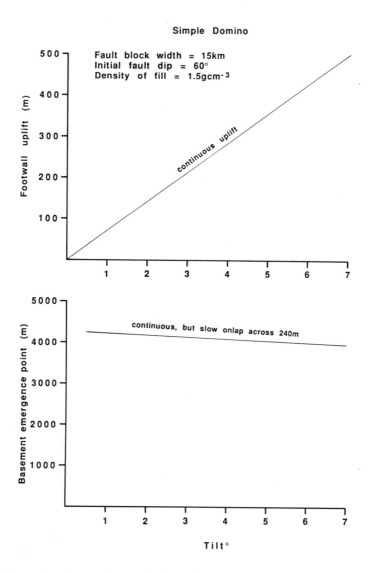

Fig. 4. Graphical illustration of the magnitude of footwall uplift (top) and the position of the basement emergence point (bottom) as a result of increased fault block tilting (≡extension), calculated using the simple domino model (cf. Fig. 3). Note continuous footwall uplift and steady (but small) onlap of the emergence point.

Modified domino, variable density of half-graben fill (1) (Figs 6 & 7)

The first attempt to introduce further complexity to the domino model involves varying the density of the half-graben load during extension. We have chosen a simple model to start with (Fig. 6), in which for the first 3° of tilt the density of fill at

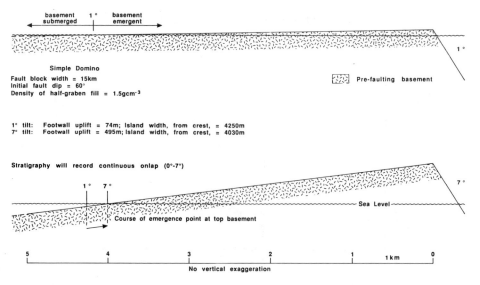

Fig. 5. True-scale cross-sections (at 1° and 7° of tilt) through the crest of a fault block derived from the model parameters and results of Fig. 4 (simple domino model). Note the steady onlap of the emergence point throughout the 7° of tilt. Pre-faulting basement is illustrated as a stratigraphic marker, the syn-rift sequence is not shown.

each new increment of tilt is $2.0 \, \mathrm{g \, cm^{-3}}$, and for the last 4° the incremental density is $1.0 \, \mathrm{g \, cm^{-3}}$. Geologically, this might represent rather extreme conditions, during which the first 3° of tilt are accompanied by complete filling of the half-graben with water-saturated sediment, at 3° the sediment supply is 'switched off', and for the next 4° of tilt the additional half-graben space is accommodated by water. In this model the average sediment density remains at $2.0 \, \mathrm{g \, cm^{-3}}$ for 3°, and then gradually diminishes to $c. \, 1.5 \, \mathrm{g \, cm^{-3}}$ at 7°, i.e. at 7° the half-graben will contain a $c. \, 50:50$ sediment : water load.

For the first 3° of tilt the results of this model follow the course of a basic domino model. After 3°, however, reduction of the density of the half-graben fill partially 'unloads' the basin. This has two effects. It causes the rate of footwall uplift to increase (Fig. 6), but more significantly it also causes the basement emergence point to retreat from the fault block crest (Figs 6 & 7). Thus, for 3° of tilt the emergence point onlaps the fault block across 110 m, but for the remaining 4° of tilt it offlaps across 1020 m.

Assuming stratigraphic relationships within the half-graben to be controlled by the basement emergence point, we would expect to see a basal onlapping sequence capped either by a younger regressive sequence or an offlap unconformity. The effect of offlap might be to raise pre-existing half-graben fill above sea-level. Assuming erosion above sea-level to be efficient this model would preserve no syn-rift sequence within $c. \, 4$ km of the fault block crest (Fig. 7).

This model, although perhaps addressing rather exaggerated geological circumstances, gives a first indication that the structural predictions of the domino fault block model may, in some circumstances, exert sufficient control on half-graben geometry to allow a complex stratigraphic sequence to evolve, without needing to consider any eustatic change in sea-level.

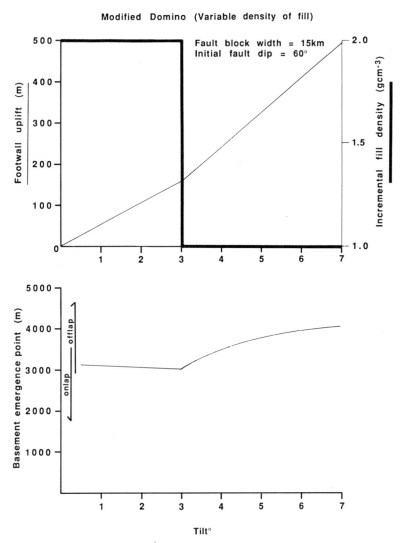

Fig. 6. Graphical illustration of the input to (fill density), and output from (footwall uplift and emergence point), a modified domino model, in which the incremental density of the half-graben fill instantaneously decreases at 3° of tilt. Note that decreasing the load causes an acceleration of footwall uplift and offlap of the basement emergence point.

Modified domino, variable density of half-graben fill (2) (Figs 8 & 9)

In the previous model the incremental half-graben load was instantaneously halved after 3° of tilt. In order to address an evolving half-graben load which might be considered geologically more plausible, an adaptation of this model was calculated.

In the new model (Fig. 8) the half-graben load added at each increment of tilt is allowed to diminish progressively, from $2.0\,\mathrm{g\,cm^{-3}}$ at 0.5° to $1.0\,\mathrm{g\,cm^{-3}}$ at 7°. Thus a steady decrease in sediment supply, relative to available space, is simulated. The final average density, at 7° ($1.55\,\mathrm{g\,cm^{-3}}$), approximates a half-graben about half-full of sediment.

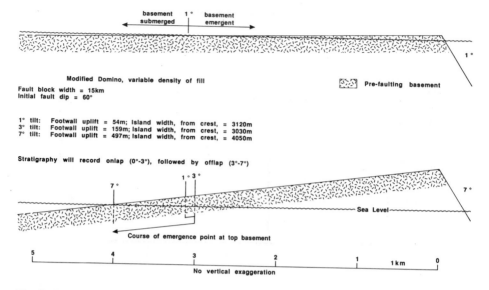

Fig. 7. True-scale cross-sections (at 1° and 7° of tilt) through the crest of a fault block derived from the model parameters and results of Fig. 6. Note the small onlap of the basement emergence point until 3° of tilt, followed by a more-rapid offlap as the half-graben load diminishes.

In this model, as the incremental and average half-graben loads become progressively lighter, so the rate of footwall uplift gradually increases (Fig. 8). More significantly, however, throughout the full 7° of tilt, the basement emergence point retreats further from the fault block crest (Figs 8 & 9). At 0.5° the dip-slope of the model island is 3140 m wide, at 7° it has enlarged to 3930 m.

It is thus anticipated that any stratigraphic succession deposited under these conditions should show a completely-opposed sequence geometry to the basic domino model. In this new model, deposition will occur under conditions of offlap and regression, whereas in the basic domino model deposition occurs under conditions of onlap and transgression.

The three models discussed so far show that on the gently-inclined dip-slope of a tilted fault block, the isostatic response to sediment loading may provide a crucial control on the stratigraphic sequence preserved near the fault block crest. Constant sediment loading should produce continuous onlap. Reduced sediment loading could, however, produce offlap and erosion, even though the background sea-level remains unchanged.

Modified domino, variable rate of faulting (1) (Figs 10 & 11)

We now turn to investigate the possible effects of background (thermal) subsidence and a variable rate of faulting on the predictions of the domino model. In the simplest case, i.e. maintaining a constant rate of fault block tilting during our chosen increment of 100 m (air-loaded) background subsidence in 30 Ma, the not-surprising effects of additional subsidence act to suppress the relief generated by a

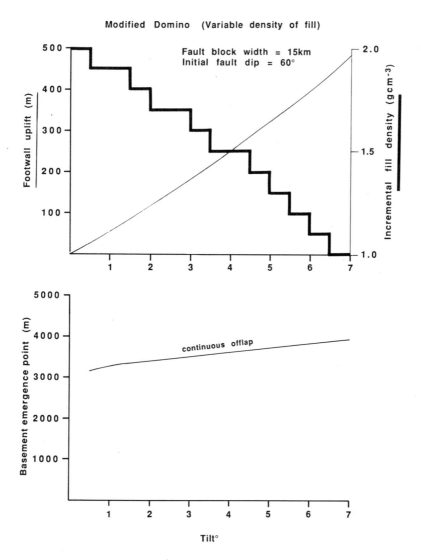

Fig. 8. Graphical illustration of the input to (fill density), and output from (footwall uplift and emergence point), a modified domino model, in which the incremental density of the half-graben fill decreases progressively as extension proceeds. This model generates continuous offlap of the basement emergence point.

basic domino model. Continuous and slow onlap still occurs, but for a basic domino model (Figs 4 & 5) with background subsidence added, onlap would occur betwen 2849 m and 2590 m from the fault block crest.

In order to investigate more-complex stratigraphic predictions, the rate of faulting relative to constant background subsidence, must be varied. In our first such model (Fig. 10) the rate of faulting/tilting is varied from slow to fast. The first 0.5° tilt increment is accompanied by 20 m of background subsidence, and in terms of the model is of 6 Ma duration. The last 0.5° is accompanied by no background

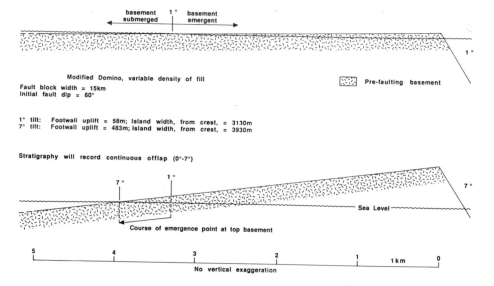

Fig. 9. True-scale cross-sections (at 1° and 7° of tilt) through the crest of a fault block derived from the model parameters and results of Fig. 8. Note the continuous offlap of the basement emergence point.

subsidence and is geologically instantaneous. Between these extremes the rate of faulting is gradually increased in 0.5° increments.

This model results in the effects of background subsidence dominating over faulting early in the rotation history, with the effects of faulting being dominant towards the end.

The addition of background subsidence to the model acts to suppress the overall magnitude of footwall uplift (Fig. 10). At 7° of tilt, 335 m of footwall uplift are predicted, by comparison with 495 m in the comparable basic domino (Fig. 4). The rate of footwall uplift, relative to the amount of tilt, is not surprisingly related to the rate of faulting. The faster the tilting occurs, the greater is the effect of footwall uplift relative to background subsidence.

The predicted course of the basement emergence point in this model is interesting and very different from the basic domino model. During the first 0.5° of tilt (6 Ma) 20 m of air-loaded background subsidence accrue. This has a marked effect on the width of footwall island, the emergence point lying only 490 m from the fault block crest. Subsequent to this, as the effects of footwall uplift begin to counteract the background subsidence, the emergence point tracks continually away from the fault block crest. At 7°, it lies 2730 m from the crest (Fig. 11). It is interesting to note, however, that while the rate of tilting and footwall uplift increase for all 7° of the model, the rate of 'island widening' is at its greatest between 0.5° and 1°. The fastest offlap occurs in this interval because fault block dip is very gentle, thus any vertical movement of the fault block has a much-exaggerated horizontal expression.

It is anticipated that a stratigraphic succession deposited under the conditions of this model should record continuous offlap and regression. Thus, we have identified a second geological circumstance under which the stratigraphic predictions of the modified domino model are markedly different to those of the comparable basic model.

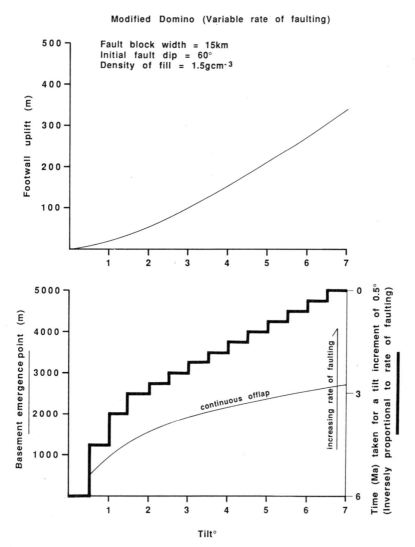

Fig. 10. Graphical illustration of the input to (variable rate of faulting), and output from (footwall uplift and emergence point), a modified domino model, in which the rate of faulting relative to continuous background subsidence, progressively increases as extension proceeds. Note that incorporation of background subsidence reduces the magnitude of footwall uplift (cf. Figs 4, 6 & 8) and increasing the rate of faulting causes continuous offlap of the basement emergence point.

Modifed domino, variable rate of faulting (2) (Figs 12 & 13)

In the previous model the final rate of tilting was left at a maximum value. In a refinement of this we investigated the effects of first increasing and then decreasing the rate of tilting, while background subsidence remained at a constant rate.

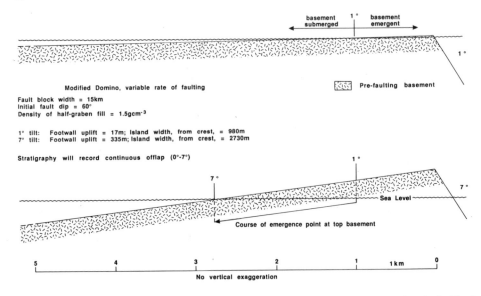

Fig. 11. True-scale cross-sections (at 1° and 7° of tilt) through the crest of a fault block derived from the model parameters and results of Fig. 10. Note the continuous offlap of the basement emergence point.

A symmetric distribution of fault rate was used in this model (Fig. 12). The first 0.5° of tilt was of 4.5 Ma duration (15 m background subsidence). The duration of 0.5° increments was then steadily decreased until at 3°, 50% of the total background subsidence had elapsed. The interval 3–4° occurred instantaneously, with no background subsidence. Then from 4–7° the duration of 0.5° increments was gradually extended to 4.5 Ma once more.

The effect of this model on the rate of footwall uplift is to produce a maximum corresponding with the maximum rate of faulting. Footwall uplift is continuous throughout the model. Even with slow faulting no footwall subsidence occurs.

The basement emergence point in this model follows a complex path. From 0° to 5° it retreats from the fault block crest quite rapidly. From 5° to 7°, however, it reverses its course and advances towards the crest. This involves an initial offlap from 1500 m to 3120 m, and then onlap to 2750 m. The renewed onlap is caused by the decrease in fault rate, with background subsidence acting to reduce the width of the footwall island. It is worthy of note, however, that the inflection from offlap to onlap is not coincident with the maximum fault rate (at 3–4°) (Figs 12 & 13). This is because between 4° and 5°, the rate of faulting relative to background subsidence, was still sufficiently fast to induce offlap.

It is envisaged that the stratigraphy developed under the conditions of this model would record an initial offlapping sequence, capped by a locally-developed erosional unconformity, which in turn would be buried during renewed transgressive onlap. This sequence of events is not unlike that thought to be recorded on the Brent/Statfjord structure (Table 1), although the precise scaling of the regressive and transgressive events requires some further fine-tuning.

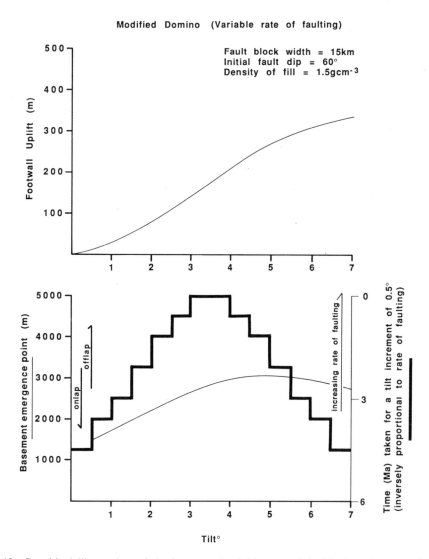

Fig. 12. Graphical illustration of the input to (variable rate of faulting), and output from (footwall uplift and emergence point), a modified domino model, in which the rate of faulting relative to continuous background subsidence, is symmetrically disposed about a maximum rate of 3–4° of tilt. This model generates offlap followed by onlap of the basement emergence point. Note that the inflexion of the emergence point is not coincident with the peak in the rate of faulting.

Modified domino, variable density of the half-graben fill and variable rate of faulting. The model for the Brent/Statfjord fault block (Figs 14 & 15)

The models presented so far have discussed the effects of varying the rate of faulting and the half-graben load independently. In reality, these two variables may be in part interdependent, as cause and effect, respectively. In general terms, slower faulting will allow more time for sediments to accumulate within a depocentre. During rapid

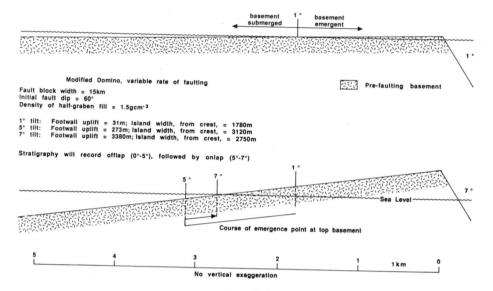

Fig. 13. True-scale cross-sections (at 1° and 7° of tilt) through the crest of a fault block derived from the model parameters and results of Fig. 12. This model generates offlap of the basement emergence point until 5° of tilt, followed by onlap from 5–7°.

extension, the rate of sediment input may struggle to keep pace with the size of the basins being created. Clearly there is more to basin-filling than assuming a constant rate of sediment supply. Increased extension will, for example, generate large uplifted areas of sediment supply. A general first-order link between increasing strain-rate and increasing sediment starvation is, however, perhaps not unreasonable.

Our model for the Brent/Statfjord structure, therefore, attempts to use these two variables as partially interdependent. The particular features of the Brent/Statfjord fault block which our refined model attempts to address are as follows (Livera & Gdula 1990; Roberts *et al.* 1987; Inglis & Gerard 1991).

1. The lower (Bathonian–Callovian) part of the Heather Formation caps the whole structure (and was deposited prior to east-flank collapse on gravity-driven slides).
2. The uppermost (Oxfordian) part of the Heather Formation is confined to a thin sequence in the westernmost, water-injection wells, 4–5 km downdip from the boundary fault. This sequence is a condensed version of that encountered in the deep, downdip well 211/28-5.
3. Heather Formation is largely absent, as a result of erosion, at the present day crest of the structure, *c.* 3 km west of the boundary fault (Fig. 2).
4. Renewed transgression during the Oxfordian/Kimmeridgian led to resubmergence of the present day crest of the fault block and a capping by Kimmeridge Clay Formation.

In our model we do not attempt to investigate the effects of gravitational collapse of the fault block crest during deposition of the upper Heather Formation. The effects of this collapse are profound and worthy of independent documentation.

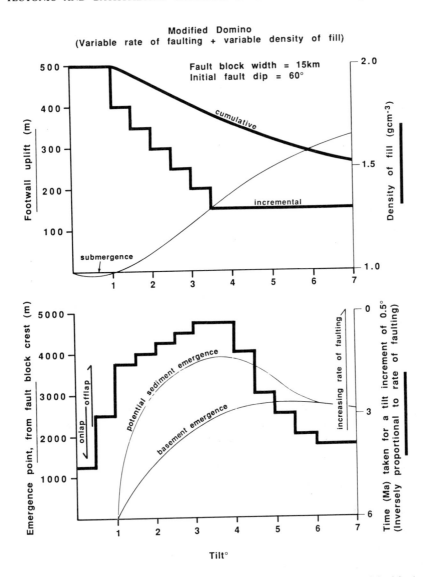

Fig. 14. Graphical illustration of the input to (fill density and variable rate of faulting), and output from (footwall uplift and emergence points), a modified domino model, in which the incremental density of the half-graben fill decreases until 3.5° of tilt and then remains constant, while the rate of faulting has a skewed distribution about a maximum at 3–4° of tilt. This model produces initial submergence of the fault block crest, followed by more characteristic footwall uplift. Upon emergence of the footwall crest (at 1°) the basement and sediment emergence points (see Fig. 17) define offlap followed by onlap (see Fig. 18). This model can be applied to the Brent/Statfjord fault block (see text).

In our model we have used a rate of faulting which increases for 4° of tilt and then decreases for the remaining 3°. The rate of faulting has been plotted both in the standard form used in this paper (Fig. 14, tilt v. time increment) and (Fig. 16a) as a more explicit plot of the rate of tilting v. time in the Late Jurassic (*sensu lato*). The

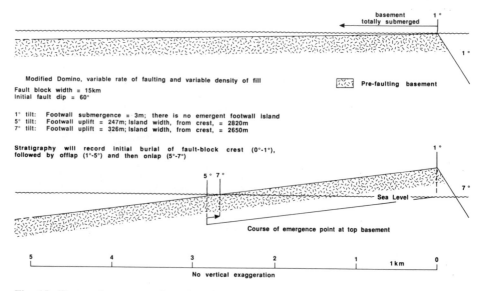

Fig. 15. True-scale cross-sections (at 1° and 7° of tilt) through the crest of a fault block derived from the model parameters and results of Fig. 14 (the sediment emergence point is not shown, see Fig. 18). Note the initial submergence of the whole fault block, followed by offlap of the basement emergence point across *c.* 3 km, with a final period (5–7°) of onlap.

rate of tilting is skewed during the 30 Ma interval, such that the maximum strain rate (3–4°) occurs after 12 Ma, i.e. at the close of deposition of the Heather Formation. Thus 4° of increasingly rapid tilt occur during Heather deposition, and 3° of tilt, at a diminishing rate, occur during Kimmeridge Clay deposition.

Incremental half-graben load during Heather deposition is given a distribution inversely related to the rate of faulting (Fig. 14). During the first 0.5° tilt increment (4.5 Ma duration), the incremental load is 2.0 g cm^{-3}. This load is steadily decreased to 1.3 g cm^{-3} at the end of Heather deposition. This value is maintained into the sediment-starved Kimmeridge Clay basin (Fig. 14). The cumulative, average density which this distribution represents is also plotted in Fig. 14. The final average density, at 7°, at 1.53 g cm^{-3} is thought to be a reasonable approximation to a basin *c.* 50% starved of sediment fill at the end of stretching (cf. Yielding 1990).

From the point of view of stratigraphic modelling the results of this model are very encouraging. The plot of footwall uplift v. tilt (Fig. 14) shows, for the first time, that uplift of the fault block crest above sea-level does not begin until 1° of tilt has been exceeded (Fig. 15). For the first 1° of tilt the model predicts submergence of the entire fault block. This results from the combined effect of a slow rate of faulting (relative to background subsidence) and a relatively dense half-graben load of 2.0 g cm^{-3}. The first degree of tilt corresponds with an elapsed time of 7.5 Ma, or end-Callovian on the time-scale in Fig. 16(a). The lower Heather Formation, which is thought to have capped the whole Brent/Statfjord structure is Bathonian–Callovian in age (Roberts *et al.* 1987) and, therefore, confined to the first degree of tilt. There is, thus, the possibility that a full, albeit condensed , lower Heather sequence could have been deposited over the crestal area of our model fault block. Hence, we have satisfied the first important criterion in our observations.

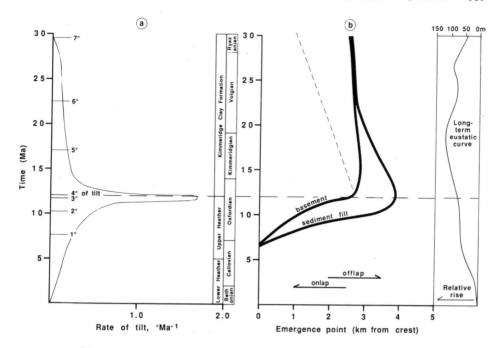

Fig. 16. (**a**) In this plot the skewed rate of faulting in Fig. 14 has been converted to a finite rate of tilting, plotted against 30 Ma of time, calibrated as intra-Bathonian to intra-Ryazanian. The corresponding lithostratigraphic units of the Humber Group 'syn-rift' sequence in the Viking Graben are also shown. As calibrated, the model fault block achieved a strain-rate peak at the end of deposition of the Heather Formation. (**b**) The course of the basement and sediment emergence points defined by the model in Fig. 14 (see also Fig. 18), plotted against the long-term, eustatic, sea-level curve of Haq *et al.* (1987). Note that the eustatic curve is out of phase with both model curves, even though the model curves provide a good fit to the stratigraphy of the Brent/Statfjord fault block (Fig. 18). The dotted line is the course of the basement emergence point incorporating new thermal subsidence after the strain-rate peak at 4°.

Subsequent to 1° of tilt, the footwall crest becomes elevated progressively higher (Fig. 14). Had the crest of the Brent/Statfjord fault block not collapsed under the influence of gravity there would probably have been no record of the early capping of the crestal area by the lower Heather.

While the footwall crest is submerged there can be no basement emergence point on our model fault block. Once 1° of tilt has been exceeded, however, the course of the basement emergence point can be followed as fault block tilt increases. From 1° to 5° of tilt, basement emergence retreats from the fault block crest for 2820 m. This period of basement offlap corresponds with the *c.* 10 Ma interval of fastest tilting (Fig. 16(a)). Subsequent to 5° of tilt, the strain rate has slowed sufficiently that background subsidence begins again to exert a significant effect. From 5° to 7° the basement emergence point onlaps towards the fault block crest from 2820 m to 2650 m (Figs 14 & 15).

Basement and sediment 'emergence points' within the half-graben. The course of the basement emergence point on our model fault block shows rapid offlap at the fault block crest, across *c.* 3 km, followed by more subdued onlap (Figs 14 & 15). The possible stratigraphic effects of this are discussed below, but first we should consider in a little more detail the possible geometric effects of offlap on the stratigraphy of an evolving half-graben.

Figure 17 shows, in cartoon form, a half-graben in which the basement emergence point has retreated from the fault block crest during the deposition of the second syn-rift unit (Unit 2). In the cartoon, Unit 1 originally extended close to the fault block crest, pinching out at the basement emergence point for Unit 1. Offlap during the deposition of Unit 2 causes retreat of the basement emergence point. This, in turn, causes the tapering edge of syn-rift Unit 1 to be elevated above sea-level. If it is assumed that erosion is efficient down to sea-level, then the tapering edge of Unit 1 will be removed, and an erosional unconformity will locally cap Unit 1 at sea-level. The proximal limit of this unconformity, and the new zero-edge to Unit 1, is defined by the basement emergence point for Unit 2. The distal limit of the unconformity is controlled by the tilt of the fault block and the geometry of Unit 1. The distal limit corresponds with the point at which the top of Unit 1 passes below sea-level. We refer to the distal limit of the erosional unconformity as the 'sediment emergence point' (distinct from the basement emergence point), as it is the point within the half-graben at which the syn-rift fill would become emergent, prior to erosion.

Assuming that deposition within the half-graben is controlled by available bathymetry, then the position of the proximal limit of syn-rift Unit 2 will be controlled by the sediment emergence point within the half-graben rather than the basement emergence point. In our cartoon we have illustrated Unit 2 tapering to a zero edge at this point (Fig. 17).

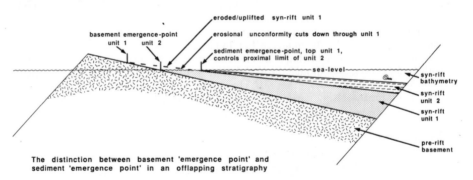

Fig. 17. Cartoon fault block illustrating the distinction between basement emergence point and sediment emergence point, during a period of offlap (see Figs 14, 16 & 18).

Figure 17 illustrates that the stratigraphy deposited, and ultimately preserved, within a half-graben is a function of the positions through time of both the basement and sediment emergence points. In an onlapping sequence these points will be coincident (there is no emergent syn-rift), but in an offlapping sequence they may be quite distinct. We have used the simplifying assumption that deposition within the half-graben extends as a tapering wedge to sea-level. With a more complex filling model the same considerations will need to be borne in mind.

Detailed stratigraphic predictions. Using the simplifying assumptions that deposition will occur as a tapering wedge extending to sea-level (Figs 3 & 17), the variable-load and variable-fault-rate model (Figs 14 & 15) have been used to construct a detailed stratigraphy for the crestal area of the model fault block. Figure 18 shows the fault block crest at 4° of tilt (end of Heather deposition) and 7° of tilt (end of Kimmeridge Clay deposition). At an aspect ratio of 1:1, the detail of the convergent tapering wedges cannot be resolved and so a vertical exaggeration of 5:1 has been used for clarity. Stratigraphic units are shown for each 1° tilt increment. The thickness of the units is controlled by incremental half-graben density. A density of $2.0 \, \mathrm{g \, cm^{-3}}$ is represented by 100% filling of the space created in that increment. A density of $1.5 \, \mathrm{g \, cm^{-3}}$ is represented by 50% filling, and the lowest incremental density, $1.3 \, \mathrm{g \, cm^{-3}}$, is represented by 30% filling.

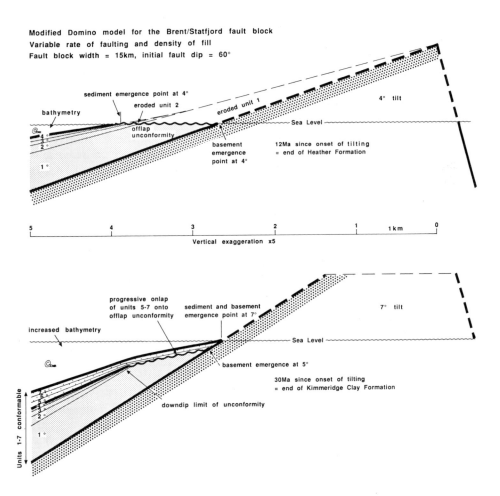

Fig. 18. Cross-sections with a vertical exaggeration of × 5 showing the stratigraphic predictions of the model described by Figs 14 & 16, and how these predictions might be matched to the Brent/Statfjord fault block. Four degrees of tilt corresponds to the end of Heather deposition, following a period of sustained offlap. Seven degrees of tilt corresponds to the end of Kimmeridge Clay deposition, following renewed onlap (see text for further explanation). Gravitational collapse of the crest of the model fault block is not incorporated. Note the substantial bathymetry developed by the end of the model.

The stratigraphy generated at 4° of tilt (end Heather) can in many respects be compared with the cartoon described above (cf. Figs 17 & 18). The basement emergence point at 4° of tilt lies 2680 m from the fault block crest. Units 1–3 were, however, deposited with basement emergence higher on the structure. Unit 1 has been constructed to cap the whole fault block. Units 2 and 3 have been constructed to taper to zero at their respective sediment emergence points (Fig. 17). As a result the sediment emergence point at 4° of tilt is located c. 3900 m, from the fault block crest. An erosional unconformity, reflecting progressive offlap, cuts down through Units 3–1, and extends across c. 1200 m, from the sediment emergence point to the basement emergence point. Updip from the basement emergence point, complete erosion of Units 1–3 has occurred.

In terms of modelling the distribution of Heather Formation on the Brent/ Statfjord structure, the model at 4° tilt shows some appealing features. It was discussed above that early submergence of the fault block crest can account for an initial cap of lower Heather Formation. The model at 4° shows that given rigid basement on the fault block, the lower Heather would have been totally eroded within c. 2700 m of the fault block crest. It is, perhaps, fortunate that gravitational collapse of the fault block crest has enabled remnants of this lower-Heather cap to be preserved on the present day east flank.

The second feature of the Heather Formation which we wish to address is the confinement of the uppermost Heather to the westernmost injector wells. This is predicted in our stratigraphic model, where the uppermost Heather unit (4°) does not encroach within c. 3900 m of the fault block crest. The injection wells on Brent and Statfjord lie 4–5 km back from the boundary fault. In our stratigraphic model, these wells alone would contain a complete sequence through the Heather Formation.

The third notable feature of the Heather is that it is largely absent at the present day crest of the structure, as a result of erosion. The present day crest of the structure lies c. 3 km west of the boundary fault (Fig. 2). It is effectively the western limit to the gravitational collapse of the fault block crest (Livera & Gdula 1990, fig. 6; Roberts et al. 1987, fig. 6; Struijk & Green 1991, fig. 2). Our end-Heather model (Fig. 18) shows that, neglecting the effects of crestal collapse, there should be no Heather Formation preserved within c. 2700 m of the fault block crest. The present day crest of the Brent/ Statfjord structure, thus, lies approximately coincident with the predicted preservational limit of the Heather. This, perhaps, explains why the present day crest, unaffected by gravity collapse, is largely devoid of Heather Formation.

We now turn to the stratigraphic model at 7° of tilt (Fig. 18). The first point to note is the increased bathymetry over that present at the end-Heather. After deposition of the Kimmeridge Clay in our model fault block, nearly half the available half-graben space is water filled. By 7° of tilt, further rotation of the fault block, combined with renewed onlap of the basement emergence point, had led to a drowning and burial of the end-Heather offlap unconformity. At 7° the basement and sediment emergence points are controlled by an onlapping sequence and they are now coincident. This predicted transgression of the Kimmeridge Clay across eroded Heather Formation is in accordance with observations (e.g. Table 1).

Our model fault block (Fig. 18) neglects gravitational collapse of the crestal area. Thus, a zero edge to Units 5–7 is constructed at the final basement emergence point. In reality, collapse of the fault block crest has allowed deposition of the Kimmeridge Clay across the present day crest and onto the east flank.

We are, therefore, much encouraged that not only does our final model replicate a sequence of events which has been identified on the Brent/Statfjord fault block, but it is also capable of scaling the magnitude of these events such that a satisfactory, synthetic stratigraphy can be derived.

The results of the stratigraphic modelling are summarized in Fig. 16(b), which provides a plot of magnitude of onlap/offlap against time. The courses of the basement and sediment emergence points are both shown. Comparison with the stratigraphic column and the time-scale shows:

1. burial of the fault block crest during deposition of the lower Heather;
2. rapid offlap and emergence during deposition of the upper Heather;
3. renewed onlap during deposition of the Kimmeridge Clay.

The additional dashed line in Fig. 16(b) shows the likely effect of incorporating 'second-phase' thermal subsidence into the model (in addition to the specified background subsidence), with thermal subsidence commencing after the 'spike' in the strain-rate plot (Fig. 16(a)). Incorporation of this additional subsidence would act to increase the rate of onlap during the final 3° of tilt.

Comparison with the long-term eustatic curve.   Each of our fault block models has been generated assuming a constant, background sea-level. We have then attempted to explain the observed stratigraphy on the Brent/Statfjord structure in terms of a largely tectonic model. It is, of course, possible that the observed stratigraphy results entirely from eustatic variations in sea-level and is not influenced by tectonism (cf. Vail & Todd 1981). We have, therefore, compared our model plot of relative onlap/offlap, which matches the observed stratigraphy, with the long-term eustatic curve of Haq *et al.* (1987) (Fig. 16). There is little correspondence between the two plots. While the stratigraphic record points to offlap (regression) during deposition of the Heather Formation, the eustatic curve indicates a steady, transgressive rise in sea-level. The two plots are in phase for the Kimmeridgian, but then an unrecognized regressive event is predicted by the eustatic curve in the Volgian–Ryazanian.

The discordance of the model plot, which matches the data, from the eustatic curve, suggests that the Humber Group stratigraphy on the Brent/Statfjord structure is not eustatically controlled. Although conversely, if there is a eustatic signature in the data, then this would indicate that the long-term curve is not correct, as it cannot match the events observed in the stratigraphic record.

Condensed sequences, palaeobathymetry and the problem of seismic resolution

In the preceding section we have attempted to model a sequence of tectonically controlled events whose stratigraphic expression might match the Humber Group stratigraphy of the Brent/Statfjord fault block. The detailed stratigraphy of the fault block crest is known because both the Brent and Statfjord fields have been penetrated by *c.* 100 exploration and development wells (Livera & Gdula 1990; Roberts *et al.* 1987). More commonly in basin analysis, our knowledge of stratigraphy may rely principally on the interpretation of seismic data.

If seismic data alone were used to evaluate the stratigraphy and geological history of the Brent/Statfjord fault block it is doubtful whether the detailed information provided by well data could be derived. A cartoon summary of the typical seismic–stratigraphic relationships seen across the crest of the Brent/Statfjord structure is shown in Fig. 19. Without supporting well data, the relationshps in this cartoon could be interpreted as follows:

1. there is no Humber Group (Heather and Kimmeridge Clay) on the eroded east flank;
2. Cromer Knoll Group (Lower Cretaceous) pinches out to zero below the present day crest. Its absence from the crest may be indicative of a regressive event following Humber Group deposition;
3. progressive onlap and transgression during the Cretaceous led to final submergence of the fault block crest during deposition of the Upper Cretaceous.

In fact none of these interpretations is likely to be correct. They arise, however, because of the inability of seismic data to resolve a thin Humber Group sequence on the east flank and a thin capping of Cromer Knoll Group across the whole structure (Livera & Gdula 1990; Roberts et al. 1987; Johnson & Eyssautier 1987; Inglis & Gerard 1991). In general, seismic data will be unable to resolve the detailed Humber Group stratigraphy across the fault block crest; well data are required to do so (Table 1).

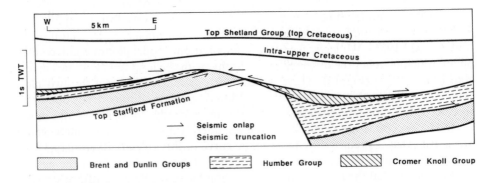

Fig. 19. Geoseismic cartoon illustrating the main seismic–stratigraphic relationships at the crest of the Brent structure. The Humber Group is visible to seismic data on the western, dip-slope of the structure and in the hangingwall basin to the east. No Humber Group is resolved on the eroded east flank, even though well data show it to be present. The Cromer Knoll Group appears to be absent from the fault block crest, onlapping lower on the structure from both east and west. In fact, a thin veneer of Cromer Knoll Group is present across even the highest parts of the fault block. The full stratigraphic history of this fault block cannot be deduced from seismic data alone.

Another similar illustration of the same resolution problem of seismic stratigraphic techniques is provided by the Snorre fault block in the northern Viking Graben (Hollander 1987; Yielding 1990). Structural cross-sections drawn across the Snorre fault block on the basis of seismic interpretation show Upper Cretaceous resting unconformably on rotated, Triassic and Jurassic pre-rift basement (e.g. Karlsson 1986; Nybakken 1991). No Upper Jurassic Humber Group or Lower Cretaceous

Cromer Knoll Group is resolved by seismic data. In fact, however, well data show there to be a uniform capping of highly-condensed Lower Cretaceous across Snorre (Hollander 1987), while the Upper Jurassic is truly absent. The Lower Cretaceous sequence is less than 10 m thick and cannot be resolved by seismic data. Thus, well data tell us that the crest of the Snorre fault block was a site of deposition early in the Cretaceous. Seismic data alone would infer that it remained an emergent site of non-deposition into the Late Cretaceous.

Condensed sequences, such as those capping Brent/Statfjord and Snorre may evolve simply as a result of stratigraphic tapering towards the crest of a structural high. Sequence condensing influenced by structural topography will be marked even in basins full to sea-level (Fig. 1) The effects of sediment starvation in bathymetrically deep half-graben may, however, act to compound the effects of structural topography (e.g. Rawson & Riley 1982; Bertram & Milton 1989; Cartwright 1991 and this volume; Barr 1991).

In a very pertinent discussion, Bertram & Milton (1989) have highlighted the pitfalls of using stratigraphic thickness data alone to make deductions about the timing of fault block rotation. They pointed out that the infilling of a bathymetrically deep half-graben by post-rift sediments would mimic the tapering wedge of a syn-rift sequence. As a case in point, they chose the Lower Cretaceous in the Viking Graben area. Figure 19 illustrates this point well. The Cromer Knoll Group sequence on either side of the Brent/Statfjord high thickens down-structure as a stratigraphic wedge. There is, however, little evidence that its deposition was accompanied by fault block rotation. We would follow similar interpretations made elsewhere by Bertram & Milton (1989), Barr (1991) and Cartwright (1991) and attribute thickness variations within the Lower Cretaceous primarily to passive infill of pre-existing bathymetry. A significant Ryazanian bathymetry is predicted by our stratigraphic model for the Brent/Statfjord structure (Fig. 18). Likewise flexural backstripping of cross-sections through the northern Viking Graben (Roberts *et al.* 1993) also indicates the likelihood of significant post-rift bathymetry within the basin.

Is the seismic stratigraphic method reliable for the analysis of tilted fault blocks?

We have already outlined two cases in which we know the resolution of seismic data to be insufficient to resolve the condensed stratigraphic relationships at the crest of tilted fault blocks. Failure to recognize the role of palaeobathymetry in stratigraphic-sequence development may also result in seismic–stratigraphic misinterpretation (Bertram & Milton 1989). The particular problem to be considered here is submarine onlap onto a bathymetric high. The seismic stratal geometries resulting from marine onlap and passive burial of a topographic high may mimic those of a transgressive sequence in which development is controlled by changing sea-level, either relative or absolute. For example, Badley *et al.* (1984) identified very pronounced seismic onlap of the Lower and Upper Cretaceous onto the west flank of the Oseberg field, offshore Norway. The eastwards migration of stratal terminations towards the crest of the Oseberg field was attributed to progressive collapse, during the Cretaceous, of a series of faulted terraces. Structural collapse of the terraces, it was argued, progressively widened the Cretaceous basin and resulted in eastwards transgression. An alternative interpretation of the same data, and one which we now favour, would recognize the importance of significant Cretaceous bathymetry in the hangingwall depocetre to the west of the Oseberg fault block. Gradual, passive accumulation of Lower and Upper Cretaceous sediments within this pre-existing depocentre would result in marine onlap onto, and progressive burial of, the west flank of the Oseberg structure. In this interpretation, all movement on the Oseberg terraces is confined to the Late Jurassic rift stage. The earlier interpretation of Badley et al. (1984) required the faulted terraces to remain active well into the post-rift history.

Careful application of seismic–stratigraphic principles clearly has a role to play in basin analysis. When applying these principles to the stratigraphic fill of rotated fault blocks we see two major shortcomings imposed by the resolution of the data.

1. Seismic data cannot distinguish the internal geometry, and sometimes the very presence, of condensed sequences on fault block crests. It may erroneously predict a stratigraphic hiatus over a structural high, where in fact there is none.
2. Without palaeobathymetric information seismic stratigraphy cannot differentiate between transgressive onlap, resulting from a migrating shoreline, and marine onlap without transgression, resulting from infill of pre-existing bathymetry.

The stratigraphic fill of tilted fault blocks within the North Sea basin is known to have been influenced by structurally controlled sequence condensing, sediment starvation and subsequent bathymetric infill. The seismic–stratigraphic technique must, therefore, be applied with caution.

The standard seismic–stratigraphic reference for the Jurassic and Lower Cretaceous of the North Sea is Vail & Todd (1981). These authors discounted the influence of tectonics on sequence development. As emphasized in the main part of this paper, we believe that the structural geometry of rotating fault blocks is likely to exert a first-order control on stratigraphic-sequence development within half-graben. As a result of this we suggest that Vail & Todd's analysis failed to take into account tectonically condensed sequences or syn- and post-rift bathymetry, and as a result, extracted from the seismic data an over-elaborate record of eustatic sea-level fluctuations.

On a more global basis, Hubbard (1988) has challenged the validity of the Jurassic and Cretaceous eustatic sea-level curve (e.g. Haq et al. 1987), suggesting that most of the 'sequence boundaries' used to construct this curve have a local tectonic influence, not a global eustatic influence. We have presented here a series of quantitative models which support Hubbard's assertion that fault block rotation and the consequent infill of half-graben depocentres may produce considerable stratigraphic complexity.

Without first 'subtracting' the tectonic influence, recognition of a eustatic signature within a half-graben's stratigraphic fill is probably, at present, impossible. We cannot uniquely 'subtract' the tectonic influence in any individual case, we can only produce a comparable forward model. Thus, we are unlikely to be able to use seismic–stratigraphic methods to define fluctuations in absolute sea-level during periods of half-graben formation and half-graben infill.

When will the seismic–stratigraphic method work?

We have outlined above some examples of geological circumstances in which rigorous application of seismic–stratigraphic principles would yield an incorrect geological history. Under what circumstances, therefore, might the seismic–strati-graphic method be applied with confidence? Seismic stratigraphy is principally concerned with evaluating the interaction between idealized depositional-systems (so-called 'systems tracts') and sea-level. The methodology will, therefore, be appli-cable if the wavelength of major topography within a subsiding basin is greater than the full width (across-strike) of a 'systems tract' entering the basin. Under these circumstances sediment supply, rather than topographic control, will be the principal control on stratal geometries. Such conditions may pertain within thermally-subsid-ing (post-rift) basins, unbuttressed continental margins (e.g. the Gulf of Mexico), and foreland basins within high-strength lithosphere.

If, however, the wavelength of major, basin floor topography (e.g. tilted fault blocks) is less than the width of individual 'systems tracts', then topography within the basin, in addition to sediment supply, will exert a major control on stratal geometries. At present, the seismic–stratigraphic literature does not acknowledge this point. When basin floor topography acts to influence the geometry of depositional systems within a basin, the seismic–stratigraphic technique cannot be used with confidence to analyse fluctuations in past sea-level.

Conclusions

In the main part of this paper, we have devised a modification of the domino fault block rotation-and-filling model. Derivation of this model was initially driven by an investigation of a major, tilted fault block in the northern North Sea, the Brent/Statfjord fault block. Like Barr's (1987a,b) initial model, however, we believe that the modified domino model has general implications for the analysis of the strati-graphic fill of evolving half-graben. In particular, the model serves to increase the range of stratigraphic sequence boundaries which can be explained as a consequence of fault block rotation, as an alternative to eustatic fluctuations in sea-level. Hubbard (1988) suggested that many apparently-global sequence boundaries in the Jurassic–Cretaceous are in fact of only local extent and reflect local tectonism within a particular basin. Application of the modified domino concept to some of Hubbard's sequences might help support this supposition.

The particular conclusions that we derive from this study are as follows.

1. Barr's (1987a,b) domino model makes useful, quantitative predictions about the nature of stratigraphic sequences within evolving half-graben. In particular, it highlights the potential for stratigraphic complexity at fault block crests.
2. The basic domino model cannot account for regressive offlap within an evolving half-graben. Such offlap is documented within the Humber Group stratigraphy of the northern Viking Graben (North Sea).
3. A modification of the domino model, in which average half-graben load decreases with time, predicts regression at the crests of half-graben and an accelerating rate of footwall uplift. In geological terms, decreasing average load within the half-graben may result from basin subsidence outpacing sediment supply or from starved sediment input to the basin. In either case it is anticipated that maximum bathymetry within the half-graben will increase as extension proceeds.
4. A further modification of the domino model can be adopted in circumstances

where the basin floor was already subsiding prior to extension, most probably as a result of thermal relaxation following earlier extension. In such circumstances, if renewed extension is rapid or geologically instantaneous, little deviation from the basic domino model will be observed. If, however, renewed extension is slow, then the effects of the ongoing 'background' subsidence act to suppress footwall uplift and the width of emergent footwall islands. An accelerating strain rate will produce accelerating footwall uplift and may induce offlap on the half-graben flank.

5. A modified domino model in which decreasing half-graben load and increasing strain rate are partially linked, as effect and cause respectively, has been used to model the syn-rift stratigraphy of the Brent/Statfjord fault block in the Viking Graben.

6. The details of the complex crestal stratigraphy on Brent/Statfjord lie below the resolution of seismic data, and are only recognized as a consequence of a large amount of well data. The observed stratigraphic relationships are out of phase with the global long-term eustatic curve. This implies either a tectonic origin for the observed stratigraphic relationships, or inaccuracy in the eustatic cure.

7. The modified domino model predicts stratigraphic complexities at the crest of tilted fault blocks, the details of which the seismic–stratigraphic technique will be unable to resolve. It also allows for the development of substantial syn-rift bathymetry. This bathymetry may be passively infilled after extension has ceased, generating marine onlap within the half-graben, entirely independent of sea-level fluctuations.

8. Before the seismic–stratigraphic technique can be successfully used to investigate the geological history of tilted fault blocks, and in particular the relationship of fault block crests to sea-level, it must be able to subtract the local, tectonic and bathymetric influence on stratigraphic relationships from the more regional, eustatic signature. This cannot be done at present. We can produce forward models which attempt to explain stratal geometries by explicit mechanisms, but there are too many unconstrained variables to allow a unique interpretation of any particular sequence of half-graben fill.

We thank Dave Barr, James Jackson and Nicky White for discussions of the domino model and its applications. The stratigraphic complexities of the Brent/Statfjord area were first made aware to us by Charles Jourdan and Terkel Olsen, whom we thank for many geological discussions. We are grateful to David Kemp for draughting the figures.

References

BADLEY, M. E., EGEBERG, T. & NIPEN, O. 1984. Development of rift basins illustrated by the structural evolution of the Oseberg feature, Block 30/6, offshore Norway. *Journal of the Geological Society, London*, **41**, 639–649.
——, PRICE, J. D., RAMBECH DAHL, C. & AGDESTEIN, T. 1988. The structural evolution of the northern Viking Graben and its bearing upon extensional modes of basin formation. *Journal of the Geological Society, London*, **145**, 455–472.
BARR, D. 1987a. Lithospheric stretching, detached normal faulting and footwall uplift. *In*: COWARD, M. P., DEWEY, J. F. & HANCOCK, P. L. (eds) *Continental Extensional Tectonics*, Geological Society, London, Special Publication, **28**, 75–94.
—— 1987b. Structural/stratigraphic models for extensional basins of half-graben type. *Journal of Structural Geology*, **9**, 491–500.

—— 1991. Subsidence and sedimentation in semi-starved half-graben: a model based on North Sea data. *In*: ROBERTS, A. M., YIELDING, G. & FREEMAN, B. (eds) *The Geometry of Normal Faults*. Geological Society, London, Special Publication, **56**, 17–28.

BERTRAM, G. T. & MILTON, N. J. 1989. Reconstructing basin evolution from sedimentary thickness; the importance of palaeobathymetric control, with reference to the North Sea. *Basin Research*, **1**, 247–257.

BOWEN, J. M. 1975. The Brent Oil-field. *In*: WOODLAND, A. W. (ed.) *Petroleum and the Continental Shelf of Northwest Europe*, Applied Science Publishers, 353–360.

BROWN, S., RICHARDS, P. C. & THOMSON, A. R. 1987. Patterns in the deposition of the Brent Group (Middle Jurassic) UK North Sea. *In*: BROOKS, J. & GLENNIE, K. W. (eds) *Petroleum Geology of North West Europe*. Graham & Trotman, London, 899–914.

CARTWRIGHT, J. A. 1991. The kinematic evolution of the Coffee Soil Fault. *In*: ROBERTS, A. M., YIELDING, G. & FREEMAN, B. (eds) *The Geometry of Normal Faults*, Geological Society, London, Special Publication, **56**, 29–40.

CLOETINGH, S. & KOOI, H. 1989. Tectonic subsidence and sea-level changes—a reappraisal. *In*: COLLINSON, J. D. (ed.) *Correlation in Hydrocarbon Exploration*, Graham & Trotman, London, 3–11.

——, LAMBECK, K. & McQUEEN, H. 1987. Apparent sea-level fluctuations and a palaeostress field for the North Sea region. *In*: BROOKS, J. & GLENNIE, K. (eds) *Petroleum Geology of North West Europe*, Graham & Trotman, London, 49–57.

——, McQUEEN, H. & LAMBECK, K. 1985. On a tectonic mechanism for regional sea-level variations. *Earth and Planetary Science Letters*, **75**, 157–166.

COLLIER, R. E. LL. 1990. Eustatic and tectonic controls upon Quaternary coastal sedimentation in the Corinth Basin, Greece. *Journal of the Geological Society, London*, **147**, 301–314.

——, LEEDER, M. R. & MAYNARD, J. R. 1990. Transgressions and regressions: a model for the influence of tectonic subsidence, deposition and eustasy, with application to Quaternary and Carboniferous examples. *Geological Magazine*, **127**, 117–128.

DAVISON, I. 1989. Extensional domino fault tectonics: kinematics and geometrical constraints. *Annales Tectonicæ*, **III**, 12–24.

EMBRY, A. F. 1989. A Tectonic Origin for Third-Order Depositional Sequences in Extensional Basins—Implications for Basin Modeling. *In*: CROSS, T. A. (ed.) *Quantitative Dynamic Stratigraphy*, Prentice Hall, 491–501.

GILTNER, J. P. 1987. Application of extensional models to the Northern Viking Graben. *Norsk Geologisk Tidsskrift*, **67**, 339–352.

GRADIJAN, S.. J. & WIIK, M. 1987. Statfjord; Nord. *In*: SPENCER, A. M. *et al.* (eds) *Geology of the Norwegian Oil and Gas Fields*, Graham & Trotman, 341–350.

HAQ, B., HARDENBOL, J. & VAIL, P. R. 1987. Chronology of fluctuating sea level since the Triassic (250 million years to present). *Science*, **25**, 1156–1167.

HOLLANDER, N. B. 1987. Snorre. *In*: SPENCER, A. M. *et al.* (eds) *Geology of the Norwegian Oil and Gas Fields*. Graham & Trotman, London, 307–318.

HUBBARD, R. J. 1988. Age and Significance of Sequence Boundaries on Jurassic and Early Cretaceous Rifted Continental Margins. *American Association of Petroleum Geologists Bulletin*, **72**, 49–72.

INGLIS, I. & GERARD, J. 1991. The Alwyn North Field, Blocks 3/9a, 3/4a, UK North Sea. *In*: ABBOTTS, I. L. (ed.) *United Kingdom Oil & Gas Fields, 25 Years Commemorative Volume*, Geological Society Memoir **14**, 63–72.

JACKSON, J. A. & McKENZIE, D. P. 1983. The geometrical evolution of normal fault systems. *Journal of Structural Geology*, **5**, 471–482.

——, WHITE, N. J., GARFUNKEL, Z. & ANDERSON, H. 1988. Relations between normal-fault geometry, tilting and vertical motions in extensional terrains, an example from the southern Gulf of Suez. *Journal of Structural Geology*, **10**, 155–170.

JARVIS, G. T. & McKENZIE, D. P. 1980. Sedimentary Basin Formation with Finite Extension Rates. *Earth and Planetary Science Letters*, **48**, 42–52.

JOHNSON, A. & EYSSAUTIER, M. 1987. Alwyn North Field and its regional geological context. *In*: BROOKS, J. & GLENNIE, K. W. (eds) *Petroleum Geology of North West Europe*, Graham & Trotman, London, 963–977.

KARLSSON, W. 1986. The Snorre, Statfjord and Gullfaks oilfields and the habitat of hydro-carbons on the Tampen Spur, offshore Norway. *In*: SPENCER, A. M. *et al.* (eds) *Habitat of Hydrocarbons on the Norwegian Continental Shelf.* Graham & Trotman, London, 181–198.

KIRK, R. H. 1980. Statfjord Field: a North Sea giant. *In*: HALBOUTY, M. T. (ed.) Giant Oil and Gas Fields of the Decade: 1968–1978, *American Association of Petroleum Geologists Memoir*, **30**, Tulsa, Oklahoma, 95–116.

KUSZNIR, N. J. & EGAN, S. S. 1989. Simple-shear and pure-shear models of extensional sedimentary basin formation: application to the Jeanne d'Arc Basin, Grand Banks of Newfoundland. *In*: TANKARD, A. J. & BALKWILL, H. R. (eds) Extensional Tectonics and Stratigraphy of the North Atlantic Margins. *American Association of Petroleum Geologists Memoir*, **46**, 305–322.

——, MARSDEN, G. & EGAN, S. S. 1991. A flexural cantilever simple-shear/pure-shear model of continental lithosphere extension: application to the Jeanne d'Arc Basin, Grand Banks and Viking Graben, North Sea. *In*: ROBERTS, A. M., YIELDING, G. & FREEMAN, B. (eds) *The Geometry of Normal Faults*, Geological Society, London, Special Publication, **56**, 41–60.

LIVERA, S. E. & GDULA, J. E. 1990. Brent Oil Field. *In*: BEAUMONT, E. A. & FOSTER, N. H. (eds) *Atlas of Oil and Gas Fields, Structural Traps II, Traps Associated with Tectonic Faulting.* American Association of Petroleum Geologists, 21–63.

MANDL, G. 1987. Tectonic deformation by rotating parallel faults—the 'bookshelf' mechanism. *Tectonophysics*, **141**, 277–316.

MARSDEN, G., YIELDING, G., ROBERTS, A. M. & KUSZNIR, N. J. 1990. Application of a flexural cantilever simple-shear/pure-shear model of continental lithosphere extension to the formation of the northern North Sea Basin. *In*: BLUNDELL, D. J. & GIBBS, A. D. (eds) *Tectonic Evolution of the North Sea Rifts*, Oxford University Press, 241–261.

McKENZIE, D. P. 1978. Some remarks on the development of sedimentary basins. *Earth and Planetary Science Letters*, **40**, 25–32.

MORTON, W. H. & BLACK, R. 1975. Crustal attenuation in Afar. *In*: PILGAR, A. & ROSLER, A. (eds) *Afar Depression of Ethiopia, Inter-Union Commission on Geodynamics. Proceedings of International Symposium on the Afar Region and related rift problems.* E. Schweizerbart'sche Verlagsbuchhandlung, Stuttgart, Germany. Scientific Report No. 14, 55–65.

NYBAKKEN, S. 1991. Sealing Fault Traps—an Exploration Concept in the Mature Petroleum Province, Tampen Spur, North North Sea. *First Break*, **9**, 209–222.

NYBERG, I. T. 1987. Statfjord Øst. *In*: SPENCER *et al.* (eds) *Geology of the Norwegian Oil and Gas Fields.* Graham & Trotman, London, 351–362.

RAWSON, P. F. & RILEY, L. A. 1982. Latest Jurassic–Early Cretaceous Events and the 'Late Cimmerian Unconformity' in North Sea Area. *American Association of Petroleum Geologists Bulletin*, **66**, 2628–2648.

ROBERTS, A. M. & YIELDING, G. 1991. Deformation around basin-margin faults in the North Sea/Norwegian rift. *In*: ROBERTS, A. M., YIELDING, G. & FREEMAN, B. (eds) *The Geometry of Normal Faults*. Geological Society, London, Special Publication, **56**, 61–78.

—— & ——, 1992. Continental Extensional Tectonics. *In*: HANCOCK, P. L. (ed.) *New Concepts in Tectonics*, Pergamon Press (in press).

——, —— & BADLEY, M. E. 1990. A kinematic model for the orthogonal opening of the Late Jurassic North Sea Rift System, Denmark–Mid Norway. *In*: BLUNDELL, D. J. & GIBBS, A. D. (eds) *Tectonic Evolution of the North Sea Rifts*, Oxford University Press. 180–199.

——, ——, KUSZNIR, N. J., WALKER, I. M. & DORN-LOPEZ, D. 1993. Mesozoic extension in the North Sea: constraints from flexural backstripping, forward modelling and fault populations. *In*: PARKER, J. R. (ed.) *Petroleum Geology of Northwest Europe: Proceedings of the 4th Conference.* Geological Society, London, in press.

ROBERTS, J. D., MATTHIESON, A. S. & HAMPSON, J. M. 1987. Statfjord. *In*: SPENCER, A. M. *et al.* (eds) *Geology of the Norwegian Oil and Gas Fields.* Graham & Trotman, London, 319–340.

SCHLISCHE, R. W. & OLSEN, P. E. 1990. Quantitative filling model for continental extensional basins with applications to early Mesozoic rifts of eastern North America. *Journal of Geology*, **98**, 135–155.

SCLATER, J. G. & CELERIER, B. 1989. Errors in extension measurements from planar faults observed on seismic reflection lines. *Basin Research*, **1**, 217–221.

—— & CHRISTIE, P. A. F. 1980. Continental Stretching: an explanation of the post mid-Cretaceous subsidence of the Central North Sea Basin. *Journal of Geophysical Research*, **85**, 3711–3739.

STEEL, R. & RYSETH, A. 1990. A Triassic–early Jurassic succession in the northern North Sea: Megasequence stratigraphy and intra-Triassic tectonics. *In*: HARDMAN, R. F. P. & BROOKS, J. (eds) *Tectonic Events Responsible for Britain's Oil & Gas Reserves*, Geological Society, London, Special Publication, **55**, 139–168.

STRUIJK, A. P. & GREEN, R. T. 1991. The Brent Field, Block 211/29, UK North Sea. *In*: ABBOTTS, I. L. (ed.) *United Kingdom Oil & Gas Fields, 25 Years Commemorative Volume*, Geological Society Memoir **14**, 63–72.

VAIL, P. R. & TODD, R. G. 1981. Northern North Sea Jurassic unconformities, chronostratigraphy and sea-level changes from seismic stratigraphy. *In*: ILLING, L. B. & HOBSON, G. D. (eds) *Petroleum Geology of the Continental Shelf of North West Europe*, Heyden, London, 216–235.

WERNICKE, B. & BURCHFIEL, B. C. 1982. Modes of extensional tectonics. *Journal of Structural Geology*, **4**, 105–115.

WHITE, N. J. 1990. Does the uniform stretching model work in the North Sea? *In*: BLUNDELL, D. J. & GIBBS, A. D. (eds) *Tectonic Evolution of the North Sea Rifts*, Oxford University Press, 217–240.

YIELDING, G. 1990. Footwall uplift associated with Late Jurassic normal faulting in the northern North Sea. *Journal of the Geological Society*, **147**, 219–222.

——, BADLEY, M. E. & FREEMAN, B. 1991. Seismic reflections from normal faults in the northern North Sea. *In*: ROBERTS, A. M., YIELDING, G. & FREEMAN, B. (eds) *The Geometry of Normal Faults*, Geological Society, London, Special Publication **56**, 79–89.

——, —— & ROBERTS, A. M. 1992. The structural evolution of the Brent Province. *In*: MORTON, A. C. *et al.* (eds) *Geology of the Brent Group*, Geological Society, London, Special Publication, **61**, 27–40.

—— & ROBERTS, A. M. (1992). Footwall uplift during normal faulting—implications for structural geometries in the North Sea. *In*: LARSEN, R. M. *et al.* (eds) *Structural and Tectonic Modelling and its Application to Petroleum Geology*, NPS Special Publication, No. 1, Elsevier, 289–304.

From WILLIAMS, G. D. & DOBB, A. (eds), 1993, *Tectonics and Seismic Sequence Stratigraphy.*
Geological Society Special Publication No. 71, 123–140.

Comments on the pattern of post-rift subsidence in the Central and Northern North Sea Basin

Aidan M. Joy

Department of Geology, Imperial College of Science, Technology and Medicine, London SW7 2BP, UK.

Abstract: Burial history analyses suggest that the post-rift subsidence history of the Central and Northern North Sea Basin is poorly explained by published models of thermal subsidence. The last rifting episode took place during the Late Jurassic. The early post-rift phase (earliest Cretaceous to Danian) was characterized by slow subsidence, with much of the sedimentation accommodated by the infilling of previously developed rift bathymetry. At this time the shoulders of the rift were supported. During the earliest Cretaceous to Danian, the Central and Northern North Sea Basin was situated in a continental interior, and its morphology and subsidence style resembled that of many modern intra-continental rifts. Sub-sequently, rates of subsidence incresed markedly; this acceleration in subsidence was particularly pronounced in the region of the rift shoulders. The timing of the acceleration was approximately mid-Palaeocene, the time at which the Norwegian–Greenland Sea opened immediately to the north of the North Sea Basin. It is suggested that there are differences between the subsidence rates and styles of extensional basins in intra-continental and continental margin settings which are not predicted by published models.

This paper concerns the central and northern regions of the North Sea Basin system. The study area lies between Scotland and Norway, north of the Mid North Sea High (Fig. 1). It lies within the Caledonian orogenic belt, in which crustal accretion was completed during the Early Devonian (Watson 1985; Glennie 1990). Since that time the tectonic history of the area has been dominated by episodes of extensional tectonism with occasional periods of weak inversion (see Glennie (1990) and Ziegler (1981, 1982) for detailed accounts of the area's tectonic evolution).

This important hydrocarbon province is well explored and a wealth of information has been gathered, and published, on its structure and stratigraphy. As Thorne & Watts (1989) point out, however, there is a major controversy concerning the role of various lithospheric processes in causing subsidence in the area. The basin system is widely believed to have been formed as a result of the extensional episodes mentioned above, accompanied and followed by thermal subsidence (Sclater & Christie 1980; Barton & Wood 1984; Hellinger *et al.* 1989; Sclater & Shorey 1989). The last extensional episode ceased during the Ryazanian (Badley *et al.* 1988; Bertram & Milton 1989; Boote & Gustav 1987). In the following section, subsidence history reconstructions are used to illustrate the progress of post-rift subsidence in the Central and Northern North Sea Basin.

Subsidence history analyses

Approach

The progress of subsidence in the study area was investigated using subsidence

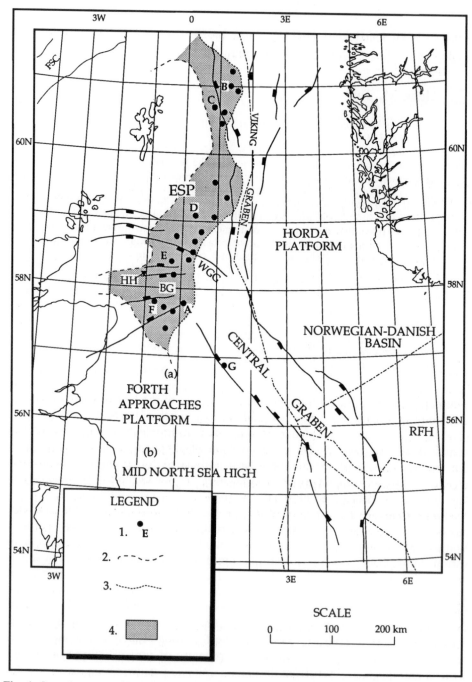

Fig. 1. Location map of North Sea Basin system. Legend: 1, Wells for which subsidence was modelled; wells illustrated in Figs 3 & 4 are lettered; 2, landward limit of Late Palaeocene; 3, basinward edge of Moray/Ninian delta top; 4, area in which Moray/Ninian delta top sediments are preserved. 2, 3 & 4 after Rochow (1981). Structural elements after Ziegler (1982). Abbreviations: BG Buchan Graben; ESP East Shetland Platform; FSC Faeroe–Shetland Channel; HH Halibut Horst, RFH Ringkobing-Fyn High; WGG Witch Ground Graben. Note the wide range of structural settings occupied by the modelled wells.

history analyses. Different parts of the study area, which may have had widely differing sedimentation histories, are best compared by mathematically correcting for loading by sediments and by eustatic sea-level fluctuations. This leaves tectonic subsidence, which may be thought of as the subsidence which the basin floor would have undergone had it been loaded by a column of sea water, the top of which was always at present day sea-level. Tectonic subsidence (TS) is calculated using the equation of Steckler & Watts (1978):

$$TS = H(\rho m - \rho s/\rho m - \rho w) - \Delta SL(\rho m/\rho m - \rho w) + \Delta WD$$

where H is sedimentary layer thickness, ΔSL is change in eustatic sea-level and ΔWD is change in water depth; ρm, ρs and ρw are the densities of asthenospheric mantle, sediment and sea water, respectively. With the exception of water depth, all of the data required to calculate tectonic subsidence in the study area are known to a sufficient degree of accuracy (though there is continuing debate over the magnitude of long-term eustatic sea-level fluctuations). The problem of water depths is a significant one, since the range of water depths which existed in the Central and Northern North Sea Basin during the post-rift phase was probably considerable.

Method and data sources

Values for thickness and density of the sedimentary layers were taken from well logs. Where density logs were unavailable (this is frequently the case, especially in the uphole section) ρs values were obtained using porosity estimates from the sonic log and appropriate grain and fluid densities. Values for surface porosity and compaction constant (f_o and c of Sclater & Christie 1980) were taken from plots constructed from well log data in the area of interest; porosity–depth plots were made for 14 different intervals since it was felt that published values might be insufficiently specific to the study area. Ages of the sedimentary layers were taken from composite logs and from Deegan & Scull (1977); these were converted to Ma using the Mesozoic–Cenozoic Cycle Chart of Haq et al. (1987). Eustatic sea-levels were also derived from the chart of Haq et al. The basin was assumed to have exhibited Airy isostasy at all times, since the flexural strength of the lithosphere in the study area is thought to be very low (Barton & Wood 1984; White & McKenzie 1988).

Water depth

Over much of the study area the sediment surface appears to have remained below wave base from the Late Jurassic to the present day. In the absence of sedimentologi-cal data diagnostic of specific water depths, palaeobathymetry is typically estimated using depth diagnostic fossils. This method is useful, if rather imprecise, for the Cenozoic of the study area, but it is typically of limited value for earlier intervals due to a combination of poor assemblages and drilling practice (Barton & Wood 1984; Bertram & Milton 1989). Following the example of Bertram & Milton, therefore, it was decided to analyse wells for which palaeobathymetric evidence is available in the form of the Moray/Ninian delta top. The coal-bearing strata of the delta top are known to have been deposited at, or very near to, sea-level at the end Palaeocene–

earliest Eocene. Bertram & Milton show how, using this *trace* (a geological horizon formed at a known water depth), subsidence curves can be 'pegged' with respect to other traces. The Moray/Ninian delta top, though geographically restricted, occurs in a wide range of structural settings; it overlies the Forth Approaches and East Shetland Platforms, the Transitional Shelf and the Buchan, Witch Ground and Viking Grabens (Fig. 1). The sample of wells which was selected for analysis, therefore, illustrates post-rift subsidence over the full range of structural settings within the Central and Northern North Sea Basin. For comparison, subsidence history plots were also constructed for a number of wells situated to the south and east of the Moray/Ninian delta top; these plots are less well constrained with respect to water depth, for reasons outlined above.

Compaction and decompaction

Subsidence history analyses must take account of compaction, since some of the space for sedimentation is made available by the progressive compaction of deeper strata. If allowance is not made for compaction, tectonic subsidence may be overestimated, especially for intervals underlain by thick sedimentary sequences.

The commonly used decompaction method of Sclater & Christie (1980) assumes a linear relationship between the natural log of porosity and depth. However, there is evidence that this method may significantly overestimate the amount of compaction which occurs at depth. Two of Sclater & Christie's porosity–depth relationships are shown in Fig. 2, with a number of other such relationships for comparison. Sclater & Christie's curves, compared to the majority of the others, indicate a less efficient porosity loss during the initial stages of burial. This is of importance for subsidence history analysis; Sclater & Christie's curves imply that a considerable amount of space for sedimentation can be supplied by compaction of deeper strata, compared with curves which indicate a more efficient porosity reduction at relatively shallow depths. In fact, normal shale compaction typically follows curves on the left of Fig. 2.1, such as curves, c, e, g and i (S. Burley, pers. comm. 1991).

Sclater & Christie's backstripping method, in which layer thickness and density were derived by decompaction prior to calculating tectonic subsidence, was shown by Thorne & Watts (1989, figure 7) to have produced 'anomalous inversion structures' in the study area. This resulted from the overestimation of porosity loss from the deeper strata during the later stages of burial, which in turn caused an underestimation of tectonic subsidence during the later stages of basin development. Even Thorne & Watts' own method, in which sediments are also decompacted prior to calculating tectonic subsidence, produced 'inversion structures', albeit much smaller.

Experimental and field evidence also suggest that the log porosity–depth relationship is not linear. Experimental data show that the earliest stages of mechanical compaction are typically responsible for a greater degree of porosity loss than is assumed by Sclater & Christie (see Rieke & Chilingarian (1974), e.g. figure 6). Field evidence is presented in the same volume (e.g. figures 19 and 23) to show that the initial stages of compaction are associated with a very high degree of porosity loss.

Consequently it was felt from the outset that the decompaction method of Sclater & Christie (1980) might introduce significant errors. The plots of tectonic subsidence are, therefore, displayed both uncorrected and corrected for compaction using Sclater & Christie's method. The corrected and uncorrected plots may be seen as the expressions of extreme views of the true role of compaction in the study area: compaction has undoubtedly occurred, but it has not produced the amount of space for sedimentation that is modelled by a linear log porosity–depth relationship. A more accurate mathematical porosity–depth model for the Central and Northern North Sea Basin is beyond the scope of this paper. However, at this stage it seems reasonable to conclude that the actual progress of tectonic subsidence is bracketed by the two tectonic subsidence plots presented.

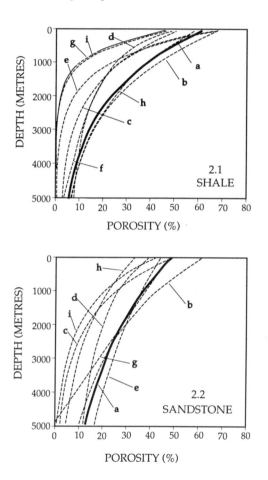

Fig. 2. Porosity–depth curves from Sclater & Christie (1980) compared with other published porosity–depth relationships. 2.1 Shale, 2.2 Sandstone. Redrawn after Gallagher (1989). Sclater & Christie's curves are highlighted. See text for discussion.

Explanation of subsidence plots

Two water depth diagnostic surfaces in the post-rift succession are cut by the wells: the Moray/Ninian delta top (age: *c*. 54 Ma) and the present day sea bed. These two points 'peg' the tectonic subsidence curve in time and space. They are highlighted on the tectonic subsidence plots.

The palaeontologically determined water depth maps of Barton & Wood (1984, figure 17) were used to calculate the tectonic subsidence curves. As mentioned ealier the values derived from this method are rather imprecise, but in the absence of water depth diagnostic surfaces in the post-rift succession they are the only available observational data.

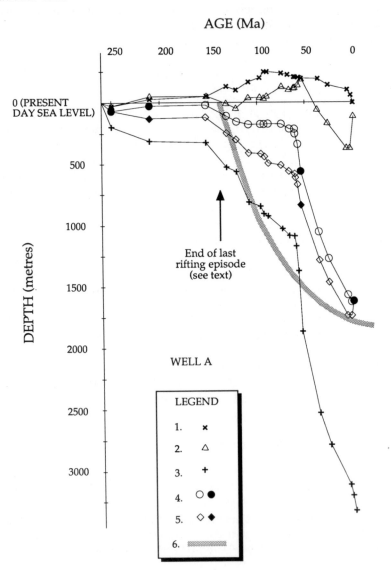

Fig. 3. Explanation of sample subsidence history plot for UK well 21/6-2 (well A on Fig. 1). Legend: 1, eustatic sea-level; 2, position of sea bed (i.e. vertical distance between 1 and 2 is water depth); 3, tectonic subsidence not corrected for compaction; 4, tectonic subsidence corrected for compaction using the method of Sclater & Christie (1980) (points on the tectonic subsidence curves for which water depth is known from sedimentological studies are filled); 5, total subsidence; 6, tectonic subsidence curve for $\beta = 2.0$, $t_0 = 140$ Ma for comparison.

Examples of the subsidence plots are shown in Figs 3 & 4. It is clear that in all wells the overall rate of Late Palaeocene–Recent subsidence was significantly greater than the earliest Cretaceous–Danian subsidence rate. The difference in subsidence rate appears to have been less marked in the grabens than on the platforms. At least some of the space for Cretaceous sedimentation in the grabens was bathymetry generated during the Late Jurassic rifting episode, as explained by Bertam & Milton (1989). No allowance has been made for rift bathymetry; this source of error has probably resulted in an overestimate of the amount of Cretaceous tectonic subsidence.

Agreement with published models

Published models of extensional basin formation such as that of McKenzie (1978) predict an asymptotic decrease in post-rift or thermal subsidence following an episode of extensional tectonism. The most recent period of rifting in the North Sea Basin system ended during the Ryazanian. Consequently the pattern of subsidence shown in Figs 3 & 4 has been a problem for workers attempting to reconcile the history of extension in the area with the progress of post-rift subsidence. Sclater & Christie (1980, figure 9) and Barton & Wood (1984, figures 19, 20, 22) all encountered well locations at which tectonic subsidence accelerated during the Palaeocene. These were interpreted as broadly conforming to published models of thermal post-rift subsidence. Bertram & Milton (1989, figure 8) also found evidence for a Palaeocene increase in post-rift tectonic subsidence in the Viking Graben; they explained this by proposing a temporary episode of uplift during the Palaeocene. There is no evidence on seismic data or from the stratigraphy for such uplift in the North Sea Basin, though early Tertiary uplift was undoubtedly important in northern Britain (Watson 1985). Cloetingh et al. (1987) have devised a model according to which a change in the stress regime during the Palaeocene may have been responsible for an increased rate of subsidence at this time. There is continuing debate, however, concerning both the timing of stress regime changes in north west Europe and whether such changes could produce observable variations in subsidence rate.

Palaeocene changes in basin morphology

The Palaeocene acceleration in subsidence is shown simply in relation to individual well locations in Figs 3 & 4. In this section, the effect of this episode of subsidence acceleration on the basin morphology is examined.

The rift shoulders, together with a number of intra-basinal horsts, formed positive features throughout the early post-rift phase. The rift shoulders were locally emergent areas of non-deposition during the Early Cretaceous (Fig. 5). Some intra-basinal highs (e.g. the Magnus Ridge; Emery et al. 1990) also appear to have remained above sea-level well into the Early Cretaceous. Other structurally positive features were covered by thin, highly condensed marine sequences (Rawson & Riley 1982). The rift shoulders continued as positive features throughout the Late Cretaceous, as suggested by the thinning of the entire Cretaceous section across these features (Fig. 6). During the Maastrichtian and Danian the positive rift shoulders acted as sources of chalk debris which was transported to the basin floor as allochthonous chalks (Hatton 1986). However, seismic profiles across the rift

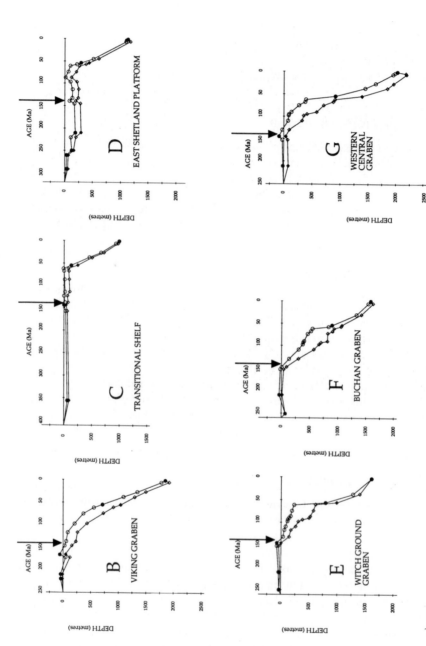

Fig. 4. Subsidence history plots of five wells which penetrated the top of the Moray/Ninian delta and one which did not do so (for well locations see Fig. 1). Symbols are the same as in Fig. 3. For clarity only two of the curves are shown: tectonic subsidence not corrected for compaction and tectonic subsidence corrected for compaction using the method of Sclater & Christie (1980). The wells are: B: 3/2-3; C: 2/15-2A; D: 8/27a-1; E: 14/20-10; F: 20/7-2; G: 29/1b-1. G is the well which did not penetrate the top of the Moray/Ninian delta. The wells are in widely different structural settings. Note that all wells show an increase in tectonic subsidence at about the end of the Early Palaeocene (60 Ma) but that this is apparently most pronounced in platform wells C and D. This may be largely because no allowance has been made for rift bathymetry (see text).

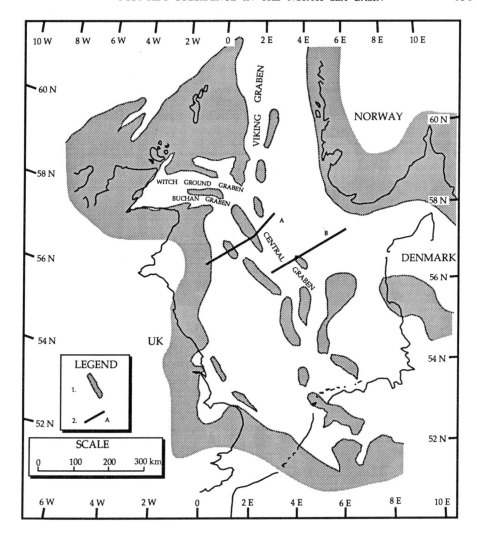

Fig. 5. Early Cretaceous palaeogeography, after Ziegler (1982, enclosure 21). Note archipelago of islands, mostly formed by uplifted shoulders of pre-Cretaceous rifts. Legend: 1, Early Cretaceous strata absent; 2, seismic lines shown in Fig. 6.

shoulders (Fig. 6) show clearly that these features are not associated with any significant thinning of the Late Palaeocene–Recent interval. This interval instead thickens gradually basinward, and isopach maps of the Cenozoic interval (e.g. Ziegler (1982) enclosure 33) show no trace of thinning over the rift shoulders. The Palaeocene episode of subsidence acceleration, therefore, profoundly changed the morphology of the basin. For the first time since extension, the areas surrounding the rifts subsided rapidly, producing the elongated saucer-shaped Tertiary sag basin and the 'steer's head' cross-sectional basin shape.

The nature of the rift shoulders, and the timing of their vertical movements, are subjects of some debate. It is not even clear, in the case of the North Sea Basin,

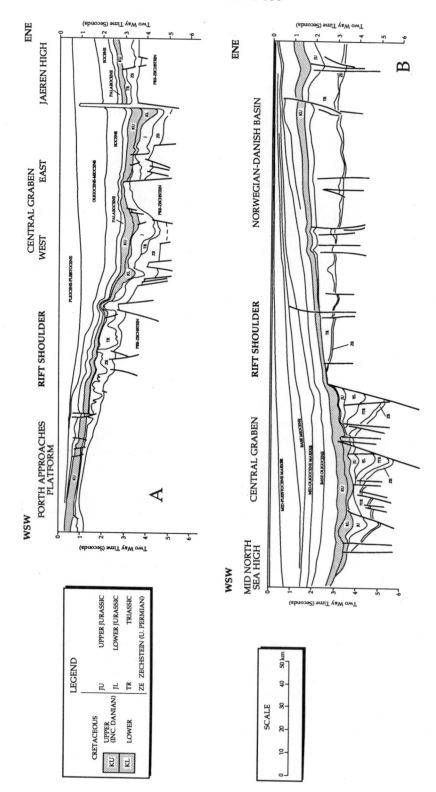

Fig. 6. Seismic line interpretations showing effects of Cretaceous–Danian (and earlier?) support of rift shoulders. Note that the rift shoulders exercised practically no control on the overall pattern of post-Danian sedimentation. Line locations shown in Fig. 5. Redrawn after Glennie (1990).

whether these features were generated by footwall uplift (as suggested by Barton & Wood (1984)), or as a response to depth-dependent stretching (see for example Keen (1987)), or by a combination of these two processes. However, the morphology of the North Sea Basin, as it evolved throughout the post-rift period, does invite some interesting comparisons with the morphology of modern extensional basins in different tectonic settings.

Comparison of North Sea Basin with other extensional basins

Published models of thermal subsidence appear to explain the patterns of post-rift subsidence in passive margins in many parts of the world (see for example Royden & Keen (1980), Burrus & Audebert (1990)). The predicted decrease in subsidence rate with time can be clearly observed in such basins; indeed it was first described from the Atlantic passive margins by Sleep (1971). Another feature of thermal subsidence is that it typically occurs over a wider area than the original rift subsidence, resulting in the progressive onlap of the basin margins during the post-rift period. Although there is some controversy concerning the reason for this pattern of subsidence (see White & McKenzie (1988) for a discussion), the onlap of the basin margins, too, is clearly seen in many passive margin settings.

Extensional basins in intra-continental settings, however, are somewhat different. Consider the Rhine Graben (Fig. 7), an intra-continental rift in which extension commenced during the middle Eocene (Illies 1978). The only subsidence which has occurred in this basin appears to have been accommodated on faults; in other words, this is syn-rift subsidence. Thermal subsidence, involving onlap of the basin margins, does not appear to have occurred in this area. In fact the rift shoulders, far from being onlapped, form positive features on either side of this rift. The distribution of active sedimentation in the Rhine Graben is consequently similar to that in the North Sea Basins during the Cretaceous–Danian: the rifts are sites where thick sedimentary sequences can accumulate to infill the pre-existing rift topography, while the platforms to either side are areas of slow sedimentation or non-deposition.

The combination of no observable thermal subsidence and rift shoulder uplift is common in intra-continental extensional basins; the East African Rifts (Fairhead 1976), Lake Baikal (Zamarayev & Ruzhich 1978), and the Rio Grande Rift (Baldridge et al. 1984) are other examples.

In Fig. 8, time since earliest rifting for a number of extensional basins is plotted against post-rift/thermal subsidence. This figure suggests that the age of the extensional basin appears to be less important in governing post-rift subsidence rates than the basin's tectonic setting: intra-continental or passive margin. Extension is still going on in at least some of the intra-continental basins plotted on Fig. 8. It might, therefore, be argued that there is some feature of active extension which suppresses thermal subsidence. Even if this is true, however, such a feature cannot account for the relatively slow thermal subsidence observed during the Cretaceous–Danian of the North Sea Basins, in which active extension ceased during the Ryazanian.

Tectonic setting of the Central and Northern North Sea Basins

During the period of extensional tectonism which formed the North Sea rifts, the Central and Northern North Sea Basin had been situated in the interior of a

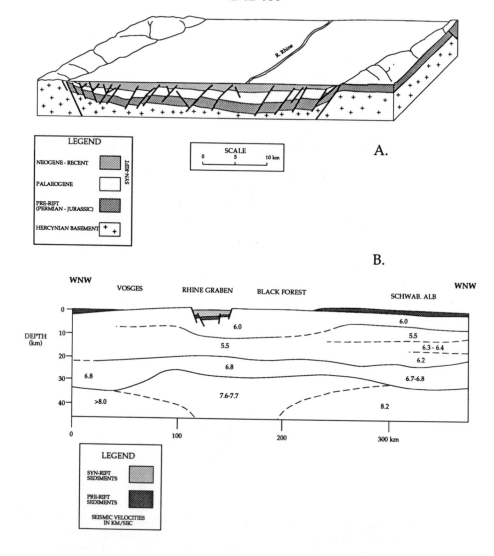

Fig. 7. Structure of an intra-continental extensional basin: the Rhine Graben. (A) Block diagram of a segment of the graben north of Karlsruhe, redrawn from Illies (1978). (B) Deep structure of the southern Rhine Graben, from Ziegler (1982). Note the uplifted rift shoulders and the predominantly fault-controlled nature of the sedimentation.

continent (Fig. 9). Indeed, it had been in an intra-continental setting, at least 1000 km from the nearest oceanic plate, since continental accretion occurred during the Middle Devonian (Smith *et al.* 1981). The intra-continental setting of this basin persisted until the Late Palaeocene. At around this time the Norwegian–Greenland Sea opened immediately to the north of the Northern North Sea Basin. Precise dating of this event is hampered by lack of agreement on correlating radiometric, magnetostratigraphic and biostratigraphic time scales. However, the earliest recognized magnetic anomaly, 24R (Knox & Morton 1988; Mutter & Zehnder 1988), is

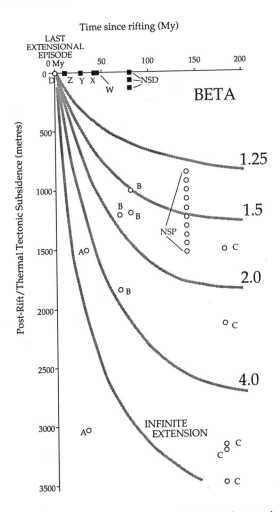

Fig. 8. Graph showing time since rifting versus post-rift/thermal tectonic subsidence for a number of intra-continental extensional basins (squares) and passive margins (circles). Tectonic subsidence curves for a variety of beta factors, according to the instantaneous stretching model (McKenzie 1978), are shown. Key: A, Gulf of Lions (from Burrus & Audebert 1990); B, Labrador Margin; C, Nova Scotia Margin (both from Royden & Keen 1980); D, Iceland; W, Rhine Graben (from Illies 1978); X, Baikal Rift (from Zamarayev & Ruzhich 1978); Y, Rio Grande Rift (from Baldridge *et al.* 1984); Z, Eastern Rift, East Africa (from Fairhead 1976); NSP, range of present day North Sea values; NSD, range of North Sea values at the end of the Danian.

dated as 52.5–55 Ma, i.e. late Thanetian to early Ypresian (time scale of Haq *et al.* 1987).

Typical values for the Central and Northern North Sea Basins, taken from wells analysed during this study, have been plotted on Fig. 8. It is suggested that the Palaeocene opening of the Norwegian–Greenland Sea adjacent to the North Sea Basins marked the transition from an intra-continental rate and style of subsidence to that more typical of oceanic margin basins. Prior to the Late Palaeocene, the

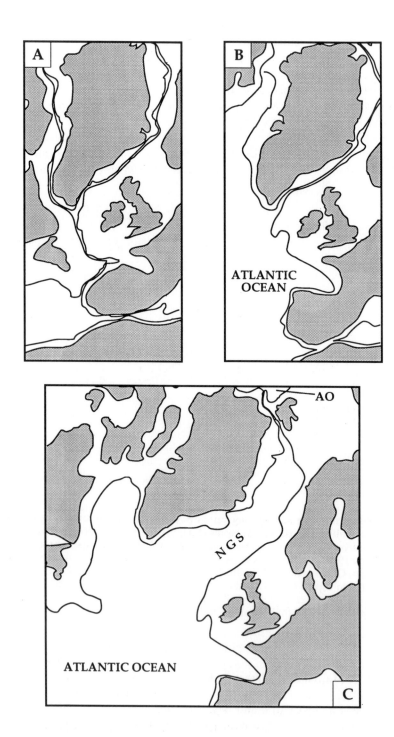

Fig. 9. Palinspastic reconstructions of the North Sea area, taken from Smith *et al.* (1981). (**A**) 140 Ma (late Jurassic, i.e. time of latest extensional episode in the North Sea Basin). (**B**) 60 Ma (Palaeocene). (**C**) 40 Ma (late Eocene). AO Arctic Ocean; NGS Norwegian–Greenland Sea.

Central and Northern North Sea Basin, situated in a continental interior, displayed features reminiscent of present day intra-continental rifts: slower than predicted post-rift subsidence, rift shoulder support and passive infill of previously-generated rift topography by sediment. From the Late Palaeocene onwards, however, with the young ocean opening adjacent to the North Sea Basin, subsidence rates were comparable with those observed on passive margins, while the previously supported areas adjacent to the rift swiftly began to subside.

The Central and Northern North Sea is not the only area in which such an increase in tectonic subsidence rate at the time of opening of a nearby ocean has been reported; Fig. 10 shows a similar pattern of subsidence as observed on the Labrador margin.

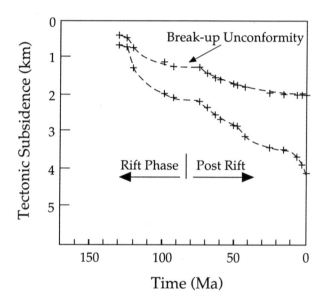

Fig. 10. Herjolf M-92 well subsidence history plot from Keen (1987). This well is located on the Labrador passive margin. Lower curve: sediment-loaded subsidence; upper curve: tectonic subsidence. Note the acceleration in subsidence at the time of oceanic lithosphere generation.

Summary and concluding remarks

The Central and Northern North Sea Basins were formed by a series of extensional episodes, the last of which ended during the Ryazanian. However, post-rift subsidence did not slow with time, as models of thermal subsidence predict. There was instead an acceleration in subsidence during the Late Palaeocene, some 80 Ma after the last extensional episode. This acceleration resulted in the subsidence of the previously supported areas adjacent to the rift itself.

Prior to the acceleration of subsidence, the Central and Northern North Sea Basins were situated in the interior of a continent. During this period, the basin exhibited features in common with present day intra-continental rifts. The acceleration of subsidence took place at the same time that the Norwegian–Greenland Sea opened immediately adjacent to the Northern North Sea Basin. Subsequently, the Central and Northern North Sea Basins have experienced subsidence at rates comparable to those exhibited by passive margin basins.

It is possible, therefore, that the Palaeocene change in rate and style of North Sea Basin subsidence is somehow connected to its transition at this time from an intra-continental setting to being situated adjacent to an ocean. It is also possible that the different styles and rates of subsidence of intra-continental rifts and passive margins reflect significant differences between the dynamics of rifting and of post-rift processes beneath continental and oceanic lithospheric plates. Elucidation of the nature of these differences, however, awaits further work on continental and oceanic extension and subsidence.

The recognition of this episode of subsidence acceleration is of particular relevance to the study of North Sea Palaeocene stratigraphy. The effects upon sedimentation of Palaeocene tectonic events within the North Sea Basin have typically been considered relatively unimportant, while eustatic sea-level change has been considered the primary control upon the stratigraphy (see, for example, Stewart 1987). The subsidence history analyses presented above suggest that tectonic processes may have been a more important factor.

This work is funded by Fina Exploration Limited, whose support is gratefully acknowledged. I would also like to thank, at Imperial College, both Dr Joe Cartwright for his constant encouragement and Dr Mike Warner for a helpful critical review of this paper. I am also grateful to Dr Stuart Burley and to an anonymous reviewer for their constructive comments.

References

BADLEY, M. E., PRICE, J. D., RAMBECH DAHL, C. & AGDESTEIN, T. 1988. The structural evolution of the northern Viking Graben and its bearing upon extensional modes of basin formation. *Journal of the Geological Society, London*, **145**, 455–472.

BALDRIDGE, W. S., OLSEN, K. H. & CALLANDER, J. F. 1984. Rio Grande Rift: problems and perspectives. *In*: BALDRIDGE, W. S., DICKERSON, P. W., RIECKER, R. E. & ZIDECK, J. (eds) *Rio Grande Rift: Northern New Mexico*, Proc. New Mexico Geological Society 35th Annual Field Conference, 1–12.

BARTON, P. & WOOD, R. 1984. Tectonic evolution of the North Sea Basin: crustal stretching and subsidence. *Geophysical Journal of the Royal Astronomical Society*, **79**, 987–1022.

BERTRAM, G. T. & MILTON, N. J. 1989. Reconstructing basin evolution from sedimentary thickness; the importance of bathymetric control, with reference to the North Sea. *Basin Research*, **1**, 247–257.

BOOTE, D. R. D. & GUSTAV, S. H. 1987. Evolving depositional systems within an active rift, Witch Ground Graben, North Sea. *In*: BROOKS, J. & GLENNIE, K. (eds) *Petroleum Geology of North West Europe*, Graham & Trotman, London, 819–833.

BURRUS, J. & AUDEBERT, F. 1990. Thermal and compaction processes in a young rifted basin containing evaporites: the Gulf of Lions, France, *American Association of Petroleum Geologists Bulletin*, **74**(9), 1420–1440.

CLOETINGH, S., LAMBECK, K. & McQUEEN, H. 1987. Apparent sea-level fluctuations and a palaeostress field for the North Sea region. *In*: BROOKS, J. & GLENNIE, K. (eds) *Petroleum Geology of North West Europe*, Graham & Trotman, London, 49–57.

DEEGAN, C. E. & SCULL, B. J. 1977. *A standard lithostratigraphic nomenclature for the Central and Northern North Sea*, Institute of Geological Sciences, Report 77/25.

EMERY, D., MYERS, K. J. & YOUNG, R. 1990. Ancient subaerial exposure and freshwater leaching in sandstones. *Geology*, **18**, 1178–1181.

FAIRHEAD, J. D. 1976. The regional gravity field of the Eastern Rift, East Africa. *In*: PILGER, A. & ROSLER, A. (eds) *Afar between continental and oceanic rifting*, Inter-Union Commission on Geodynamics Scientific Report **16**, 113–130.

GALLAGHER, K. 1989. An examination of some uncertainties associated with estimates of sedimentation rates and tectonic subsidence. *Basin Research*, **2**, 97–114.

GLENNIE, K. 1990. North Sea history and structural framework. *In*: GLENNIE, K. (ed.) *Introduction to the Petroleum Geology of the North Sea*, 3rd edn, Blackwell, Oxford, 34–77.

HAQ, B. U., HARDENBOL, J. & VAIL, P. R. 1987. Chronology of fluctuating sea levels since the Triassic (250 million years ago to present). *Science*, **235**, 1156–1166.

HATTON, I. R. 1986. Geometry of allochthonous Chalk Group members, Central Trough, North Sea. *Marine and Petroleum Geology*, **3**, 79–98.

HELLINGER, S. J., SCLATER, J. G. & GILTNER, J. 1989. Mid-Jurassic through mid-Cretaceous extension in the Central Graben of the North Sea—part 1: estimates from subsidence. *Basin Research*, **1**, 191–200.

ILLIES, J. H. 1978. Two stages Rhinegraben rifting. *In*: RAMBERG, I. B. & NEUMANN, E. R. (eds) *Petrology and Geochemistry of Continental Rifts*, D. Riedel, Holland, 63–71.

KEEN, C. E. 1987. Dynamical extension of the lithosphere during rifting: some numerical model results. *In*: FUCHS, K. & FROIDEVEAUX, C. (eds) *Composition, structure and Dynamics of the Lithosphere–Asthenosphere System*, American Geophysical Union/Geological Society of America, 189–203.

KNOX, R. W. O'B. & MORTON, A. C. 1988. The record of early Tertiary North Atlantic volcanism in sediments of the North Sea Basin. *In*: MORTON, A. C. & PARSON, L. M. (eds) *Early Tertiary Volcanism and the Opening of the NE Atlantic*, Geological Society, London, Special Publication, **39**, 407–419.

MCKENZIE, D. 1978. Some remarks on the development of sedimentary basins. *Earth and Planetary Science Letters*, **40**, 25–32.

MUTTER, J. C. & ZEHNDER, C. M. 1988. Deep crustal structure and magmatic processes: the inception of spreading in the Norwegian–Greenland Sea. *In*: MORTON, A. C. & PARSON, L. M. (eds) *Early Tertiary Volcanism and the Opening of the NE Atlantic*, Geological Society, London, Special Publication, **39**, 35–48.

RAWSON, P. F. & RILEY, L. A. 1982. Latest Jurassic–Early Cretaceous events and the 'Late Cimmerian Unconformity' in North Sea area. *American Association of Petroleum Geologists Bulletin*, **66**(12), 2628–2648.

RIEKE, H. H. & CHILINGARIAN, G. V. 1974. *Compaction of Argillaceous Sediments*, Elsevier, Amsterdam.

ROCHOW, K. A. 1981. Seismic stratigraphy of the North Sea 'Palaeocene' deposits. *In*: ILLING, L. V. & HOBSON, G. D. (eds) *Petroleum Geology of the Continental Shelf of North-West Europe*, Institute of Petroleum, London, 255–266.

ROYDEN, L. & KEEN, C. E. 1980. Rifting process and thermal evolution of the continental margin of eastern Canada determined from subsidence curves. *Earth and Planetary Science Letters*, **51**, 343–361.

SCLATER, J. G. & CHRISTIE, P. A. F. 1980. Continental stretching; an explanation of the post-mid Cretaceous subsidence of the Central North Sea Basin. *Journal of Geophysical Research*, **85**(B7), 3711–3739.

—— & SHOREY, M. D. 1989. Mid-Jurassic through mid-Cretaceous extension in the Central Graben of the North Sea—part 2: estimates from faulting observed on a seismic reflection line. *Basin Research* **1**, 201–215.

SLEEP, N. H. 1971. Thermal effects of the formation of Atlantic continental margins by continental break-up. *Geophysical Journal of the Royal Astronomical Society* **24**, 325–350.

SMITH, A. G., HURLEY, A. M. & BRIDEN, J. C. 1981. *Phanerozoic Palaeocontinental World Maps*, Cambridge University Press.

STECKLER, M. S. & WATTS, A. B. 1978. Subsidence of the Atlantic-type continental margin off New York. *Earth and Planetary Science Letters*, **41**, 1–13.

STEWART, I. J. 1987. A revised stratigraphical interpretation of the Early Palaeogene of the central North Sea. *In*: BROOKS, J. & GLENNIE, K. (eds) *Petroleum Geology of North West Europe*, Graham & Trotman, London, 557–576.

THORNE, J. A. & WATTS, A. B. 1989. Quantitative analysis of North Sea subsidence. *American Association of Petroleum Geologists Bulletin*, **73**(1), 88–116.

WATSON, J. 1985. Northern Scotland as an Atlantic–North Sea divide. *Journal of the Geological Society, London*, **142**, 221–243.

WHITE, N. & MCKENZIE, D. 1988. Formation of the 'steer's head' geometry of sedimentary basins by differential stretching of the crust and mantle. *Geology*, **16**, 250–253.

ZAMARAYEV, S. M. & RUZHICH, V. V. 1978. On relationships between the Baikal Rift and ancient structures. *Tectonophysics*, **45**, 41–47.

ZIEGLER, P. A. 1981. Evolution of sedimentary basins in North-West Europe. *In*: ILLING, L. V. & HOBSON, G. D. (eds) *Petroleum Geology of the Continental Shelf of North-West Europe*, Institute of Petroleum, London, 3–39.

—— 1982. *Geological Atlas of Western and Central Europe*, Elsevier, Amsterdam.

From WILLIAMS, G. D. & DOBB, A. (eds), 1993, *Tectonics and Seismic Sequence Stratigraphy.*
Geological Society Special Publication No. 71, 141–162.

Analogue sandbox modelling of Miocene extensional faulting in the Outer Moray Firth

W. G. Higgs[1] & K. R. McClay[2]

[1]*Chevron UK Ltd, 2 Portman Street, London, W1H 0AN, UK.*
[2]*Department of Geology, Royal Holloway and Bedford New College, University of London, Egham, Surrey, TW20 0EX, UK.*

Abstract: The Palaeogene sequence of the Outer Moray Firth in the UK sector of the North Sea consists of a series of stacked submarine-fans and associated shelf deltaic deposits. The sequence was derived from the elevated Shetland Platform to the northwest. The clastic material was transported southeastwards along the axis of the Witch Ground Graben towards the basin low in the Central Graben.

Towards the top of the Palaeogene submarine-fan slope deposits, there is a disturbed sequence, Oligocene in age, which is interpreted to have been deformed by Miocene age extensional faulting. A semi-regional study of Quadrants 15, 16, 21 and 22 has revealed that the faults, which cut the Eocene to Lower Miocene section, terminate at the Middle Miocene unconformity. Fault activity coincided with a Middle Miocene tilting event indicated by the onlap of Upper Miocene sequences higher on the shelf slope. This tilting event acted as a trigger for extensional fault movement.

Detailed study of the extensional fault geometries illustrates the complex nature of the deformation. The dominant fault trend is northeast–southwest, commonly with the downthrown side towards the northwest. The faults do not exhibit a marked listric geometry nor do they have a common detachment horizon. A common feature is the decrease in observed brittle deformation with depth.

Analogue sandbox modelling illustrates the development of extensional faults associated with the gravitational collapse of a tilted sequence. Deformation within the sandbox models is dominated by non-rigid block rotation.

The Miocene-aged faulting in the Outer Moray Firth is interpreted to be a result of the gravitational collapse of the Palaeogene slope sequence. Fault dip towards the shelf was probably controlled by shear stresses within the deforming sequence and a downslope resistance to deformation. A non-rigid block rotation model is proposed as a possible mechanism for the deformation. A basal detachment is not a requirement of this model.

The Witch Ground Graben, which underlies part of the Outer Moray Firth, is a northwest–southeast trending asymmetric extensional graben that forms one of the three arms of the Central North Sea graben system (Fig. 1). To the southeast the Witch Ground Graben intersects with the north–south trending Viking Graben and north-northwest–south-southeast trending Central Graben. To the northeast the Witch Ground Graben is bound by the southerly extension of the elevated Shetland Platform, the Fladen Ground Spur. The boundary to the southwest is less distinct but can be considered to be marked by the Renee Ridge.

Tectonic extension initiated the basin in the Permian and continued into the early Cretaceous (Beach 1985; Glennie 1986; Harker *et al.* 1987). However, the most active periods of tectonic subsidence occurred in the late Jurassic (Volgian) and early Cretaceous (Valanginian to Aptian) (Beach 1985). Thick sequences of Cretaceous sediments were deposited in the graben, which continually subsided, due initially to tectonic extension followed by later thermal subsidence. By the beginning of the Palaeocene much of the basin topography had been infilled and blanketed, leaving only subtle highs associated with the more prominent footwall blocks of the buried basin structure. The much wider Tertiary to present day basin forms the Outer Moray Firth.

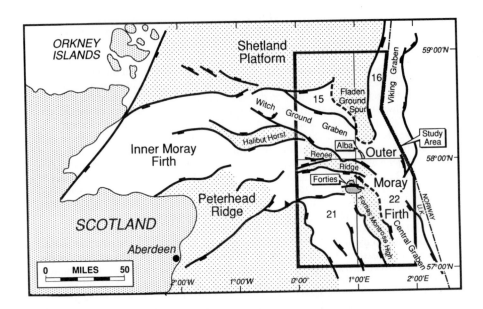

Fig. 1. Location map of the Outer Moray Firth in the North Sea.

Uplift and rejuvenation of the Shetland Platform in the early Palaeocene (Knox *et al.* 1981; Lovell 1986; Morton 1979, 1982; Ziegler 1982, 1988) resulted in a return to clastic deltaic, shelf and submarine-fan deposition within the Outer Moray Firth. The detailed stratigraphy of the Palaeogene is complex. Many seismic, lithostratigraphic and biostratigraphic markers have been identified from the wealth of seismic and well information (Harding *et al.* 1990; Latham & Mattingly in press; Stewart 1987). In grossly simplified terms this period of sedimentation in the Outer Moray Firth can be considered as a time of progradation of a large Palaeogene clastic wedge from the northwest to the southeast along the axis of the former Witch Ground Graben. The sequence is sand-prone towards its base and northwestwards towards the palaeoshelf, but is more shale-prone towards the southeast and towards the top of the stratigraphic section (Harding *et al.* 1990; Stewart 1987).

An Oligo–Miocene sequence characterized by a high amplitude seismic signature is commonly observed within the Outer Moray Firth. Over a wide zone, trending roughly northeast–southwest across Quadrants 15, 16, 21 and 22, this sequence is also characterized by short reflection segments that dip towards the southeast. Interpretation of the high quality recent seismic data as well as reprocessed older data indicates that these dipping reflectors are associated with Miocene extensional faulting that has deformed the underlying Palaeogene sequence.

LINE C1588-115

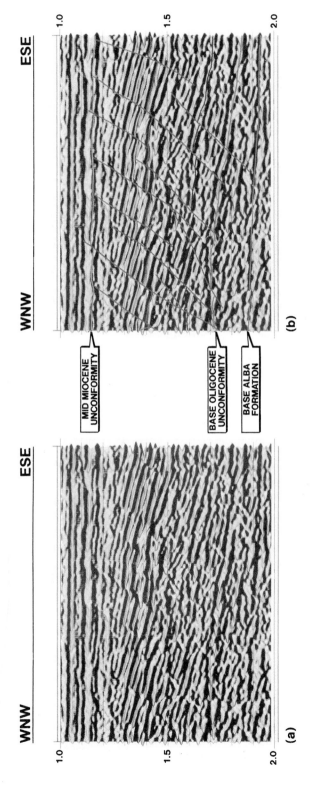

MID MIOCENE UNCONFORMITY

BASE OLIGOCENE UNCONFORMITY

BASE ALBA FORMATION

Fig. 2. Segment of seismic line CON-C1588-115. (**a**) Uninterpreted section showing characteristic short reflections segments dipping towards the southeast. The high amplitude Oligo-Miocene sequence is used as a regional marker horizon to delineate the deformation. (**b**) Interpretation of line CON-C1588-115. Extensional fault movement is dated by the Middle Miocene unconformity which developed concurrently with the faults. The faults commonly dip and have their downthrown side towards the northwest. They also show a decrease in the amount of fault-related deformation with depth.

In this paper we will discuss the characteristics of this faulting and document the results of analogue sandbox modelling undertaken to constrain possible mechanisms for the deformation.

Fault geometries

A detailed study of the extensional fault geometries illustrates the complex and widespread nature of the deformation. The segment of line CON-C1588-115 (Fig. 2) demonstrates several characteristics of the extensional deformation. First, the high amplitude Oligo–Miocene sequence can be used as a regional marker horizon to delineate the deformation (Fig. 2(a)). The terminations of marker reflectors in this sequence define extensional offsets of up to 60 m (65 msec) at this level. Second, the interpretation in Fig. 2(b) illustrates that the faults commonly dip and are down-thrown towards the northwest, i.e. away from the basin. This direction is opposite to that observed in the Niger Delta (Merki 1972; Whiteman 1982) and Gulf Coast (Bruce 1973; Busch 1975; Murray 1961; Ocamb 1961) regions where gravitationally driven extensional growth faults are commonly downthrown towards the basin. Third, the period of most active fault movement is dated by the truncation of many of the faults by a Middle Miocene unconformity, although, minor displacements are observed on some faults in the Upper Miocene Sequence above the unconformity. Also commonly observed throughout the deformed zone is a high density of faults with offsets up to 65 msec (c. 60 m) in the high amplitude Oligo–Miocene sequence. However, the fault density and offset at the Base Oligocene Unconformity is considerably reduced (Fig. 2(b)). There is no evidence that either the frequency of the seismic data or the velocity of the interval vary sufficiently to explain the observed decrease in offset with depth (a 60 m offset at the Base Oligocene Unconformity would produce an offset of 60 msec on a time seismic section). Therefore, this observation is interpreted as a decrease in the amount of brittle deformation with depth.

The fault geometries are dominated by sub-planar fault segments (Fig. 2); strongly listric fault geometries are rarely observed within the Oligocene to middle Eocene sequence. However, the exact geometry of the faults deeper in the section is difficult to define; partly because of the decrease in fault displacement with depth (Fig. 2). The faults generally have short map traces which trend northwest–southeast. The high density of the faults and their discontinuous nature, limits detailed correlation on two-dimensional seismic data.

The true geometry of the extensional faults can be assessed by converting the time seismic sections to depth and drawing them to true scale. Figure 3 illustrates the true scale depth conversion of line CON-C1588-103. The dips of the faults range from 30° to 60°, which is within the common range of extensional fault plane dips (Higgs 1988; Walsh & Watterson 1988a). The line re-emphasizes the common occurrence of faults with downthrown sides towards the northwest, i.e. towards the Palaeogene shelf. A simple line length restoration of the Oligo–Miocene marker indicates that the Oligo–Miocene sequence has been extended by up to 11% across this region.

In some instances, where detailed definition of seismic reflection offsets has been possible, the displacement distribution over the fault section can be assessed. This has been done for a small number of faults within the area. The results suggest that the ratio of the maximum marker offset and the fault length from fault tip to maximum

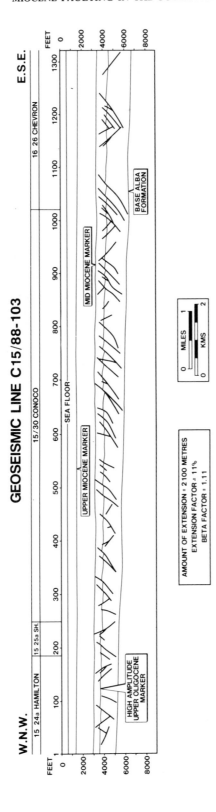

Fig. 3. Depth conversion of seismic line CON-C1588-103, which highlights the common occurrence of faults with their downthrown sides and fault plane dip towards the Palaeogene shelf in the northwest. The basinward tilt of the Palaeogene sequence is illustrated by the dip of the base Eocene Alba Formation.

offset (the Apparent Displacement Magnitude of Higgs & Williams 1987) is in the range 5–20%. This range is in the highest range of values previously obtained for extensional faults (Barnett *et al.* 1987; Higgs 1988; Muraoka & Kamata 1983; Rippon 1985; Walsh & Watterson 1988b). This may be due in part to the mechanical properties of the material undergoing deformation. The undercompacted and dominantly shale sequences of the interval can inhibit the propagation of the fault surface, which results in a high ratio of maximum displacement to fault length (see Williams & Chapman 1983). There are also errors, however, in measurement. The fault sections considered represent only chord lengths of the fault surface as it is unlikely that they cut the nucleation point of the fault. Errors such as these have been discussed by Muraoka & Kamata (1983) and Walsh & Watterson (1987) who concluded that they should be small. The limits of seismic resolution mean that marker offsets of less than 30 m are not distinguished at the depths under consideration. While these errors will affect the displacement magnitude, the results obtained will represent a maximum value of the ratio of displacement to fault length (Muraoka & Kamata 1983; Walsh & Watterson 1988b).

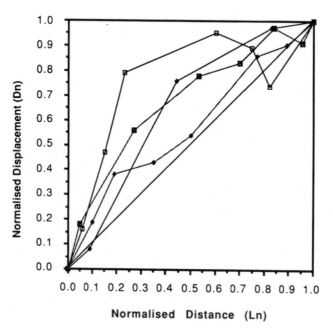

Fig. 4. Graph of normalized fault displacement versus normalized distance along fault trace (Higgs & Williams 1987), illustrating the characteristic displacement distribution for four Miocene faults studied. The convex upwards profile with depth suggests local strain accommodation within undercompacted sediments.

   The displacement gradients associated with these fault surfaces have also been assessed. Figure 4 illustrates a normalized displacement versus normalized distance plot (Higgs & Williams 1987) for a number of the faults. This form of displacement distribution, with a convex upwards profile and displacement efficiency values (Higgs & Williams 1987) in the range 50–75%, is characteristic of the faults studied. These results suggest that the decreases in displacement with depth are consistent with extensional faults propagating through undercompacted sediment (Higgs 1988; Walsh & Watterson 1988b).

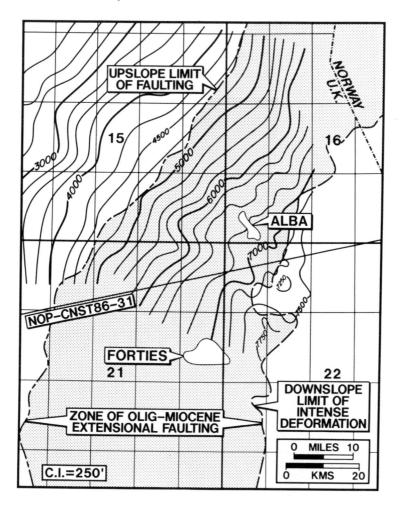

Fig. 5. Regional distribution of Miocene faulting within the study area superimposed on the base Eocene Alba Formation structure map after Harding *et al.* (1990). The zone of Miocene faulting is parallel to the structural contours. The zone of deformation has a well-defined upslope limit but a more poorly defined downslope limit.

Regional distribution of faulting

The Miocene faulting in the Outer Moray Firth has a finite limit, both upslope and downslope, which can be mapped over the study area (Fig. 5). The zone of deformation trends northeast–southwest across Quadrants 15 & 16 but turns to trend north-northeast–south-southwest across Quadrants 21 & 22. These trends mimic the form of the underlying Palaeogene sequences as indicated by the depth structure map of the base Eocene Alba Formation (Harding *et al.* 1990), also shown on Fig. 5. This relationship is also highlighted on the regional seismic line CNST86-31 (Fig. 6).

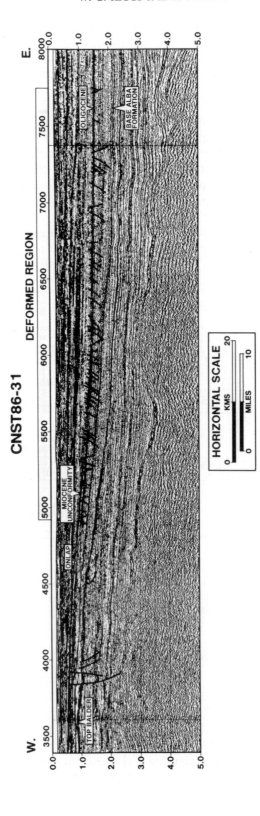

Fig. 6. Regional NOPEC seismic line CNST86-31 from west to east across the zone of Miocene faulting (see Fig. 5 for line location). The location of Miocene faulting shows a strong correlation to the position of more steeply dipping Palaeogene sediments. The tilting of the Palaeogene sequence occurred concurrently with the onset of faulting as indicated by the onlap of mid- to late Miocene sediments onto the Middle Miocene unconformity surface.

Although the line is oblique to the deformation trend (Fig. 5), it illustrates the spatial relationship between the faulting and the steeper dips of the underlying Palaeogene.

Within the zone of faulting, the deformation is most intense in the centre and dies in intensity towards the boundaries (Fig. 6). The downslope boundary of the deformed zone is poorly defined, being both diffuse (Fig. 6) and having an irregular map outline (Fig. 5). In contrast, the upslope boundary has a regular map outline (Fig. 5) and there is a sharp break between the deformed and undeformed regions (Fig. 6). An important characteristic of the upslope boundary is the marked north-westwards onlap of the Middle to Upper Miocene sequences. The Middle Miocene unconformity coincides both temporally and spatially with the onset of Miocene faulting. Tilting of the Palaeogene sequence in the Middle Miocene may have acted as a triggering device for the faulting.

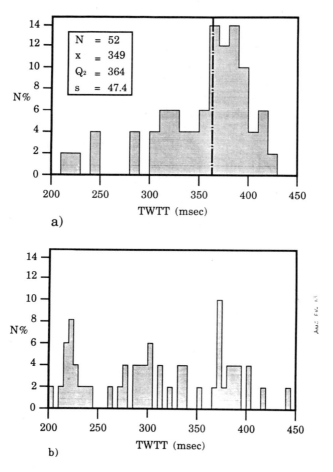

Fig. 7. Histograms of the interval thickness, measured in two-way travel times (TWTT) along the upslope boundary of Miocene faulting. (**a**) From the Middle Miocene unconformity to the base of the Eocene Alba Fomation; and (**b**) from the Middle Miocene unconformity to the top of the Palaeocene Balder Formation. The values were calculated at 52 locations along the boundary. The upper histogram (**a**) has a skewed distribution with a mode of 364 msec, however, the lower histogram (**b**) shows a random distribution suggesting that the depth of penetration of the deformed zone is not to the Balder Formation level. See text for details.

The relationship between the trend of the Miocene extensional faulting and the dip of the underlying Palaeogene sequence suggests that the faulting resulted from the gravitational collapse of the Palaeogene sequence. The irregular nature of the downslope limit of faulting is consistent with this interpretation. There is evidence that extensional tectonic activity on the shelf occurred in the Oligo–Miocene; the extensional faults near shot point 4000 (Fig. 6) displace Oligo–Miocene strata. Earthquake seismicity associated with this faulting may have provided an additional stimulus for the Palaeogene sequence to become unstable.

The control on the position of the upslope limit of faulting is somewhat more enigmatic. There is no direct relationship between the location of the upslope limit of faulting and any marked gradient change in the underlying Palaeogene sequence (Figs 5 & 6). The Tertiary section below the Middle Miocene unconformity reduces in thickness from the area of faulting upslope towards the northwest. Therefore, a possible control on the position and sharpness of the upslope limit is the critical overburden required for the gravitational collapse of the sequence. To test this hypothesis the 'thickness' of the interval from top Middle Miocene to base Alba Formation was assessed at 52 localities along the upslope boundary. Figure 7(a) is a histogram of the thickness of this interval measured as two-way travel time (TWTT). The base Alba Formation was selected because it is a prominent regional marker (Latham & Mattingly, in press) and it is near to, or at, the base of the deformed sequence. The histogram shows a distribution that is skewed towards the higher values (Fig. 7(a)). The median value of thickness is 364 msec, which suggests this may be the critical overburden thickness required for the onset of faulting. As a control study, the TWTT thickness from the Middle Miocene to the top Balder Formation at the same 52 localities was also plotted (Fig. 7(b)). The random distribution suggests that there is no relationship between the thickness of this interval and the positive of the upslope limit of faulting. This further suggests that the base of the deformed sequence is above the top Balder Formation level.

Analogue sandbox modelling

The study of the Miocene extensional faulting in the Outer Moray Firth has indicated five key observations.

1. there is a relationship between the location of the Miocene faulting and the dip of the underlying Palaeogene sequences;
2. the common extensional fault trend is northeast–southwest with the dominant faults having downthrown sides towards the northwest, back towards the shelf;
3. the amount of observed brittle deformation decreases with depth;
4. most faults are truncated by the Middle Miocene unconformity; however, limited faulting continued into the Upper Miocene section;
5. the Middle Miocene unconformity coincides, both temporally and spatially, with a tilting event interpreted from the onlap towards the northwest of the Mid–Upper Miocene sequence.

With these observations in mind, two analogue sandbox model experiments were constructed to develop a kinematic model for the Miocene faulting. The first of the two experiments is described in detail. The second produced similar results demonstrating the reproducibility of the modelling.

Experimental procedure

Deformation was achieved by moving the box relative to an end wall, which was fixed to a static base (Fig. 8). Uniform extension was achived by using a basement comprising a rubber sheet fixed between the stationary and moving walls of the deformation apparatus.

DEFORMATION APPARATUS

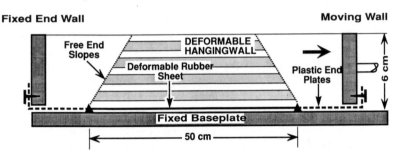

Fig. 8. Schematic diagram of the deformation apparatus used in the analogue sandbox model experiments. Extension between the fixed section of the box and the moving section of the box was accommodated by uniform extension on a rubber sheet at the base of the model.

To produce geologically valid results the models were appropriately scaled giving a scaling factor between 10^{-4} and 10^{-5} (i.e. to represent brittle crustal thicknesses between 1 km and 10 km). Assuming a brittle Coulomb-type failure criterion for both the crust and the modelling material, a similar scaling factor was applied to the modelling material properties. As a result, a weak, cohesionless material (McClay & Ellis 1987) consisting of a dry, bleached pottery sand, with an average grain size of 300 μm and and internal angle of friction of 31°, was used. However, scaling was not perfect as the relatively large grain size resulted in the formation of narrow shear zones rather than discrete fault planes (Horsfield 1977).

The models were prepared within the sliding box by carefully sieving alternating coloured and white sand into layers until a composite model was constructed. There is no difference in the mechanical properties of the coloured (dyed) and white sand layers, i.e. the model is isotropic. The box was not filled to the end walls in order to reduce edge effects. Instead the model was constructed with a free surface at either end. The box was extended, using a motor-driven worm screw, at a displacement rate of 4×10^{-4} cm sec^{-1}. Data were recorded using 35 mm time-lapse photography after every 1 cm of extension. After each 1 cm increment, sand was added to represent the growth sequence and to maintain the continuity of the model. The models were extended by 50%.

A wedge geometry was used as an analogue to the Palaeogene sediment package in the Outer Moray Firth. The sliding box was inclined to 5° before the addition of the sand layers. Addition of the layers to the box resulted in a wedge of sand, which onlapped onto the base (Fig. 9(a)). This resulted in initial model dimensions of 60 cm × 25 cm with a variable depth from 5–9.5 cm.

SANDBOX EXPERIMENT 1

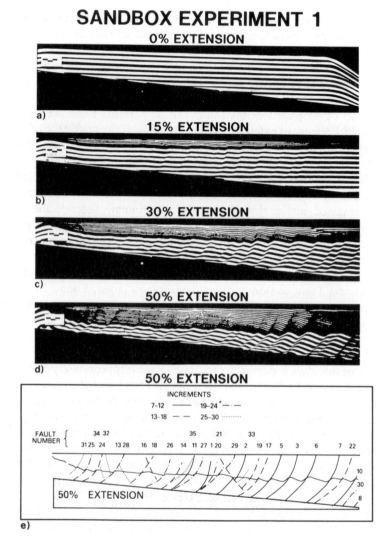

Fig. 9. (**a**) Initial configuration of sandbox model. The model dimensions are 25 cm × 60 cm with a variable thickness from 5–9.5 cm. (**b**) Sandbox model after 15% extension illustrating the development of high angle faults with their downthrown sides and fault plane dip towards the updip end of the model. The narrow bands of sand towards the top of the model represent the growth sequence as an additional layer is added after each increment of extension. (**c**) Sandbox model after 30% extension. The initially planar faults have been rotated into more listric fault profiles with the associated rotation of bedding. At this time there is a subordinate development of faults with their downthrown sides towards the downdip end of the model. (**d**) Sandbox model after 50% extension. Faults have been rotated to shallow angles within the 'pre-rift' and steepen upwards within the growth sequence. (**e**) Fault sequence diagram with faults coded according to the increment after which they were first observed. The early formed faults commonly initiated at the downdip end of the model with their downthrown sides towards the updip end of the model. The later formed faults show a mix of downdip and updip faults.

Results

Figure 9 shows the results after 0%, 15%, 30% and 50% extension. The most striking feature of the experiment is the development of faults which dip and are downthrown toward the slope. This is the dominant fault orientation with only a subordinate development of antithetic 'down-to-basin' faults. Most of the antithetic faults form at the upslope end of the wedge. This is similar to the distribution of Miocene faults within the deformed zone of the Outer Moray Firth.

The sequential development of the faults can be assessed from the photographs taken after each increment of extension. A line drawing of the final stage of the model (after 50% extension) is illustrated in Fig. 9(e). The faults are coded according to the increment of extension at which they were first observed. The resulting pattern is complex with no obvious trends except that the earliest faults initiated in the downslope half of the model. There are three other points to note. First, most of the early faults remained active throughout the experiment. Second, the antithetic 'down-to-basin' faults formed late in the deformation history and are more common in the upslope half of the model. Finally, some late faults formed as footwall splays to earlier faults, e.g. faults 20, 29 and 35 (Fig. 9e).

The majority of the faults nucleated in the upper layers of the sand model and propagated up and down section as the extension continued. Figure 10 details the displacement variation over one fault within the system. The final geometry of the fault is complex involving divergent splay faults. The successive offsets from the top of the 'pre-rift' (marker 6) decrease down the fault system to the point where there is no apparent offset at the level of marker 19 (Fig.10(b)). Figure 10(c) shows a plot of displacement versus distance along the fault trace (Muroka & Kamata 1983; Williams & Chapman 1983) for the summed displacement over the fault system. The curve can be divided into three regions. Region 1 defines the growth sequence added during the development of the model. This shows a marked decrease in displacement towards the top of the model as expected for the successive deformation of a growth sequence (Barr 1987; Gibbs 1983). Region 2 marks the area of almost uniform maximum displacement. This defines the region where the fault nucleated and a region where the fault is extremely displacement efficient (Higgs & Williams 1987). Region 3 defines the section of the fault system where the displacements are decreasing with depth. This decrease in displacement is accommodated in the volume surrounding the fault by more pervasive grain flow as illustrated by the thickness changes.

The development of individual faults can be assessed both geometrically and with respect to other faults within the system. Figure 11(a) illustrates the sequential development of one early formed fault (No. 7 in Fig. 9(e)) from its initial development after increment 9 (15% extension) to increment 30 (50% extension). This demonstrates how initially planar and steep fault segments become less steeply dipping and listric as the model develops. Associated with this process is the rotation of marker beds to steeper angles as illustrated by the initial (increment 9) and final (increment 30) positions of one marker bed (Fig. 11(a)). A second feature illustrated in Fig. 11(a) is the movement of the fault continuously downslope with respect to the external reference frame of the fixed wall of the apparatus. This is due to the extension applied to the base of the model by pulling away the right-hand side.

An important aspect of the development of the faults is demonstrated by the

SANDBOX EXPERIMENT 1
SERIAL SECTION OF HORSETAILING FAULT SYSTEMS

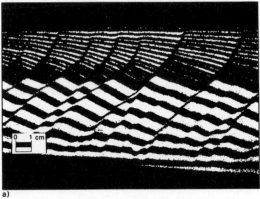

a)

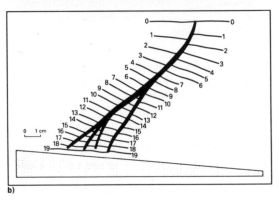

b)

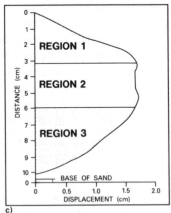

c)

Fig. 10. (**a**) Details of fault profiles from serial section made after completion of model at 50% extension. The discontinuities show strongly listric profiles in the upper section but increase in dip with depth. The offset on the discontinuities decreases towards the base of the model. (**b**) Line drawing of fault system in the centre of (**a**) showing marker bed correlation. (**c**) Diagram of fault-parallel displacement versus distance along the fault trace from the top of the model for the fault system in (**b**). The diagram can be divided into three regions of differing displacement profiles (see text for details).

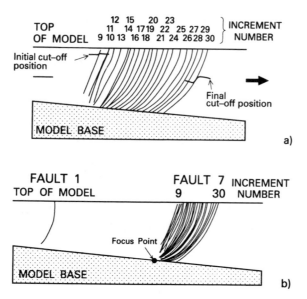

Fig. 11. (a) Sequential development of fault 7 illustrating the change from planar to listric fault geometries as the model developed. There is a corresponding rotation of bedding to higher dip angles as indicated by the initial and final positions of one marker bed within the model. (b) Sequential relationship between two faults within the system. The top of fault 7 is moving downslope more quickly than its base and the updip fault 1. This implies a component of differential shear within the model. The top and base of the model apparatus provide a fixed reference frame for the analysis.

sequential development of fault 7 with respect to fault 1 (Fig. 11(b)). After each increment of movement, the distance between fault 1 and fault 7 has been plotted by successively laying the initial trace of fault 1 over its new position and drawing the corresponding position of fault 7. These two faults were selected as they were early faults with sufficient spacing to enable tracking over the 30 increments. There are two important observations from the relationship between these faults. First, the traces of fault 7 appear to focus towards one point at the base of the model, indicating that the base of fault 7 is moving at the same rate as fault 1. This is to be expected as the rubber sheet at the base of the model is undergoing uniform extension. Second, the traces are divergent towards the top of the model. This suggests that there is a differential shear downslope associated with the rotation of the faults, i.e. the top of fault 7 is moving downslope faster than the base of fault 7 and with respect to the updip fault 1.

A further indication of the nature of motion within the hangingwall block comes from the analysis of vector motions over several increments. Figure 12 illustrates the vector motions documented for the movement of the model between increments 25 to 28. The vectors vary in both direction and magnitude over the section of the model. As a rule, the magnitudes of the vectors appear to increase both from left to right (downdip) and from bottom to top (up-section), with the downdip increase being by far the greater. This indicates that while there may be a uniform extension across the base of the model there is non-uniform extension within the hangingwall block. The distribution of the vectors indicates that the right-hand side of the model is moving further than the left. This is consistent with an active footwall block moving to the right with potential voids being filled by the passive collapse of the hangingwall block.

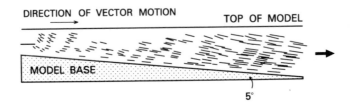

Fig. 12. Vector trajectories for the sandbox model over five increments show an increase in magnitude of the vectors downdip and down-section. The vectors are not parallel to the base of the model.

A second important feature of the vector distribution illustrated in Fig. 12 is the non-parallel nature of the vectors. These non-parallel vector motions document the rotation of the faults and intervening blocks. This is illustrated in more detail in Fig. 13, where the footwall cut-off position of fault 6 and the hangingwall cut-off position of fault 7 (Fig. 9(e)) have been traced from increment 19 to increment 23. The resulting traces define the vector motions of the block between faults 6 and 7. Over the five increments considered, the vector direction for each side of the block appears to be constant. There is, however, an angular difference between these two vector orientations. The vector defining the footwall cut-off position of fault 6 makes an angle of 12° to the horizontal compared to 16° for the vector defining the hangingwall cut-off to fault 7 (Fig. 13). A second feature highlighted in Fig. 13 is the decrease in the magnitude of vectors down-section on both sides of the block.

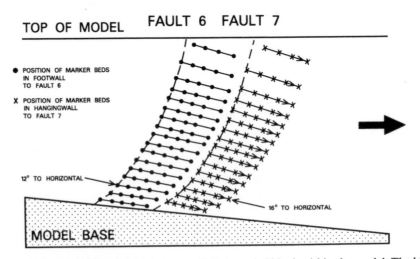

Fig. 13. Details of the vector motion for one fault bounded block within the model. The block is bound on its footwall side by fault 6 and on its hangingwall side by fault 7. The magnitude of the vectors decreases with depth and the vector direction for the footwall side of the block is different from that on the hangingwall side.

Geometric model for non-rigid block faulting

The information on the variations in both magnitude and direction of the displacement vectors in the sandbox models can be used to document how the faults and the
intervening blocks rotate and deform. These results in turn can be used to suggest
possible mechanisms for the Miocene faulting in the Outer Moray Firth. Deformation within the sandbox models is driven by the rubber base of the model, i.e.
decollement driven. However, the 'deformation mechanism' within the sand is a
combined pure shear (deeper levels)/simple shear (higher levels) model which results
in non-rigid block rotation above the decollement. If the analogy between the
sandbox models and the deformation in the Outer Moray Firth is exact then a basal
decollement, transmitting the extension towards the southeast, would be expected.
However, there is no evidence for compressional structures at the downslope limit of
faulting (Figs 5 & 6), which would be required in such a model. There are also no
dramatic changes in bulk rock densities or sonic transit times at the level a
decollement might be expected. Using the information from the sandbox models, it
can also be demonstrated, that a basal decollement is not a requirement for non-rigid
block rotation.

   This is best illustrated in two dimensions (Fig. 14(a)) by considering faults AD and
BC as initially vertical and the intervening fault block, ABCD, a square. From the
observations above, we know that each corner moves with a separate vector
magnitude $(\bar{a}, \bar{b}, \bar{c}\ \&\ \bar{d})$ and that vectors $\bar{a}$ and $\bar{d}$ have the same direction, as do
vectors $\bar{b}$ and $\bar{c}$. The magnitudes of vectors $\bar{a}$ and $\bar{b}$ are greater than those of $\bar{c}$ and $\bar{d}$,
and the direction of vectors $\bar{b}$ and $\bar{c}$ makes a greater angle with the horizontal than do
vectors $\bar{a}$ and $\bar{d}$. A new position of the block after deformation can be defined by
A'B'C'D' if we assume that bed length, x (=AB), is maintained. The result is that
both the intervening block and the boundary faults are rotated in such a fashion that
the deformation can be considered as non-rigid block rotation.

   The treatment of the deformation in terms of vector motion can be expanded to
include the adjacent fault blocks. Definition of the trajectories of the block between
faults 3 and 6 (Fig. 9(e)) indicates that deformation of the adjacent block follows
similar trajectory paths to those shown by Fig. 13. We can, therefore, define the
deformation of the adjacent block ADFE (Fig. 14(b)). The major constraint on the
location of the adjacent block is the need to maintain the continuity of the model.
Therefore, the new hangingwall position of point A must lie on the line A'–D'
defined by the neighbouring block. This point, A", is thus defined by the intersection
of the vector $\bar{a}_1$ with the line A'–D'. The same principle applies to the hangingwall
position of point D, which lies at the intersection of the vector $\bar{d}_1$ and the extension of
line A'–D' (Fig. 14(b)). As described above for the one block model (Fig. 14(a)), the
new positions of points E and F are governed by the point of intersection of the arc
radius x centred on A" and D" with the vectors e and f, respectively (Fig. 14(b)). The
two block model demonstrates how the displacement decreases down the fault as the
offset of A' to A" is greater than the offset of D' to D". This is consistent with the
observations of the Miocene faulting in the Outer Moray Firth (Fig. 3) and within
the sandbox models (Fig. 10(c)).

   The above model can be expanded for a suite of blocks (Fig. 14(c)). The Figure
illustrates important features of the vector motions and depth to 'detachment' in the
model. In addition to the decrease in displacement with depth on individual faults,

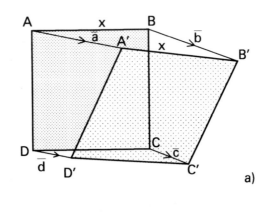

a)

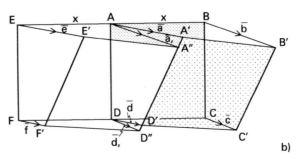

b)

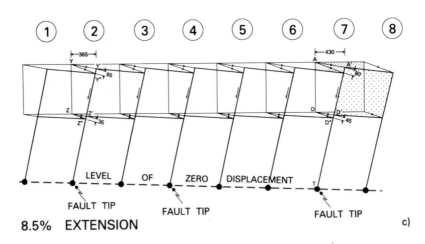

c)

8.5% EXTENSION

Fig. 14. (a) Schematic definition of non-rigid block rotation for one fault block initially bound by vertical faults A–D and B–C. The deformed block can be defined from the vector trajectory observations in Fig. 14. (b) The deformed state of the adjacent block within the system can be defined by maintaining the law of continuity (see text for details). The fault A′–D″ shows a decrease in displacement with depth. (c) A non-rigid block rotation fault model can consist of a series of faults which decrease to zero displacement with depth. The blocks have undergone an angular shear rotation. A decreasing angular shear with depth may be expected in an overall undercompacted sequence that shows increasing compaction with depth.

the amount of bed rotation also decreases with depth in each fault block. The relative displacement on the faults also decreases from right to left. These features are illustrated by the change in displacement between faults 1 and 7 (Fig. 14(c)). Associated with the right-to-left decrease in displacement is a decrease in vector magnitude, illustrated by the comparison of vectors A–A' and Y–Y'. These observations are consistent with the observations from the sandbox model (Fig. 12) and are similar in style to the model proposed by Morton & Black (1975) for extensional block rotation.

Another feature of the model presented in Fig. 14(c) is that the depth to the base of the deforming sequence can be calculated. This depth is defined by the point of intersection of the original fault position and the final fault position, i.e. for fault 7 at point T (Fig. 14(c)). In this model, the base of the deformed sequence is dipping, which is consistent with the sandbox models and probably with Miocene deformation in the Outer Moray Firth. However, the prediction of the depth to the base of the deformed model does not aid the prediction of the base of the deformed sequence in the Outer Moray Firth because we cannot define the original positions and dips of the faults. Deformation accommodated by non-rigid block rotation as defined by this model also negates the use of rigid block deformation models to calculate the amount of extension (cf. Le Pichon & Sibuet 1981; Wernicke & Burchfiel 1982).

Discussion and conclusions

The timing of events within the Outer Moray Firth was critical to the style of deformation that occurred. An important aspect appears to be that the Tertiary sequence until early Miocene time was deposited with no gravity-driven deformation. This resulted in two important influences on the deformation. First, there was no free surface downslope within the deforming sequence. The sequence deposited in the deeper parts of the basin appears to have acted as a buttress to the deformation upslope and to have restricted the development of a basal decollement. Second, the vertical gradient of compaction established within the sequence prior to deformation may have enhanced the development of top-towards-the-basin shear and, consequently, non-rigid block rotation. The sediments towards the base of the deforming sequence exhibited a greater resistance to downslope motion than the sediments towards the top of the sequence because of the increase in compaction with depth. Such a process would result in an angular shear strain within the deforming unit.

The timing of the tilting event was also critical in that it appears to have occurred as a single event late in the deposition of the Lower Miocene sequence. A return to more sand-prone deposition within the Miocene sequence above the Miocene unconformity in the Outer Moray Firth suggests an associated rejuvenation of the hinterland. The driving mechanism for this tilting event remains unclear. Basin subsidence due to sediment loading and thermal decay cannot readily explain a single tilting event. Tectonic rejuvenation of the basement structure as a result of Alpine-related foreland deformation (Ziegler 1987) and/or changes in intra-plate stresses associated with the development of the Atlantic spreading axis to the northwest of Britain (Ziegler 1988) may have been responsible. We will not, however, fully understand this tilting event until a suitable explanation for the wider issue of Tertiary hinterland uplift and basin subsidence has been developed.

The intimate relationship between the dip of the Palaeogene sequence and the distribution of Miocene extensional faulting suggests that there is an important link between basin configuration and faulting. This style of deformation can be tracked regionally (Fig. 5) and has also been identified outside the area of study in the south Viking Graben. The evidence indicates that the deformed sequence penetrates to at least the base of the Eocene Alba Formation but probably not to the top of the Palaeocene Balder Formation. The fact that fault displacements are much reduced at the level of the Base Oligocene Unconformity favours such an interpretation.

A problem that this study has been unable to resolve is the accommodation of the observed extension at the downslope limit of deformation. No compressional toe region has been identified at this deformation limit. Non-rigid block rotation requires that the intervening blocks change shape and volume. This may be accommodated by flexural slip along easy slip planes or by bulk flexural shear within the deforming sequence (Higgs *et al.* 1991) and by sediment compaction. Such deformation mechanisms could be accommodated within the Palaeogene sequence of the Outer Moray Firth, which was undercompacted at the time of deformation. If the deforming sequence is pinned at its base, the amount of extension that needs to be accommodated at the downslope boundary may be equivalent only to the angular shear within the deformed zone (an angular shear of 5° on a fault initially dipping at 50° would result in the order of 11% extension as observed in Fig. 3 (Le Pichon & Sibuet 1981)). Volume change within the undercompacted sediments at the down-slope limit of faulting may be able to accommodate such values of extension as shales can compact in excess of 45% of their original volume (Baldwin & Butler 1985).

In conclusion, Miocene extensional faulting in the Outer Moray Firth is inter-preted to be a result of the gravitational collapse of the Palaeogene slope sequence. Fault dip towards the shelf is probably controlled by shear stresses within the deforming sequence and a downslope resistance to deformation. A non-rigid block rotation model is proposed as a possible mechanism for the deformation. A basal detachment is not a requirement of this model.

We wish to thank Chevron UK Ltd, the partners of UK CS Block 16/26, Conoco UK Ltd and NOPEC UK Ltd for permission to publish proprietary seismic data and geological infor-mation. WGH wishes to thank the many colleagues at Chevron UK Ltd and COPI, especially H. H. Bretthauer, E. L. Couch, A. W. Harding, C. F. Kluth, A. Latham, D. W. Lewis, D. C. Mann, K. J. Reed and K. J. Thompson for technical discussions which greatly improved the text. We would also like to thank Andy Scott at R.H.B.N.C. for his help in running the sandbox models and the CUK drafting department for providing the figures.

References

BALDWIN, B. & BUTLER, C. O. 1985. Compaction curves. *American Association of Petroleum Geologists Bulletin*, **69**, 622–626.

BARNETT, J. A. M., MORTIMER, J., RIPPON, J. H., WALSH, J. J. & WATTERSON, J. 1987. Displacement geometry in the volume containing a single normal fault. *American Association of Petroleum Geologists Bulletin*, **71**, 925–937.

BARR D. 1987. Lithospheric stretching, detached normal faulting and footwall uplift. *In*: COWARD, M. P., DEWEY, J. F. & HANCOCK, P. L. (eds) *Continental Extensional Tectonics*. Geological Society, London, Special Publication, **28**, 75–94.

BEACH, A. 1985. Some comments on sedimentary basin development in the Northern North Sea. *Scottish Journal of Geology*, **21**, 493–512.

BRUCE, C. H. 1973. Pressured shale and related sediment deformation: mechanism for development of regional contemporaneous faults. *American Association of Petroleum Geologists Bulletin*, **57**, 878–886.

BUSCH, D. A. 1975. Influence of growth faulting on sedimentation and prospect evaluation. *American Association of Petroleum Geologists Bulletin*, **59**, 217–230.

GIBBS, A. D. 1983. Balanced cross-section construction from seismic sections in areas of extensional tectonics. *Journal of Structural Geology*, **5**, 153–160.

GLENNIE, K. W. 1986. The structural framework and pre-Permian history of the North Sea area. *In*: GLENNIE, K. W. (ed.) *Introduction to the Petroleum Geology of the North Sea*, Blackwell, 25–62.

HARDING, A. W., HUMPHREY, T. J., LATHAM, A., LUNSFORD, M. K. & STRIDER, M. H. 1990. Controls on Eocene submarine fan deposition in the Witch Ground Graben. *In*: HARDMAN, R. F. P. & BROOKS, J. (eds) *Tectonic Events Responsible for Britain's Oil and Gas Reserves*, Geological Society, London, Special Publication, **55**, 353–367.

HARKER, S. D., GUSTAV, S. H. & RILEY, L. A. 1987. Triassic to Cenomanian stratigraphy of the Witch Ground Graben. *In*: BROOKS, J. & GLENNIE, K. (eds) *Petroleum Geology of North West Europe*. Graham & Trotman, London, 809–818.

HIGGS, W. G. 1988. The Geometries and Kinematics of Extensional Faults. PhD thesis, University of Wales.

—— & WILLIAMS, G. D. 1987. Displacement efficiency of faults and fractures. *Journal of Structural Geology*, **9**, 371–374.

——, —— & POWELL, C. M. 1991. Evidence for flexural shear in extensional fault-related folds. *Geological Society of America Bulletin*, **103**, 710–717.

HORSFIELD, W. T. 1977. An experimental approach to basement controlled faulting. *Geologie en Mijnbouw*, **56**, 363–370.

KNOX, R. W. O'B., MORTON, A. C. & HARLAND, R. 1981. Stratigraphical relationships of Palaeocene sands in the UK sector of the Central North Sea. *In*: ILLING, L. V. & HOBSON, G. D. (eds) *Petroleum Geology of the Continental Shelf of North-West Europe*, Institute of Petroleum, London, 267–281.

LATHAM, A. & MATTINGLY, G., in press. Lithostratigraphy of the Eocene in the area around UKCS Block 16/26, North Sea. *Marine and Petroleum Geology*.

LE PICHON, X. & SIBUET, J.-C. 1981. Passive margins: a model of formation. *Journal of Geophysical Research*, **86**, 3708–3720.

LOVELL, J. P. B., 1986. Cenozoic. *In*: GLENNIE, K. W. (ed.) *Introduction to the Petroleum Geology of the North Sea*, Blackwell Scientific, London.

McCLAY, K. R. & ELLIS, P. G. 1987. Analogue models of extensional fault geometries. *In*: COWARD, M. P., DEWEY, J. F. & HANCOCK, P. L. (eds) *Continental Extensional Tectonics*, Geological Society, London, Special Publication, **28**, 109–126.

MERKI, P. 1972. Structural geology of the Cenozoic Niger Delta. *In*: DESSAUVAGIE, T. F. J. & WHITEMAN, A. J. (eds) *African Geology*, Ibadan University, 635–646.

MORTON, A. C. 1979. The provenance and distribution of the Palaeocene sands of the Central North Sea. *Journal of Petroleum Geology*, **2**, 11–21.

—— 1982. Lower Tertiary sand development in the Viking Graben, North Sea. *American Association of Petroleum Geologists Bulletin*, **66**, 1542–1559.

MORTON, W. H. & BLACK, R. 1975. Crustal attenuation in Afar. *In*: PILGER, A. & ROSLER, A. (eds) *Afar depression of Ethiopia, Inter-union Commission Geodynamique Science Report* Schweizerbart'sche Verlagsbuchhandlung, Stuttgart, 55–65.

MURAOKA, H. & KAMATA, H. 1983. Displacement distribution along minor fault traces. *Journal of Structural Geology*, **5**, 483–495.

MURRAY, G. E. 1961. *Geology of the Atlantic and Gulf coastal province of North America*, Harper & Row, New York.

OCAMB, R. D. 1961. Growth faults of south Louisiana. *Gulf Coast Association Geological Society Transactions*, **11**, 139–175.

RIPPON, J. H. 1985. Contoured patterns of throw and hade of normal faults in the coal measures (Westphalian) of northeast Derbyshire. *Proceedings of the Yorkshire Geological Society*, **62**, 147–161.

STEWART, I. J. 1987. A revised stratigraphic interpretation of the early Palaeogene of the central North Sea. *In*: BROOKS, J. & GLENNIE, K. (eds) *Petroleum Geology of North West Europe*, Graham & Trotman, London, 557–576.

WALSH, J. J. & WATTERSON, J. 1987. Distribution of cumulative displacement and seismic slip on a single normal fault surface. *Journal of Structural Geology*, **9**, 1039–1046.

—— & —— 1988a. Dips of normal faults in British Coal Measures and other sedimentary sequences. *Journal of the Geological Society, London*, **145**, 859–874.

—— & —— 1988b. Analysis of the relationship between displacements and dimensions of faults. *Journal of Structural Geology*, **10**, 239–248.

WERNICKE, B. & BURCHFIEL, B. C. 1982. Modes of extensional tectonics. *Journal of Structural Geology*, **4**, 105–115.

WHITEMAN, A. 1982. *Nigeria: its petroleum geology, resources and potential*, Vol 2. Graham & Trotman, London.

WILLIAMS, G. D. & CHAPMAN, T. J. 1983. Strains developed in the hangingwalls of thrusts due to their slip/propagation rate: a dislocation model. *Journal of Structural Geology*, **5**, 563–571.

ZIEGLER, P. A. 1982. *Geological Atlas of Western and Central Europe*, Elsevier Science Publishers, Amsterdam.

—— 1987. Late Cretaceous and Cenozoic intra-plate compressional deformations in the Alpine foreland—a geodynamic model. *Tectonophysics*, **137**, 389–420.

—— 1988. *Evolution of the Arctic–North Atlantic and Western Tethys*. American Association of Petroleum Geologists Memoir, **43**.

From WILLIAMS, G. D. & DOBB, A. (eds), 1993, *Tectonics and Seismic Sequence Stratigraphy.*
Geological Society Special Publication No. 71, 163–191.

Seismic sequence stratigraphy and tectonics offshore Namibia

M. P. R. Light, M. P. Maslanyj, R. J. Greenwood & N. L. Banks

Intera Information Technologies, Highlands Farm, Greys Road, Henley-on-Thames, Oxon, RG9 4PS, UK.

Abstract: High quality seismic data recently acquired offshore Namibia have
revealed the complex interplay between sedimentation and rifting that accompanied the breakup of Gondwanaland. Seismic sequence analysis has demonstrated a complex series of superimposed phases of rifting.
   Jurassic early-rift sediments were deposited in a Basin & Range setting with
marine embayments. Mid- to Late Jurassic extension probably culminated in
acidic to intermediate volcanicity. Subsequently, late-rift fill sedimentary accumulations were terminated locally by a major period of plateau-forming effusive
activity. This was coincident with the start of Early Cretaceous spreading in the
South Atlantic. Shelf, slope and basinal facies are clearly defined in the post-rift
succession.
   Although virtually undrilled, the area is considered to have very considerable
petroleum potential. Seismic stratigraphy will continue to play a vital role in
defining the critical juxtapositions of source rock, reservoir and seal.

The passive margin offshore Namibia is one of the largest unexplored continental
shelves in the world. Some 110 000 km^2, 240 000 km^2 and 310 000 km^2 lie between the
coastline and the 200 m, 1000 m and 2000 m isobaths, respectively.

   This paper discusses the interpretation of a regional grid of more than 10 600 km^2
of speculative, non-exclusive, high resolution seismic, gravity and magnetic surveys
acquired offshore Namibia by Intera (formerly ECL)/HGS in 1989/90, integrated
with published and open-file data. It has culminated in the development of a model
of the regional tectono-stratigraphic and geological history of Gondwanaland since
the Permian.

   The model recognizes a passive Basin & Range, and two active rifting phases
within the Namibian offshore area. Rifting was succeeded in the Early Cretaceous by
oceanic spreading in the South Atlantic with concomitant thermal sag and passive
margin development.

   The principal regionally extensive seismic sequence boundaries have been mapped
out in order to evaluate the various depositional units. Horizons are designated
utilizing a similar nomenclature to that applied by previous authors to the Orange
Basin (Gerrard & Smith 1982), although other unconformities (Horizons Q, G & A)
are newly specified.

   Geological control is based on the three closely spaced Kudu wells in the Orange
Basin to the south. However, these did not penetrate down to Horizon Q, and
recognition of deeper events is based on published reports dealing with the South
African part of the Orange Basin.

   A seismic facies analysis was carried out in order to derive geological information from reflection character and patterns. To achieve this aim with a degree of confidence, it is desirable to tie in geological control from well or outcrop data. Since the only wells on the Namibian shelf (which extends more than 1200 km from south to north) are the three closely spaced Kudu wells, the conclusions and interpretations presented are necessarily speculative.

Gas fields occur in the western and northern parts of the Orange Basin; oil plays are developed in Jurassic graben further to the east. Although undrilled, the Luderitz and Walvis Basins, also have potential for large plays.

Structural framework

The passive margin offshore Namibia essentially consists of an eastern Graben Province, separated from an extensive coast-parallel Central Half-Graben by a Medial Hinge Line. The Central Half-Graben is bounded in the west by the Marginal Ridge. Four major sedimentary basins can be recognized within the Central Half-Graben. From south to north these are the Orange, the Luderitz, the Walvis and the Namibe (Fig. 1). The northernmost two are separated by the Walvis Ridge, and as a result the Namibe Basin has a closer affinity with the Angolan shelf than with the basins further south.

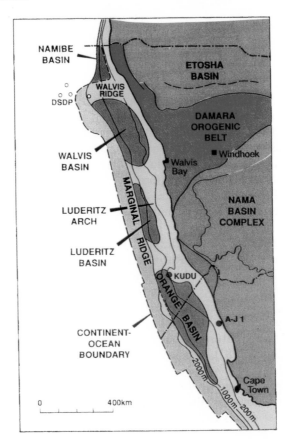

Fig. 1. Location map.

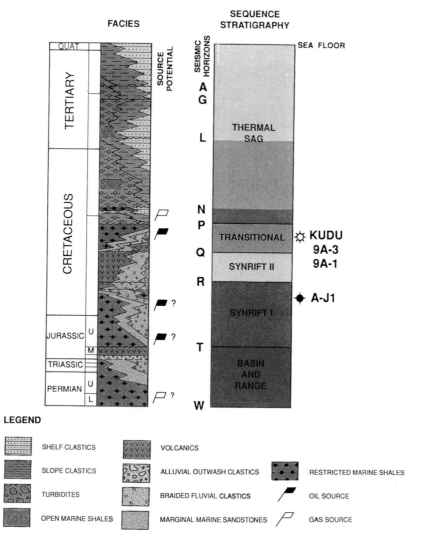

Fig. 2. Stratigraphy and seismic horizons.

Tectono-stratigraphic sequences

The stratigraphy of Permian to Recent sediments can be subdivided into five main tectono-stratigraphic sequences (Fig. 2):

Thermal Sag	(Horizon P–sea floor)
Transitional	(Horizon Q–P)
Syn-rift II	(Horizon R–Q)
Syn-rift I	(Horizon T–R)
Basin & Range	(Horizon W–T)

The sequence boundaries defining these tectono-stratigraphic units are illustrated on regional line ECL 89-011 which passes through the Kudu 9A-3 well (Fig. 3).

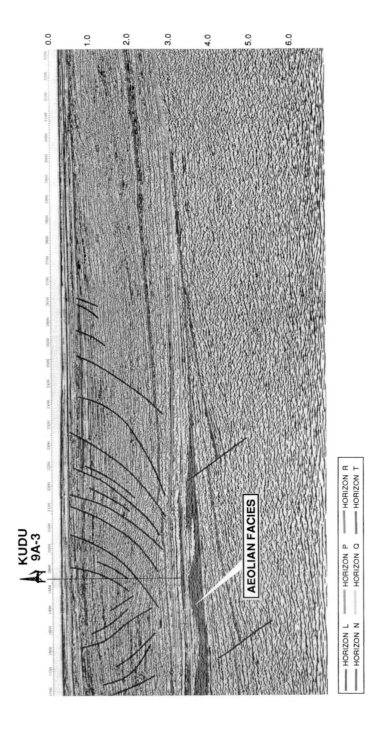

Fig. 3. Seismic line ECL 89-011.

- Horizon T is the Late Jurassic angular unconformity at the top of the Basin & Range section. It is marked by a very high amplitude continuous reflector.
- Horizon R has previously been given two different ages; Valanginian by Gerrard & Smith (1982) and Hauterivian by McLachlan & McMillan (1979). In the present study, two separate unconformities, Horizon Q (Hauterivian) and Horizon R (Valanginian), are proposed. The major period of volcanic activity, correlated with the Etendeka volcanics (Karoo Group), is bounded by these two unconformities.
- Horizon P is the Middle Aptian unconformity, which is the breakup unconformity north of the Walvis Ridge. It forms a continuous reflector of moderate to high amplitude, overlies extensive Lower Aptian source/seal shales and, to the east of the Hinge Line, truncates Horizons R & T. It represents the top of a prograding sequence, and there is downlap of overlying beds.
- The Turonian unconformity, Horizon N, occurs at the top of a prograding sequence and is continuous to the east. In the west it deteriorates into a zone of slumping. Overlying beds downlap in the west, and onlap in the east.
- The base of the Tertiary, Horizon L, is a continuous high amplitude reflector at the top of a prograding sequence and is usually disconformable. There is onlap and downlap of overlying beds, and the underlying sequence exhibits toplap/erosion.
- North of the Walvis Ridge, Horizon G (Oligocene) and Horizon A (Middle Miocene) form erosional unconformities that are dissected by several transverse channels.

Rift phase

Basin & Range rifting began earliest in the south and propagated northwards towards the Walvis Ridge. The effects of this continued during later rift events, and the first syn-rift phase (Syn-rift I) is confined to the southern half of the offshore area, whereas the second syn-rift phase (Syn-rift II) is present, and thickens rapidly northwards, within the Walvis Basin (Fig. 4).

Basin & Range Megasequence

Structural evolution Gondwanaland developed during the Late Proterozoic from the fusion of cratonic fragments along suture zones (the Pan-African belts, see Lawrence (1989)).

The transverse Damara (Pan-African) orogenic belt, which separates the Kalahari and Congo cratons (Fig. 5), has coast-parallel extensions, the Kaoko and Gariep/Saldanha–Malmsbury belts, and underlies the passive margin offshore Namibia. During the collision of the Kalahari and Congo cratons between 600 and 535 Ma, Nama Group sediments were deposited in foredeep and foreland basins in Namibia. Eastward-verging Pan-African thrusts have acted as detachments for Late Jurassic/Early Cretaceous rifting and Late Cretaceous/Tertiary inversion.

Karoo sag basins developed in the southern portion of Gondwanaland during the Permo-Carboniferous (Kent 1980) and their structural evolution and depositional patterns were influenced by its subsequent breakup.

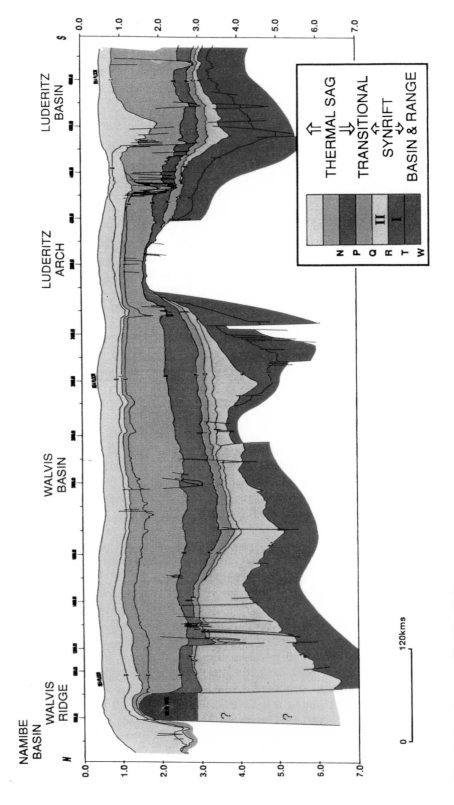

Fig. 4. Geoseismic profile ECL 89-50.

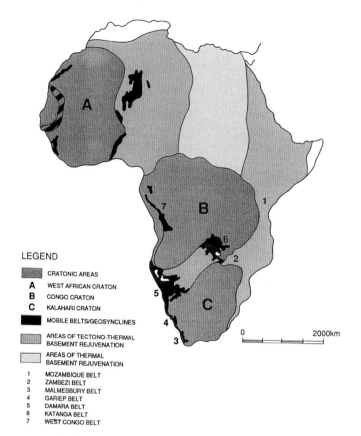

LEGEND

	CRATONIC AREAS
A	WEST AFRICAN CRATON
B	CONGO CRATON
C	KALAHARI CRATON
	MOBILE BELTS/GEOSYNCLINES
	AREAS OF TECTONO-THERMAL BASEMENT REJUVENATION
	AREAS OF THERMAL BASEMENT REJUVENATION
1	MOZAMBIQUE BELT
2	ZAMBEZI BELT
3	MALMESBURY BELT
4	GARIEP BELT
5	DAMARA BELT
6	KATANGA BELT
7	WEST CONGO BELT

Fig. 5. Craton-orogen—basin system.

The stratigraphy and structure of Basin & Range continental clastics and acid to intermediate volcanics, are comparable with the Basin & Range Province in the US (Bruhn *et al.* 1978; Dalziel 1980; Bust *et al.* 1985; Light *et al.* 1992). Extensive rift basins developed on the Argentine margin in concert with an outer basement ridge 80 km wide (Urien *et al.* 1981). When combined with the giant half-graben systems found on the Namibian margin, the section is remarkably similar to a 'simple shear' model of the Basin & Range region USA after Wernicke (1981, 1985), which demands the existence of a wedge of mantle beneath the basin or Central Half-Graben (Fig. 6). A large coast-parallel gravity anomaly exists along the Central Half-Graben offshore Namibia, and has a striking correlation with the regional Hinge Line, forming its eastern flank, indicating that the anomaly and the hinging process are structurally related. This anomaly can be largely derived by varying the depth to the Moho, and a mantle wedge similar in form to that in Wernicke's Basin & Range model is interpreted to underlie the Central Half-Graben (Fig. 6).

During the Late Jurassic/Early Cretaceous, a set of en échelon (Riedel) graben formed northwest of Walvis Bay, in response to clockwise rotation of the southern part of Africa along pre-existing Pan-African sinistral shear zones. Listric extension along pre-existing, east-verging Pan-African thrusts formed post-Horizon T basins in the region of the thrust ramp, east of the Hinge Line, in southern offshore Namibia (Fig. 6).

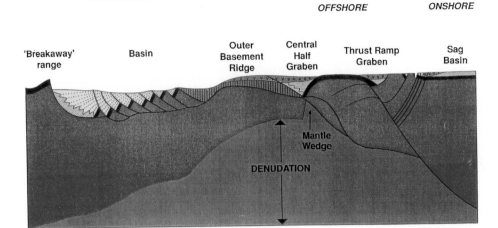

Fig. 6. Cross-section—end Basin & Range.

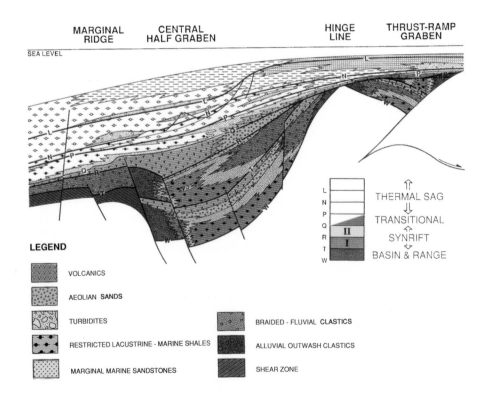

Fig. 7. Rift phase sequences.

Stratigraphy The Basin & Range Megasequence consists essentially of the Karoo formations as defined within the main Karoo Basin and southern Namibia (Fig. 7) (Kent 1980).

It is difficult to interpret the seismic facies of this unit with confidence due to the general deterioration in seismic signature with increasing depth, and there is almost total character loss in places, particularly beneath overlying highly reflective intervals. Furthermore, there is no well control to confirm sub-Horizon T facies interpretation except in the South African portion of the Orange Basin.

Along a broad north/south-trending belt, west of the Medial Hinge Line, seismic reflectors display a complex pattern of high amplitude, discontinuous, irregular and hummocky events, probably representing arid continental deposits with aeolian dunes, fluvial sands, lower energy braidplain silts and shales, and extensive tracts of subaerially extruded lavas.

In the western part of the Orange Basin, seismic reflection character suggests a rather more uniform sequence, where reflectors are generally more continuous. This aspect might indicate a shallow water-lain sand and shale sequence, possibly of shallow marine origin. In fact, following the Dwyka glacial period, during the initial (Permian) stages of Basin & Range rifting, a marine embayment developed in the Namibian offshore area within the Central Half-Graben, and also extended onshore (Fig. 8) (Martin 1973).

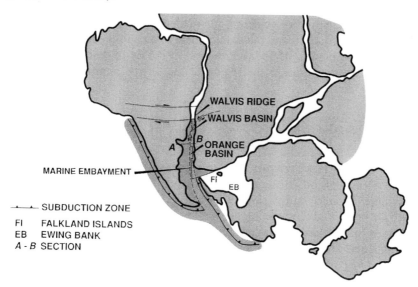

Fig. 8. Triassic–Mid-Jurassic Basin & Range.

A series of major deltaic systems formed later in the Permian, building out westwards from Central Africa (Nossob, Early Auob and Upper Wankie Sandstones) into the marine environment in Namibia, where they were reworked by marine processes (Intera 1990).

Formations equivalent to the marine reworked deltaic complexes of the Nossob and Auob (Early and Middle Ecca) may be present within the Central Half-Graben, probably as sand/shale sequences. These units are believed to undergo a series of facies changes to the west of the Medial Hinge Line, passing from a clastic apron (alluvial fans) through fluvial systems, reworked deltaic facies and shallow marine units to deep water sand/shale sequences in the core of the Central Half-Graben (Fig. 7). Similar facies changes may occur east of the Hinge Line in smaller graben that are rotated on listric detachments located on older Pan-African thrusts (Fig. 7). Seismic reflection character implies that these are infilled with marginal alluvial fans grading laterally and vertically into fluvial and lacustrine sediments. Both oil (Whitehall and Irati Formation oil shales) and gas (Lower and Upper Carboniferous shales) source rocks are thought to be present within these units.

In the Mid- to Late Triassic (240–200 Ma), uplift and rifting in northern Namibia impeded westward-directed drainage and allowed fluvial and lacustrine sediments to aggrade in the Haub River valley (Martin 1976). Prior to or during this period the continental Gai-As red beds and Omingonde Formation were deposited in northern Namibia (Kent 1980). Basin & Range rifting continued through the Early Jurassic, and deposition of the extensive Clarens or Plateau aeolian sandstones indicates a continuation of arid conditions in Namibia and in the main Karoo Basin at this time (Kent 1980).

The period of aridity preceded and coincided with extensive volcanicity in the Mid- and Late Jurassic, when acid to intermediate volcanics erupted in the Orange Basin, and more-basaltic rocks formed flows within Central Namibia (the Kalkrand lavas).

Regional uplift   The period of acidic to intermediate volcanism was terminated by regional uplift, block rotation and the development of a regional unconformity in the Kimmeridgian–Oxfordian ($\pm$155 Ma) at the end of the Basin & Range rifting event (Fig. 6). Uplift exceeded 1 km in the region of the Great Escarpment, east of the modern Namib Desert.

Syn-rift I Megasequence

Structural evolution   The southern African continental shelf underwent a major period of east/west tension during the Late Jurassic that led to the development of syn-sedimentary normal faults parallel to the continental margin (Schommarz 1988). Syn-rift I heralded the opening of the South Atlantic in the Early Cretaceous, when a new set of rift basins was localized offshore Namibia, west of the Basin & Range rift (Central Half-Graben (Fig. 9).

Stratigraphy   The Syn-rift I interval represents a wedge-shaped, generally west-wards-thickening sequence, which pinches out at the Medial Hinge Line in the east, usually due to erosion. No wells in the Namibian offshore have penetrated this sequence, therefore facies interpretations are speculative. The general stratigraphy is illustrated in Fig. 7.

East of the Hinge Line, narrow elongate thrust ramp graben and half-graben occur, which were syn-tectonically filled with alluvial and fluvial sediments during the waning phases of rifting (Fig. 10). Progradational and chaotic reflection patterns along the margins of many of these graben indicate that clastic fans were developed marginally, and grade laterally and vertically into fluvial, braidplain and, perhaps, lacustrine sequences, marked by more regular, more continuous and parallel reflectors. East of the Orange Basin in South Africa, drilling has proven a rift fill sequence of lacustrine shales and sandstones in one of these Jurassic-age grabens.

West of the Hinge Line, deposition in the Orange Basin continued with a similar facies distribution to that of the underlying Basin & Range sequence. A zone of chaotic, highly disturbed reflectors extends away from the Hinge Line, through a region of rather high amplitude, semi-continuous to discontinuous, often hummocky reflectors, to an area in the west where reflectors are less disturbed and have a greater continuity. This pattern seems to indicate a fringe of alluvial fans, sometimes with volcanic material associated, comprising conglomerates and coarse-grained sands, feeding westwards into a fluvial wadi system where medium and fine sands predominate. This fluvial regime is separated from a probably shallow marine sand/shale sequence in the west by an apron where aeolian dune sands appear to have developed under the influence of southwesterly winds (Fig. 11) which prevailed in the Mesozoic (Martin 1973; Horsthemke *et al.* 1990). An aeolian origin is implied by the similarity of seismic character to that of the interval cored at Kudu (Fig. 12) where well-developed dune cross-bedding occurs at the base of the Transitional Megasequence (Q–P) interval. These wind-blown sands are probably closely associated with subaerial volcanics and fluvially deposited sands and shales.

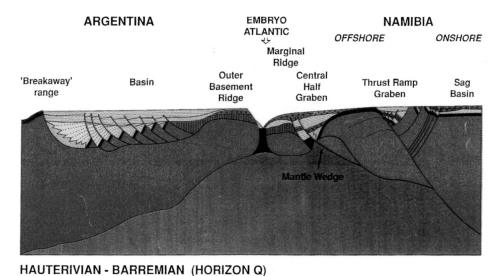

HAUTERIVIAN - BARREMIAN (HORIZON Q)

Fig. 9. Cross-section—end Syn-rift II.

Further to the north, in the Luderitz basin, the Central Half-Graben is quite narrow, and the T–R interval thickens rapidly away from the Hinge Line. It seems likely that a marginal fluvial facies grades westwards through shoreline clastics, possibly into a rather shallow marine sand/shale facies in the central part of the basin. The basin is separated from the Marginal Ridge in the west by a fault system, and chaotic reflection patterns here suggest a rim of clastic fans feeding eastwards into the basin, where a narrow, elongate zone of semi-continuous and discontinuous, irregular and wavy reflectors implies a more distal, probably shallow-water fan development.

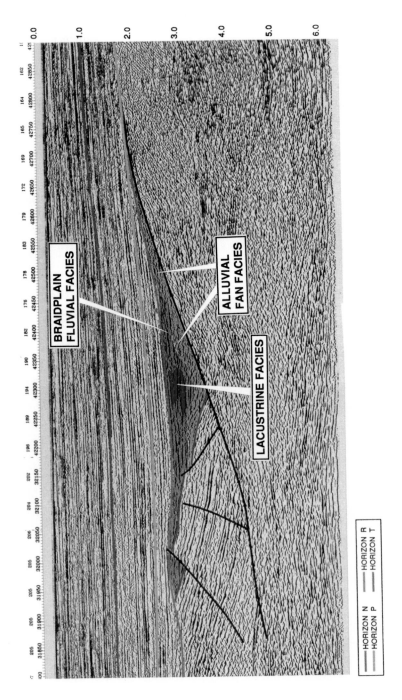

Fig. 10. Seismic line ECL 89-7.

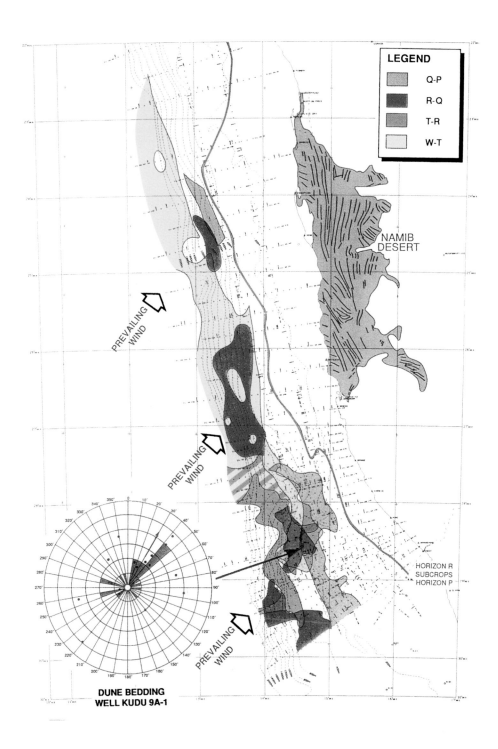

Fig. 11. Northeasterly younging of aeolian facies.

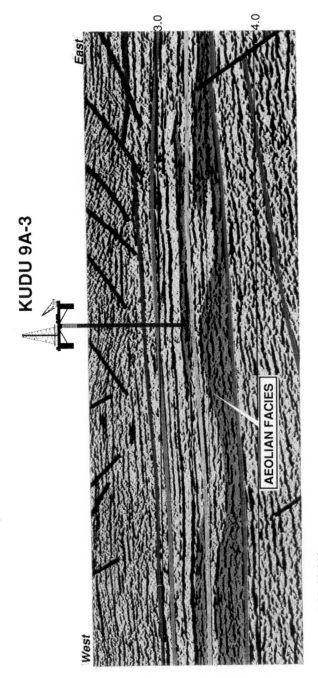

Fig. 12. Seismic line ECL 89-011.

Seismic reflections on the Marginal Ridge itself are mostly high amplitude, continuous to discontinuous, often irregular and hummocky. It is interpreted on regional grounds to be primarily a fluvial system, perhaps with associated volcanics. Areas of more continuous reflectors suggest lower energy braidplain or lacustrine sand/shale deposits.

Regional uplift   The first syn-rift event was brought to a close by a period of fault block rotation, and the formation of an angular unconformity (Horizon R). This is correlated with the Early Cretaceous initiation of sea floor spreading in the South Atlantic (Gerrard & Smith 1982) and the related Valanginian global oceanic low stand (Vail *et al.* 1977).

Syn-rift II Megasequence

Structural evolution   A second syn-rift event, Syn-rift II, developed in the northern part of offshore Namibia and was associated with widespread volcanicity, related to the Walvis Ridge mantle plume (130–120 Ma) (Dingle *et al.* 1983). The Etendeka (Kaoko Group) Volcanics are dated between 114 and 136 Ma (Kent 1980) and are inter-bedded with aeolian and fluvial sands (Etjo/Doros; Dingle *et al.* 1983).

A volcanic plateau, with well-developed escarpments on its western flank, developed above the north-trending Marginal Ridge to the west of the Central Half-Graben between Horizon R (Valanginian) and Horizon Q (Hauterivian–Barremian) (Fig. 13).

Stratigraphy   Onshore, aeolian and wadi sandstones are inter-bedded with volcanics throughout the Kimmeridgian to Barremian interval (136–114 Ma), which indicates that climatic conditions had again become arid in Namibia (Fig. 7). These dune sands were deposited by westerly palaeowinds (Martin 1973) (Fig. 11).

Immediately west of the Medial Hinge Line, seismic reflection characteristics in the Orange and Luderitz Basins are essentially rather low amplitude, semi-continuous to discontinuous, sometimes wavy, with inter-bedded quieter and transparent zones. Very low angle prograding units are sometimes developed. There is no evidence to support the existence of a prominent shelf break, and much of the sediment fill within the Central Half-Graben is interpreted to be moderate energy fluvial sands and shales. Only rarely is marginal alluvial fan development seen. Distally, the fluvial sediments pass into lower energy braidplain and lacustrine silt and shale deposits, characterized by mostly continuous reflectors of high and low amplitude. Some areas of irregular, discontinuous and wavy reflectors also contain scattered, very short, low angle clinoforms with variable orientation (Fig. 12). These are interpreted to represent patches of aeolian reworking with dune formation, similar to the cored sequence in Kudu 9A-1 well.

In the southwestern part of the Orange Basin it is possible that shallow marine to shoreline sand/shale deposition continued, forming the western limit of the aeolian plain. North west of Luderitz, the marginal Ridge is characterized by extremely high amplitude, low frequency, irregular and hummocky reflectors, representing very thick plateau lava flows, with marginal escarpments (Fig. 13).

The Syn-rift II desert/wadi erg system appears to have developed within an intra-

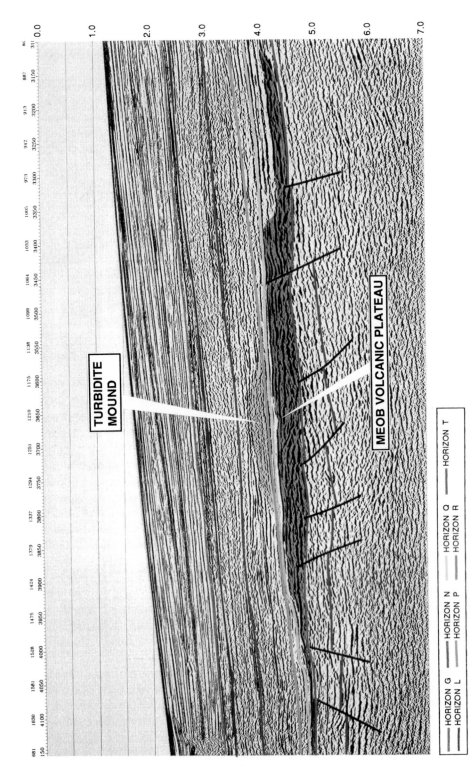

Fig. 13. Seismic line ECL 89-31.

continental basin between a palaeo-escarpment to the east, and a volcanic plateau or marine shoreline to the west. It may be comparable to the present day Namib Desert which is confined between the Great Escarpment to the east and the Atlantic shoreline to the west.

The R–Q (Syn-rift II) interval in the Walvis Basin is a very distinctive facies. It thickens very rapidly both northwards and westwards, filling a trough related to the major east–west pre-Karoo fracture system that trended along the Walvis Ridge. Low to moderate angle aggradational progradation is developed. Reflectors are mostly discontinuous and wavy, but some are more continuous. This sequence is interpreted to be a prograding deltaic unit where there was very rapid deposition of shales, silts and sands. Fluctuating shorelines probably gave rise to inter-bedded fluvial and aeolian clastics. A zone of listric faulting has developed in the west.

The Syn-rift II sequence is not evident north of the Walvis basin due to erosional truncation.

Regional uplift   The angular unconformity, marked by Horizon Q (Hauterivian–Barremian age), terminates the second syn-rift event. It is itself truncated by Horizon P (Mid-Aptian unconformity) which becomes the end syn-rift unconformity north of the Walvis Ridge.

Rift/drift phase

Transitional Megasequence

Structural evolution   The Transitional Megasequence marks the initial effects of thermal sag following the end of rifting, and is the first to contain signs of a developing shelf break. Equivalent deposits in the San Jorge Basin in Argentina are continental, indicating the progressive growth and damming effect of the basement Marginal Ridge, which confined marine systems to the east and continental sediments to the west (Dingle *et al.* 1983). It is bounded below by Horizon Q (Hauterivian–Barremian), and above by Horizon P (Mid-Aptian).

Stratigraphy   Most of the Q to P succession has been intersected in the Kudu wells west of the Medial Hinge Line, where it ranges from continental beds (basalts, and aeolian to fluvial sands) in the lower part, through shallow marine sandstones containing abundant carbonate cements, to shelly sandstones that locally grade into lagoonal shales, and deeper marine siltstones and sapropelic shales at the top. The major Aptian marine transgression correlates with a global sea-level high stand (Vail *et al.* 1977). An interpreted facies distribution map of the basal part of this sequence is shown in Fig. 14. It effectively represents and summarizes the latest phase of rifting prior to the onset of thermal sag.

Drilling to the east of the regional Hinge Line, adjacent to the Orange Basin, has shown that the Transitional Megasequence consists essentially of fluvial sediments in Jurassic-age grabens (Fig. 7) (Gerrard & Smith 1982; Dingle *et al.* 1983). A number of similar graben and half-graben occur east of the Walvis Basin. Centrally, these contain a more or less transparent seismic sequence, with discordant low amplitude reflectors adjacent to the fault scarps. The graben might also be filled with fluvial sediments grading into a more uniform sequence of siltstones and lacustrine shales.

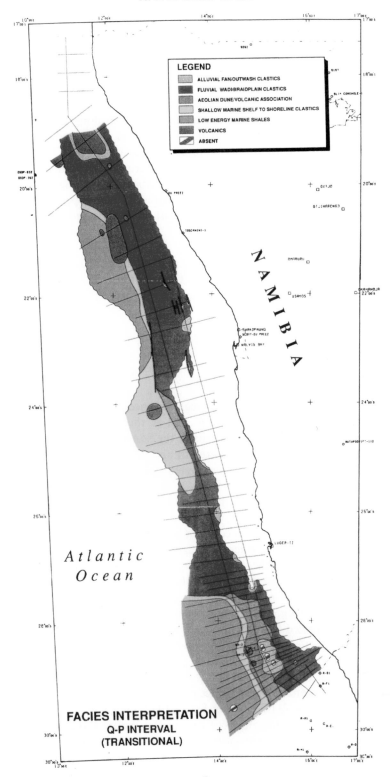

Fig. 14. Facies interpretation Q–P interval.

In the Orange Basin a fluvial-wadi facies developed to the west of the retreating platform edge, characterized by irregular, discontinuous reflectors with inter-bedded quieter zones. High energy sands probably dominate the sequence, but local patches of semi-continuous, parallel reflectors indicate sand/shale inter-beds, perhaps in shallow water environments.

Aeolian gas-bearing sands at the base of the section in the Kudu wells have a seismic signature characterized by moderate to high amplitude, discontinuous, irregular and wavy reflectors, with very short, discordant clinoforms (Fig. 12). An area with similar seismic character, extending north and south through Kudu, is thus interpreted to represent a broad, arid, coastal plain with aeolian sands organized into dune fields by southwesterly prevailing winds. These are inter-bedded with fluvial and braidplain sands, silts and shales, together with extruded volcanics.

West of this coastal plain is a narrow belt where the Q–P interval thins gradually westwards, associated with weak indications of low angle prograding reflectors, and beyond this a region of continuous high and low amplitude reflectors. The whole probably represents the earliest stages of a marine transgressive sequence with sands and inter-bedded shales.

The Luderitz Basin is characterized by discontinuous, irregular reflectors and associated quieter zones, and is probably entirely continental in aspect. Occasional marginal clastic fans are interpreted to have fed into a low to moderate energy fluvial sand and shale regime with a central low energy braidplain where fine-grained sands, silts and shales accumulated. Over much of the western part of this area, the Q–P interval is very thin.

A marginal fluvial to braidplain sequence, with similar seismic features to that of the Luderitz Basin, borders the Walvis Basin in the east, and grades westwards into a shallow marine transgressive facies, defined by a narrow belt with low angle progradation. This shallow marine facies may encroach southwards into the northern part of the Luderitz Basin. An area with more continuous, parallel reflectors further west might indicate a deeper marine, low-energy shale-rich basin, into which some clastic turbidites have been introduced, as suggested by discontinuous, highly disturbed reflectors.

In the Namibe Basin, north of the Walvis Ridge, Horizon P is interpreted to form the top of a truncated syn-rift section in rotated fault blocks of possible Early Cretaceous age. A regional basement high forms the early shelf edge here with a succession of northwest-trending graben to the east and a series of rotated fault blocks in the west.

In the eastern graben, Horizon P is interpreted to overlie a transitional marine facies with good source potential that developed above the end syn-rift unconformity (Horizon Q). The syn-rift sequences beneath Horizon Q are probably aeolian and fluvial systems similar to those developed further south along the Luderitz Arch.

The Q–P Transitional Sequence apparently represents a period of marine transgression. Thus, in the Kudu wells, continental and lagoonal to shallow marine sediments are overlain by progressively deeper water argillaceous deposits, and the uppermost part of the interval consists of deep marine shales. The lateral equivalents of these deep water sapropelic shales have been intersected at DSDP site 360 in the Cape Basin, and also off the Falkland Islands. In both areas they are strongly oil prone.

Thermal sag phase

P–N Megasequence

Structural evolution The P–N Megasequence of Aptian and Turonian age developed during continued sagging and tilting of the continental margin offshore Namibia (Fig. 15). It is characterized by a progradational succession that downlaps onto Horizon P. In the region of the Hinge Line, Horizon N is frequently truncated and displaced by a major Late Cretaceous/Tertiary-age listric slump detachment system that extends down close to the level of Horizon P.

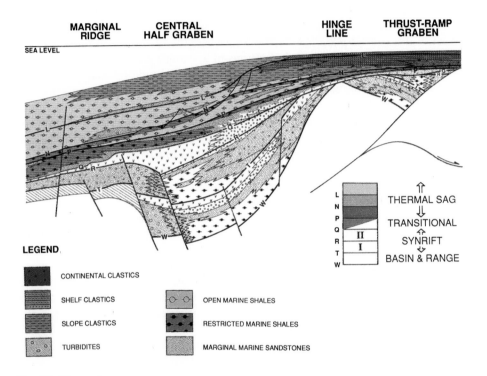

Fig. 15. Thermal sag sequences.

The top of the sequence represents a major transgression of abyssal marine shales during a related oceanic high-stand in the Turonian (Haq *et al.* 1987). A large volcanic mound erupted on the eastern end of the Walvis Ridge at this time, and contained within it a succession of prograded tuffaceous rocks developed above Horizon P (Mid-Aptian unconformity) and beneath Horizon N (Turonian). Volcanism on the Walvis Ridge and in the San Jorge Basin of Argentina, are probably related to the Albian–Aptian episode of rapid spreading (Larson & Pitman 1972), and associated calc-alkaline volcanism.

Stratigraphy The P–N Megasequence is illustrated in Figs 15 & 16. Biostratigraphical data from the Kudu wells indicates that the P to N succession is deep marine and consists entirely of basinal shales (McLachlan & McMillan 1979). South of the

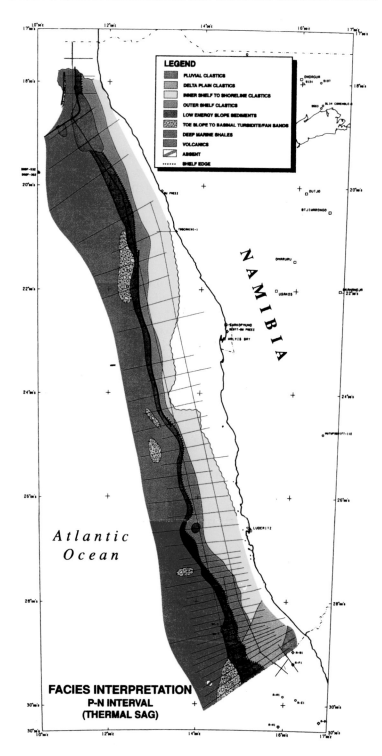

Fig. 16. Facies interpretation P–N interval.

Walvis Ridge a major transgression began after Horizon N and the sea transgressed over the Hinge Line further to the east than in the preceding Transitional Megasequence.

The individual basins south of the Walvis Ridge had, by this time, more or less lost their separate identities, and almost the entire offshore Namibia area has a well-defined east/west tripartite subdivision into shelf, slope and basin. This interval represents a continuation of the marine transgression which characterizes the underlying transitional sequence.

Seismic reflectors on the shelf are essentially parallel, but with slight evidence of coastal onlap. In the eastern part they are more or less discontinuous or semi-continuous, with inter-bedded quieter zones, and represent a sequence of high-energy shoreline to shallow marine inner shelf sands, with inter-laminated shales, and perhaps thin limestones. The western area of the shelf is typified by more continuous reflectors, again with quieter and transparent inter-beds, which signify lower energy, outer shelf sands and shales below and beyond the influence of wave energy and inshore currents.

In the southern part of the region, off the Orange River, most of the shelf area is characterized by parallel, semi-continuous and discontinuous reflectors. These are interpreted to represent the earliest phase of the Orange River delta plain facies, with silts, shales, channel sands, and perhaps thin coals. Mouth bar sands are likely to be developed in the submarine portion of the delta plain.

The shelf break is now well defined south of the Walvis Ridge, characterized by low or very low angle progradation. In places it has been affected by faulting. Slope sediments throughout the offshore area are most likely to be fine-grained clastics, dominated by clays and silts, but fine-grained sands may be found at the top of the slope.

Seismic reflections beyond the base of the slope, on the basin floor, are predominantly lowish amplitude, discontinuous and wavy, inter-bedded with some slightly more continuous reflections. This character suggests muddy and silty turbidites. Within the basin there are areas of discontinuous, wavy, chaotic reflectors, some-times with mounding, suggestive of sandy turbidites (Fig. 13). These are most commonly present off the Orange River delta, and between Walvis Bay and the Walvis Ridge in the north.

In the Namibe Basin the P–N (Aptian to Turonian) Megasequence is interpreted to represent a progradational build-out of the shelf edge, with some volcanicity occurring along the eastern flank of the continental basement ridge. Lower to Middle Albian and Cenomanian–Turonian sapropelic source rocks may occur.

Contemporaneous with magmatic activity on the Andean margin, and the eruption of Late Cretaceous Mina del Carmen tuffs on the Argentine shelf, a giant volcanic dome developed on the eastern end of the Walvis Ridge. These magmas apparently erupted along the pre-existing right lateral strike-slip system that extended westwards across South America to the Pacific margin (Unternehr *et al.* 1988). On the Walvis Ridge, the volcanic dome is bounded beneath by Horizon P and above by Horizon N indicating that it is of Aptian to Turonian age. Thick and extensive sets of prograding reflectors occur within the core of the volcano, probably representing rapidly deposited tuffaceous units which built-out to the west and north. Pyroclastic deposits probably extend more than 10 km south of the volcano, beneath Horizon N, where seismic lines are characterized by strong diffractions.

N–L Megasequence

Structural evolution   A thick marine sequence developed offshore Namibia between Horizon N (Turonian) and Horizon L (Base Tertiary), representing a period of rapid progradation of the shelf due to sagging of the passive margin edge during the Late Cretaceous (Fig. 15).

A phase of major extension occurred during the Late Cretaceous and Early Tertiary, probably related to the differential anti-clockwise rotation of South America relative to Africa, which resulted in trans-tensional forces and regional intra-plate stress (Fitzgerald *et al.* 1990). A set of Late Cretaceous/Early Tertiary intrusions (Gerrard & Smith 1982) may be related to this tectonic event offshore Namibia. This movement also resulted in strike-slip displacement along zones aligned with South Atlantic transforms (Windhausen 1924; Francheteau & Le Pichon 1972). Associated with, and probably triggered by, this period of strike-slip displacement are a succession of large-scale slumps (Gerrard & Smith 1982) that are best developed in the lower part of the Horizon N (Turonian) to Horizon L (Base Tertiary) sequence. These slumps show classic listric head scarp fractures, basal detachment planes and toe areas (Figs 17 & 18). West of Luderitz and off the Orange River delta, zones of large-scale high angle listric faulting have caused rotation of downfaulted blocks of sediment, imparting high angle reverse dip (Fig. 17).

The position of the main detachment for these Tertiary-age slump faults has often been localized by the seaward position of the shelf edge at the time of formation of the Horizon L unconformity (Palaeocene–Base Tertiary). This complex slump system has a steep westward-dipping listric surface to the east that extends down to flatten out above the Horizon N (Turonian) unconformity, possibly on top of early deposited pre-delta clays. Further to the west, slumping often terminates in a mounded toe region, or in a succession of mass flow gravity slides, slumps and stacked thrusts (Fig. 18).

Stratigraphy   South of the Walvis Ridge, the N–L Megasequence contains within it several discontinuities and represents a stacked succession of progradational build-outs with intervening periods of transgression that developed during the Late Cretaceous (Gerrard & Smith 1982) (Fig. 15). Over much of the area, Horizon K is identified between Horizons N and L.

The shelf/slope/basin pattern established in the P–N interval is still broadly developed, and there is a reasonably well-defined shelf break. The Orange Basin deltaic sequence is much more extensive, and channels traverse the shelf in the central and northern areas. This increase in downcutting activity and the introduction of large sediment volumes suggest that there was a relative fall in sea-level towards the end of this interval, apparently culminating in a lowstand at the time of Horizon K (?Maastrichtian).

In the easternmost part of the shelf area north of Luderitz, there is a narrow zone which has a mostly quiet and transparent seismic character, with occasional discontinuous high amplitude reflectors. This is thought to represent low energy fluvial to nearshore or lagoonal facies, made up predominantly of clays, with perhaps thin limestones.

Over most of the shelf area, high energy, inner shelf to shoreline sands and shales are characterized by parallel, short, wavy, discontinuous reflectors with inter-bedded

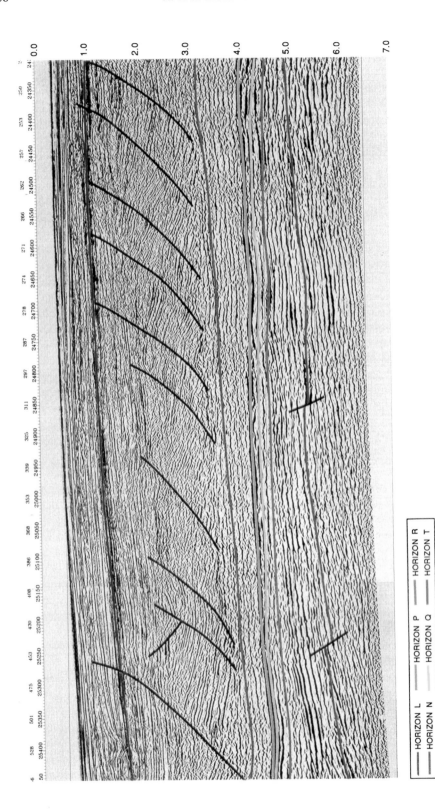

Fig. 17. Seismic line ECL 89-4.

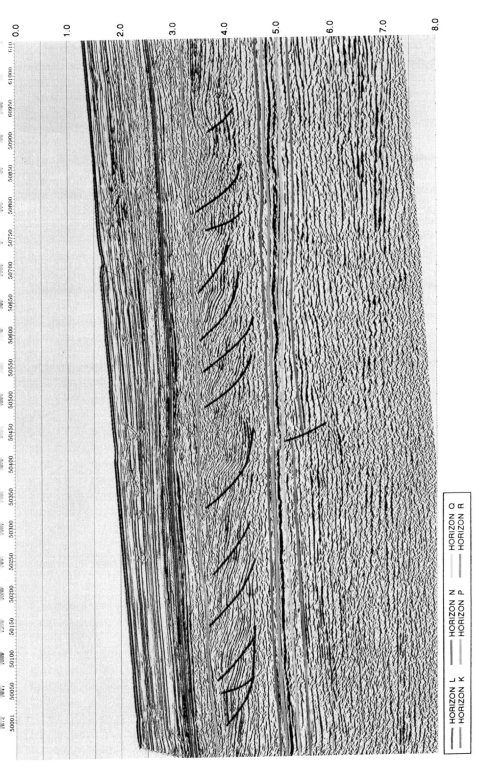

HORIZON L   HORIZON N   HORIZON Q
HORIZON K   HORIZON P   HORIZON R

Fig. 18. Seismic line ECL 89-7.

semi-continuous and quieter zones. Low energy, outer shelf sands and shales are indicated by more continuous reflectors, extending outwards to the shelf break, sometimes showing evidence of toplap.

The shelf is traversed by a number of features, most notably the thick delta plain deposits in the Orange Basin. These are indicated by inter-bedded, parallel, semi-continuous and discontinuous, rather high amplitude reflectors, with associated quieter zones. Elsewhere, in the north and central parts of the Namibian offshore, the shelf is cut down into by a number of east–west and northeast–southwest orientated channels. These are probably infilled with coarse-grained clastics along their margins and base (sometimes displaying well-defined progradation units), and finer-grained, parallel-bedded abandonment fill.

Throughout the Namibian offshore, south of the Walvis Ridge, the slope is well defined by rather low angle prograding units, which downlap into the basin and onlap the shelf. Toplap is locally seen. In places the slope is deformed by listric faulting and fault-induced slumped masses.

The net effects of listric faulting and gravity sliding, particularly west of Luderitz and in the Orange Basin, have been to carry shelf sands into a more basinal setting, and to provide potentially good reservoirs in highly rotated fault block structures. The zone of listric faulting was in fact the primary objective of the Kudu 9A-1 well, but it failed to encounter good sand development. The interval penetrated consists predominantly of deep marine shales, claystones and siltstones, with occasional 5 m to 10 m thick sands. In fact the Kudu wells appear to be marginally located for well-developed sands, and this play has not been adequately tested.

The seismic character of basinal facies within the area studied is usually typified by discontinuous, wavy, irregular reflectors, indicating a distal muddy turbidite regime, but more continuous, parallel reflectors with inter-bedded transparent zones occur in the outer part of the Walvis Basin indicating low energy, deep marine shale deposition. The channels which cut through the shelf edge and upper slope usually terminate in toe slope mounds in which seismic reflectors vary from chaotic to contorted to gently prograding. These probably represent turbidite sand build-ups.

North of the Walvis Ridge, correlations are uncertain, but in the Namibe Basin, a sequence has developed to the east in the shelf area between Horizons N (Turonian Unconformity) and G (Oligocene Unconformity) and may represent a period of shelf build-out. To the west of the basement high a succession of Upper Cretaceous–Palaeocene deep water sandstones accumulated.

L–sea floor Megasequence

Structural evolution   The Tertiary Megasequence developed during continued sagging of the passive margine (Fig. 15). North of the Walvis Ridge, Tertiary sections are thick in contrast to the thin syn-rift sequences, whereas south of the Walvis Ridge the Basin & Range and syn-rift successions are extremely thick, and the Tertiary relatively thin. This is further evidence of the long standing effect of the regional shear system that existed in the area of the Walvis Ridge, and the early subsidence of basins to the south.

Stratigraphy   Tertiary depocentres are generally located seawards of those of the Mesozoic, and continue the open marine sedimentation begun in mid-Cretaceous times. The shelf break has also migrated westwards, although in the north, just south of the Walvis Ridge, it is difficult to locate precisely due to the very broad zone of flexure. In the Namibe Basin, it is affected by faulting and canyon cutting which developed during the Oligocene low stand.

Tertiary sediments throughout the Namibian shelf are generally very thin. Their seismic character is mostly transparent, with some high amplitude, continuous reflectors, and occasional zones of discontinuous, slightly wavy reflectors. The general impression given is that the sequence represents rather low energy conditions, with deposition of clays and sands, and occasional thin beds of shelly limestones and extensive erosional episodes by offshore, coast-parallel, marine currents.

Basinal sediments appear to be mostly low energy clays, marked by continuous and semi-continuous parallel reflectors. Mounded build-ups occur in places, particularly west of Luderitz, where reflectors are discontinuous, irregular and wavy, signifying turbidite sands.

Conclusions

The Namibian offshore area was affected by two major phases of tectonism related to the breakup of Gondwanaland.

- Regional extension and rifting was initiated during the Mesozoic, producing a general north–south margin-parallel structural grain, with some east–west-orientated fractures. Four depocentres can be identified within the zone of greatest subsidence (the Central Half-Graben); from south to north these are the Orange, Luderitz, Walvis and Namibe Basins. The Basin & Range, and Syn-rift sequences within these basins are characterized by rotated and eroded fault blocks, and sedimentation was predominantly in a continental environment.
- Following breakup and the onset of drift, structuring is essentially confined to thermal sag and the influence of eustatic sea-level changes is paramount. Individual basins lose their separate identities, and thermal sag sequences have a well-defined subdivision into marine shelf, slope and basinal environmental settings.

Rift phase sequences appear, on regional evidence, to represent broadly regressive cycles where marine sediments deposited in the central and deepest parts of the Central Half-Graben were progressively overlain by westerly advancing deltaic and continental facies. Well-defined unconformities separate the sequences, and tensional, rotated fault blocks are often truncated. All evidence points to a tectonic control of sedimentation and facies distribution during the rifting phase of the Namibian offshore region.

Towards the end of the Transitional Sequence, almost all of the offshore area was subject to marine sedimentation. Thermal Sag sequences have a reasonably well-defined subdivision into shelf, slope and basinal environments, and it is evident that control for the transgressive/regressive cyclicity is almost entirely due to changes in eustatic sea-level.

The integration of regional geology with seismic–stratigraphical studies suggests that reservoirs, source and seal are expected to occur in most of the megasequences recognized. Aeolian and fluvial reservoirs dominate the pre-breakup sequence, but shallow marine and turbidite sandstone reservoirs are developed in the N to P interval. The most prospective reservoirs found in the P–L sequence are likely to be related to deltaic sequences and progradational shelf units, with turbidites developing locally at the base of the continental slope.

Oil- and gas-prone shales of Permian age exist, and marine shales occur in post-Horizon T sequences. Oil has been discovered in the graben province to the east of the Orange Basin and, although the central Orange Basin appears to be gas prone, some of the source rocks in the other offshore basins fall within the zone of oil generation.

Shale seals exist below Horizon Q, and within the Transitional Megasequence between Horizons Q and P. They occur extensively within the Aptian.

The structural and stratigraphical model predicts a variety of plays, most having a favourable juxtaposition of reservoir, source and seal, but with variable degrees of risk. This integrated study suggests that there is excellent potential for giant hydrocarbon accumulations offshore Namibia. Unequivocal evidence supporting its prospectivity are the discoveries at Kudu, and other fields in the Orange Basin. The region has all the ingredients required for the development of a major new hydrocarbon province.

The results discussed in this paper are part of an Intera HGS regional survey commissioned by NAMCOR. The authors are indebted to Ian Horn and Ken Davidson for use of their interpretations and useful discussions. Seismic data were processed by HGS, Bedford, England. Gravity and Magnetic data were processed and interpreted using LCT Software.

References

BRUHN, R. L., STERN, C. R. & DEWIT, M. J. 1978. Field and geochemical data bearing on the development of a Mesozoic volcano-tectonic rift zone and back-arc basin in southernmost South America. *Earth and Planetary Science Letters*, **41**, 32–46.
DALZIEL, I. W. D. 1980. Comments and reply on Mesozoic evolution of the Antarctic Peninsula and Southern Andes. *Geology*, **8** (6), 260–262.
DINGLE, R. V., SIESSER, W. G. & NEWTON, A. R. 1983. *Mesozoic and Tertiary Geology of Southern Africa.* A. A. Balkema, Rotterdam, 1–231.
FITZGERALD, M. G., MITCHUM, R. M., ULIANA, M. A. & BIDDLE, K. T. 1990. Evolution of the San Jorge Basin Argentina. *American Association of Petroleum Geologists Bulletin*, **74** (6), 879–920.
FRANCHETEAU, J. & LE PICHON, X. 1972. Marginal fracture zones as structural framework of continental margins in South Atlantic Ocean. *American Association of Petroleum Geologists Bulletin*, **56**, 991–1007.
GERRARD, I. & SMITH, G. C. 1982. Post Palaeozoic succession and structure of the southwestern African continental margin. *In*: WATKINS, J. S. & DRAKE, C. L. (eds) *Studies in Continental Margin Geology.* American Association of Petroleum Geologists Memoir **34**, 49–74.
GUST, D. A., BIDDLE, K. T., PHELPS, D. W. & ULIANA, M. A. 1985. Associated Middle to Late Jurassic volcanism and extension in southern South America. *Tectonophysics.* **116**, 223–253.
HAQ, B. U., HARDENBOL, J. & VAIL, P. R. 1987. Chronology of fluctuating sea levels since the Triassic (250 million years ago to present). *Science*, **235**, 1156–1167.
HORSTHEMKE, S., LEDENDECKER, S. & PORADA, H. 1990. Depositional environments and stratigraphic correlations of the Karoo sequence in North Western Damaraland. *Communications of the Geologial Survey of Namibia*, **6**, 63–73.
INTERA, (formerly ECL) REPORT. 1990. *The Petroleum Potential of Offshore Namibia.* Non-exclusive report, Intera ECL Petroleum Technologies, Oxon.

KENT, L. E. 1980. *Stratigraphy of South Africa*. Geological Survey of South Africa, Handbook 8.

LARSON, R. L. & PITMAN, W. C. 1972. World-wide correlation of Mesozoic magnetic anomalies and its implications. *Geological Society of America Bulletin*, **83**, 3645–3662.

LAWRENCE, S. R. 1989. Prospects for petroleum in Late Proterozoic/Early Palaeozoic basins of southern central Africa. *Journal of Petroleum Geology* **12** (2), 231–242.

LIGHT, M. P. R., MASLANYJ, M. P. & BANKS, N. L. New geophysical evidence for extensional tectonics on the divergent margin offshore Namibia. *In*: STOREY, B. C., ALABASTER, T. AND PANKHURST, R. J. (eds) *Magmatism and the Causes of Continental Break-up*, Geological Society, London, Special Publication (in press).

MCLACHLAN, I. R. & MCMILLAN, I. K. 1979. Microfaunal biostratigraphy, chronostratigraphy and history of Mesozoic and Cenozoic deposits on the coastal margin of South Africa. *In*: VAN BILJON, W. J. & ANDERSON, A. M. (eds) *Geokongress '77*, Geological Society of South Africa Special Publication **6**, 161–181.

MARTIN, H. 1973. The Atlantic margin of southern Africa between Latitudes 17° South and the Cape of Good Hope. *In*: NAIRN, A. E. M. & STEHLI, F. G. (eds) *The Ocean Basins and Margins 1. The South Atlantic*, Plenum, New York, 277–300.

—— 1976. A geodynamic model for the evolution of the continental margin of southwestern Africa. *Anais da Academia Brasileira de Ciencias*. **48**, 169–177.

SCHOMMARZ, R. E. 1988. *The coal potential of the Toscannini area. Skeleton Coast Park*. Geological Survey of Namibia—Economic Mineral Report.

UNTERNEHR, P., CURIE, D., OLIVET, J. L. & BEUZART, P. 1988. South Atlantic fits and intraplate boundaries in Africa and South America. *Tectonophysics*, **155**, 169–179.

URIEN, C. M., ZAMBRANO, J. J. & MARTINS, L. R. 1981. The basins of southeastern and eastern Argentina including the Atlantic paleogeographic evolution. *In*: *Comite Sudamericano Del Jurassico Y Cretacico: Cuencas Sedimentarias Del Jurassico Y Cretacico De America Del Sur S.L.*, S.C.P.I., 45–125.

VAIL, P. R., MITCHUM, M., TODD, R. G., WIDMIER, J. M., THOMPSON, S., SANGREE, J. B., BUBB, J. N. & HATLELID, W. G. 1977. Seismic stratigraphy and global changes of sea level. *In*: PAYTON, C. E. (ed.) *Seismic stratigraphy—applications to hydrocarbon exploration*. American Association of Petroleum Geologists Memoir **26**, 49–212.

WERNICKE, B. 1981. Low-angle normal faults in the Basin and Range Province; nappe tectonics in an extending orogen. *Nature*, **291**, 645–648.

—— 1985. Uniform-sense normal simple shear of the continental lithosphere. *Canadian Journal of Earth Sciences* **22**, 108–125.

WINDHAUSEN, A. 1924. Lineas generales de la constitucion geologica de la region situada al oeste del Golfo de San Jorge. *Academia Nacional de Ciencias Boletin*, **27**, 167–320.

From WILLIAMS, G. D. & DOBB, A. (eds), 1993, *Tectonics and Seismic Sequence Stratigraphy*.
Geological Society Special Publication No. 71, 193–219.

Relationships between thrust tectonics and sequence stratigraphy surfaces in foredeeps: model and examples from the Pyrenees (Cretaceous–Eocene, France, Spain)

Joachim Deramond,[1] Pierre Souquet,[2] Marie-José Fondecave-Wallez[3] and Martin Specht[4]

[1] *Laboratoire de Géologie structurale et Tectonophysique, Université Paul Sabatier, 38, Rue des Trente-Six Ponts, 31400 Toulouse, France.*
[2] *Laboratoire de Géologie sédimentaire et Paléontologie, URA CNRS 1405, Université Paul-Sabatier, 39, Allées Jules Guesde, 31062 Toulouse Cedex, France.*
[3] *Laboratoire de Géologie et Géochronologie, Université Paul Sabatier, 39, Allées Jules Guesde, 31062 Toulouse Cedex, France.*
[4] *Institut Français du Pétrole, BP 311, 1–4, Rue du Bois-Préau, 92506 Rueil-Malmaison, France.*

Abstract: A new method of chronological and geometrical analysis is used for understanding the sedimentary and tectonic evolution of perisutural basins (foredeep and foreland basins). It may be applied to synorogenic basins whose infilling was controlled by sea-level fluctuations and where, as a result, the tectonic structures are well preserved. This method is based on the mapping of depositional sequence boundaries and maximum flooding surfaces defined by sequence stratigraphy. These planar markers are considered as synchronous and their numerical ages are determined by classical chronostratigraphic methods, by dating and by comparison with the eustatic global cycle chart.

The evolution of the studied perisutural basins is controlled by the propagation in space and time of a syn-depositional thrust-and-fold system including a fault-propagation anticline and two synclines (a foreland and a hinterland syncline) over and in front of a blind basal sole thrust. The propagation of this thrust-and-fold system toward the foreland is connected to unconformable depositional sequence sets, which indicate for each system a time span for thrusting of several eustatic cycles.

The evolution of a single thrust-and-fold system corresponds to a shortening accommodated by upward imbrication of second-order thrusts inside the anticline. Each of these thrusts is related, at least, to one depositional sequence lying unconformably on the external side of the fold and deformed by the successive development of the branch lines toward the hinterland. This tectono-sedimentary correlation indicates a time span sometimes as short as one eustatic cycle for each second-order thrust.

Thrusting and sea-level changes are not exactly synchronous, as the depositional sequence sets (which are tectonic in origin) do not systematically correlate with eustatic supercycles. The apparent time correlation between the two groups of independent phenomena is an artefact of the method which calibrates the tectonic evolution by comparison with eustatic fluctuations.

Applied to the South Central Pyrenees, the method has specified the structure of the Late Cretaceous foredeep basin and has revealed the successive stages of forward thrust-and-fold system migration (4 to 5 Ma for each one from 89 Ma) and of hindward second-order thrust migration (1 to 4 Ma for each one).

In the North Central Pyrenees as in the South Central Pyrenees, Late Cretaceous foredeeps are characterized by syntectonic turbidite deposits (from 89 Ma onward) and by a significant shortening due to a symmetrical and synchronous structural evolution. The Eocene foreland is a foreland syncline developed in the footwall of the North Pyrenean Thrust. This syncline is due to the occurrence of blind thrusts and it is infilled by fluvial deposits.

The practice of sequence stratigraphy in mobile belts (Pyrenees: Fondecave-Wallez *et al.* 1988; 1989; Fondecave-Wallez & Souquet 1991; Souquet & Déramond 1989; Rif: Ben Yaich *et al.* 1989) allows us to make use of a new method (Specht *et al.* 1991) for analysing the relationships between tectonics and sedimentation in foredeep and foreland basins. This method is a combination of sequence stratigraphy (Vail *et al.* 1977; Vail 1987)—which characterizes numerically dated synchronous surfaces—and thrust tectonics (Boyer & Elliott 1982; Suppe 1983)—which uses these surfaces as deformation markers. Thus it becomes possible to determine the age, the duration and the velocity of the sedimentary and tectonic processes. The method is based on a tectono-sedimentary model, constructed from outcrop and well-log data, which is explained and illustrated as a basis for interpretation of perisutural basins from the Pyrenees.

Model of synsedimentary thrust-and-fold systems

Model description

Perisutural basins (Bally & Snelson 1980) are created by tectonic shortening, and thrust propagation determines the migration of the maximum subsidence areas. This evolution generates intrabasinal structures which are organized in a synsedimentary thrust-and-fold system (Fig. 1) including: (1) an uplifting fault propagation anticline; (2) two synclines (a foreland and a hinterland syncline), which represent sub-basins and where tectonic and eustatic processes combine to cause relative changes of sea-level and then to control the accommodation space.

According to our observations, the synsedimentary synclines and particularly the foreland syncline, which is the special topic of this paper, show two transverse depositional systems: a synorogenic system overlying with unconformity ('progressive unconformity'; Riba 1976) the active part of the fault propagation anticline (with immature gravity flow deposits) and a backstepping system on the opposite flank of the syncline (with dominant platform facies on the cratonic margin of the basin). A longitudinal system distributes mature foreland-derived sediments and remobilized synorogenic deposits.

In perisutural basins the relationships (Fig. 1A) between tectonics and sedimentation can be examined at two scales:

- at the basin scale: relationships between synsedimentary thrust-and-fold systems and depositional sequence sets (migration of foreland sub-basins);
- at the thrust-and-fold system scale: relationships between thrust branches and depositional sequences (infilling of sub-basins).

Use and limitations of the model

Tectono-sedimentary structures similar to the model are preserved in areas where the space available for sediments is created by flexural loading and by eustatic rise and

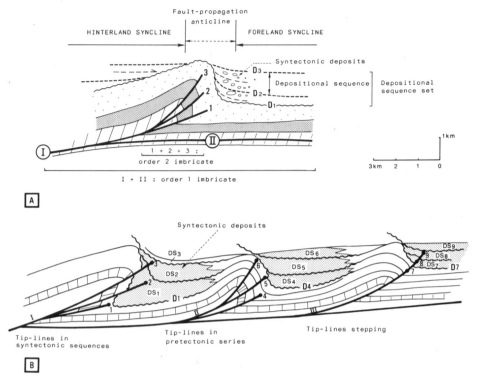

Fig. 1. The synsedimentary thrust-and-fold system. (**A**) The model. I–II: major thrusts forming first-order imbricates; 1, 2, 3: second-order imbricates. The foreland and the hinterland synclines are filled by a sequence set in relation with the main thrust motion. The D1, D2, D3 unconformities relate to second-order thrust motion. (**B**) Thrust-and-fold propagation at the basin scale. Different patterns of anticline growth: tip-lines in syn-tectonic sequences as observed in the North Pyrenean Late Cretaceous foredeep; tip-lines in pre-tectonic series as observed in the South Pyrenean Late Cretaceous foredeep (San Corneli anticline); tip-line stepping as observed in the North Pyrenean Eocene foreland (North Pyrenean Frontal thrust).

fall of sea-level (without eustatic fluctuations, the uplift structures are destroyed by erosion or incompletely protected by a continental sedimentary cover). Thus, the field of application of the method corresponds to marine or exorheic basins in which sequence stratigraphy allows identification and mapping of depositional sequences (DS), depositional sequence sets (DSs), systems tracts and synchronous surfaces.

In such foreland sub-basins, the problem is to determine if the unconformities, which are the sequence boundaries, are generated or enhanced by tectonic events. On the active flank of the foreland syncline, the sequences and the unconformities show increasing dips both with depth and proximity to the anticline. This provides evidence that the anticline grows during the infilling of the syncline with an uplift rate equal to or greater than the sedimentation rate. In the passive setting of the sub-basin, where the sequence boundaries are conformable, it becomes possible to compare the thrust propagation rate with the eustatic cycles recorded there without tectonic influence.

Sequence boundary mapping shows a physical continuity between the deformed unconformities (step or reverse erosional surfaces) observed on the anticline and the disconformities or correlative conformities identified in the syncline. In this basin setting, these surfaces are dated at their minimum hiatus and time-correlated with eustatic sea-level falls shown in the global curve by Haq *et al.* (1987). This is illustrated in Figs 4, 5 and 6A (sequence boundaries dated at 80, 79, 77.5, 75 Ma in the Las Vilas foreland syncline) and in Figs 4, 6B and 7 (sequence boundaries dated at 75, 71 68 Ma at the western termination of the San Corneli Fault propagation anticline).

These correlations result from ages determined with an accurate chronostratigraphic resolution by means of (1) biostratigraphic zonations (planktonic foraminifera); (2) numerical ages given by grade-dating. This method (Gourinard 1983) is based on the chronometric calibration of a lineage evolution thanks to a biometric index variation and datum-planes (K/Ar ages or well-dated palaeontological events). The chronometric tool used in this study is the evolution curve of *Rosita fornicata* lineage (Fondecave-Wallez *et al.* 1989, 1990) through Senonian times (between 89 and 66 Ma). This technique can differentiate ages to a resolution of 0.2 Ma.

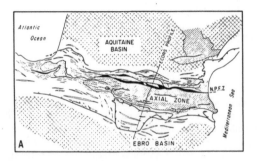

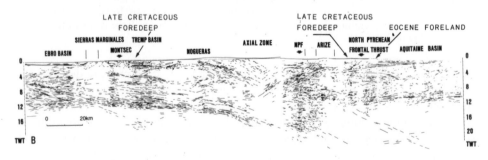

Fig. 2. Location of studied examples on the ECORS–Pyrenees seismic section. (**A**) Location of the profile. (**B**) Line drawing and location of the North and South Pyrenean Late Cretaceous foredeeps, and of the North Pyrenean Eocene foreland. (From ECORS-TEAM 1990).

Illustration of the model

Illustrative examples are given from the two sides of the Central Pyrenees along the ECORS profile (Fig. 2):

- from the South Pyrenean Late Cretaceous foredeep where the model was developed;
- from the North Pyrenean Late Cretaceous foredeep and Eocene foreland where the model is used to explain complex tectono-sedimentary structures.

Application to the Central Southern Pyrenees

The example described is the newly recognized (Puigdefabregas & Souquet 1986; Souquet & Déramond 1989) Late Cretaceous foredeep basin where the method has revealed four stages of synsedimentary thrust-system migration.

The Late Cretaceous foredeep

Geological framework   The Late Cretaceous thrust-fold belt (Fig. 3) is involved in an Eocene thrust sheet (Central South Pyrenean Unit (Séguret 1972) which overrides a wedge of Eocene strata (Specht 1989) and moved to the south above the A-subduction surface of the Iberian plate (Fig. 2; ECORS team 1990). The recognition of this allochthonous foredeep has demonstrated that the tectono-sedimentary evolution of the Southern Pyrenees was controlled by a south-verging piggy-back thrust sequence beginning at Early Coniacian times (89 Ma).

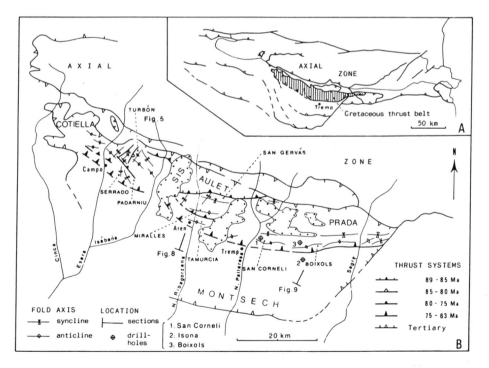

Fig. 3. The South Pyrenean Late Cretaceous foredeep (Spain). (**A**) Location. (**B**) Map of the thrust-and-fold systems.

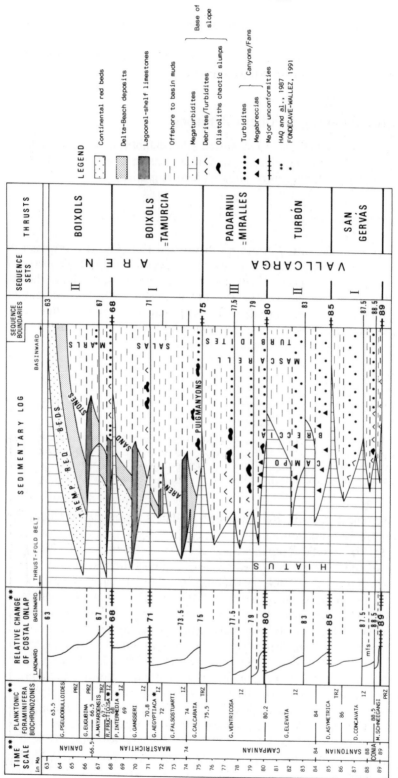

Fig. 4. Integrated tectono-stratigraphic records of the Late Cretaceous foredeep in the South Central Pyrenees (between Esera and Noguera Pallaresa valleys, Spain).

Sequence stratigraphy (Fig. 4). **Vallcarga sequence sets**:   This unit is a group of eight depositional sequences identified in turbidite series (Campo Breccia, Mascarell Turbidites: Mey *et al.* 1968) and time-correlated with the eustatic global cycle chart (Haq *et al.* 1987) between 89 and 75 Ma (Fondecave-Wallez *et al.* 1989).

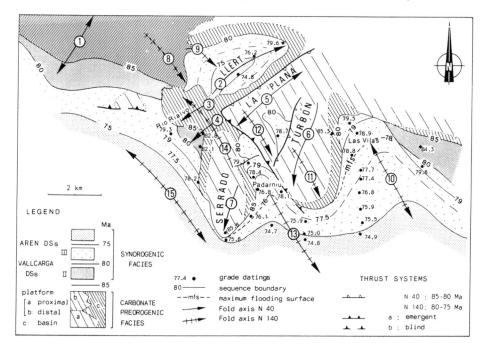

Fig. 5. Map of interference structures and of depositional sequences in the Turbón area (Spain). See location on Fig. 3. 1–15: fold numbers. One thrust-and-fold system begins at 85 Ma with progressive unconformities in the 1, 2, 4 syn-depositional synclines; the other begins at 80 Ma with progressive unconformities in the 10, 13, 15 synclines.

Due to syn-tectonic deposition, the sequence boundaires are submarine truncation surfaces (Vail's type 1 unconformities) easily mappable (Fig. 5) below large turbidite or debrite bodies. The lowstand systems tracts show (Fig. 6A) thick slope fans with two interfering systems: carbonate slope aprons (slumps, olistoliths, breccia sheets, mudstones); terrigenous canyon fills or channel-lobe fans driven by syncline axes (turbiditic sandstones or sandy-biocalcarenites with facies B, C, D and E from Mutti & Ricchi Lucchi (1972), carbonate debrites or debrite-turbidite couplets (Souquet *et al.* 1987) mudstones). There are no basin fans, probably because of the inversion of the basin and the erosion of its deeper part. There are no thick turbidite bodies or neritic facies that can be linked to prograding wedges, which indicates a relatively low sediment supply. The highstand systems tracts are predominantly mudstones.

Three main unconformities dated at 89, 85 and 80 Ma separate three sequence sets (numbered I, II, III) which are located (Figs 4, 5) in different synclines and onlap syn-depositional anticline highs. Vallcarga I DSs (89 to 85 Ma) is restricted to the incipient basin (central northern area around the Noguera Ribagorzana valley) where three DS are shown against a steep slope onlapped by debrites (DS 89, DS 88.5), then carbonate Bouma turbidites (DS 87.5). Vallcarga II (85 to 80 Ma) fills

200   J. DERAMOND *ET AL.*

several transverse depo-axes, in syncline canyons (DS 85, DS83: Campo Breccia in
Esera valley, West Turbón), in channel-lobe fans (DS 83, Isábeña valley, East
Turbón) and at the base of slopes (Noguera Ribagorzana, Noguera Pallaresa
valleys). Vallarcaga III (80 to 75 Ma) extends along the basin showing slope facies
(Esera valley), channellized deposits (Isábeña valley), and basin to slope facies
(Noguera Ribagorzana, Noguera Pallaresa valleys).

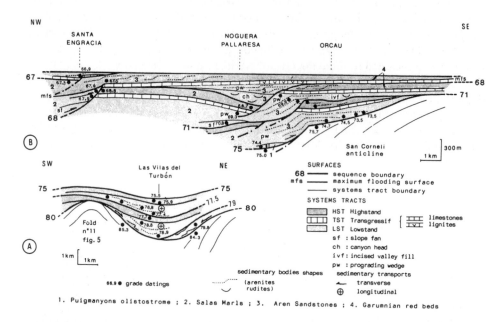

Fig. 6. Models of syn-tectonic depositional sequences and sequence sets (DSs). (A) In the
turbiditic Vallcarga III DSs (80 to 75 Ma) from a cross-section through the las Vilas del
Turbón syncline (number 10 in Fig. 5). (B) In the Aren DSs (75 to 63 Ma) from a longitudinal
section of the Tremp syncline, western termination of the San Corneli anticline (see Fig. 7),
Modified from Fondecave-Wallez *et al.* (1988).

Aren sequence sets: This unit includes four depositional sequences which have been
identified (Fondecave-Wallez *et al.* 1988) in the Latest Campanian to Danian
formations (Puigmanyons Olistostrome, Mascarell Turbidites, Salas Marls, Aren
Sandstones, Garumnian red beds from the Tremp Formation (Mey *et al.* 1968)) and
which have been time-correlated with the global cycle chart between 75 and 63 Ma.
The stratigraphic surfaces have been mapped (Fig. 7) using criteria of subaerial
erosion or submarine tectonic truncation (enhanced unconformities) and criteria of
hard-ground or bioturbation (maximum flooding surfaces). They cross the formations and are involved in the synsedimentary compressional structures of the San
Corneli anticline and the Boixols thrust. The systems tract organization is visible
along a cross-section parallel to the foreland axis (Fig. 6B), which reveals a
prograding margin with listric normal faulting propagating basinward.

The slope fans are mud-rich and characterized by slope apron debrites (DS 75:
Puigmanyons Olistostrome), slumps (DS 71: Salas Marls, N. Pallaresa valley) and
channellized turbidites (DS 75, DS 68, Mascarell Turbidites, Isábeña valley). The

lowstand prograding wedges are predominantly offshore blue-grey marls associated with aggradationally offlapping bioclastic limestone (DS 75, DS 67, Aren Sandstones) or shoreline sandstones (DS 71, Aren Sandstones) or Gilbert delta to estuarine sandstones (DS 68, Aren Sandstones). The transgressive systems tracts are carbonates consisting of biogenic limestones with orbitoides, rudistids or chara (DS 75, DS 71, DS 67) or of lime storm deposits to mollusc coquina with lignites (DS 68). The highstand systems tracts correspond to hemipelagic mudstones (Salas Marls) in the open basin, associated with various depositional systems characterized in Aren Sandstones: sigmoidal offlapping offshore bioclastic bars (DS 75) and oblique beach complexes (DS 71, DS 68, DS 67). Sediment gravity flow deposits derived from the shelf are also included in these open-shelf mudstones near the major unconformities. They can be interpreted as shelf-perched lowstand deposits due to tectonic uplift and slope failure (see the unconformity of 71 Ma in Fig. 4).

A major unconformity associated with a thick slope fan dated at 68 Ma divides the Aren unit into two sequence sets (Aren I and II). Their tectonic origin is suggested by the recognition of folds and cleavage megaclasts of Maastrichtian age and of distal ramp facies.

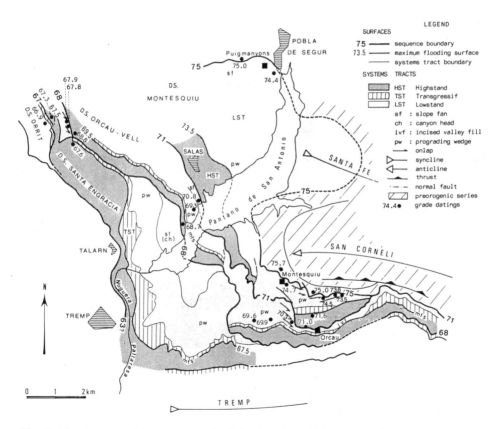

Fig. 7. Sketch map of the western end of the San Corneli anticline (Spain) see location on Fig. 3. This anticline is bounded northward by the Tremp syn-depositional foreland syncline. The isochrons (sequence boundaries, maximum flooding surfaces) have a strong dip on the external flank of the anticline due to the second-order thrust propagation.

Synsedimentary tectonics. Migration of the thrust and fold system in time and space is best illustrated in the central part of the basin (Noguera Ribagorzana valley) by a sequence of south-vergent thrust systems ordered from North to South: San Gervas, Miralles, Tamurcia (Figs 3, 8). E–W-trending exposed anticlines have been related to blind thrusts (Garrido 1973; Simó 1985) and later to blind imbricate fans in a geometrically constrained restoration (Laborderie *in* Souquet & Déramond 1989). The successive foreland synclines show basal unconformities enhanced above rotated and eroded strata and syn-tectonic depositional sequence sets becoming younger southwards (Fig. 8).

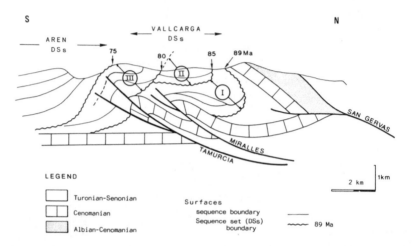

Fig. 8. First-order imbricates and associated depositional sequence sets in the central part of the South Pyrenean foredeep (section of the Noguera Ribagorzana valley, location on Fig. 3).

The San Gervas foreland syncline is filled by the Vallcarga I DSs related to a cycle from 89–85 Ma. The Miralles synclinal infill corresponds to the Vallcarga III cycle from 80–75 Ma. The Tamurcia synclinal infill corresponds to the Aren cycle from 75–63 Ma. There are locally transverse structures (approximately N–S) connected with the Vallcarga II cycle from 85–80 Ma. Similar anomalous features develop in the Western part of the basin where they are well exposed (Turbón).

The Boixols thrust and the associated San Corneli anticline is the best example of thrust system evolution in the eastern part of the basin. The structural features have been established by Specht (1989) and Specht *et al.* (1991) and from sub-surface data (San Corneli, Boixols, Isona drill holes; ECORS seismic profile).

Geometry of the structure (Fig. 9): From the surface data, the San Corneli fold appears as an EW anticline in which the external SE limb is cut by a high-angle reverse fault showing a small offset (Late Cretaceous in the hangingwall and in the footwall). The deformed strata have been eroded and unconformably overlain by the Aren sequence sets beginning at 75 Ma. The San Corneli well data show a thrust system characterized in depth by: (1) larger displacement than that at surface (Triassic evaporites over overturned Jurassic strata); (2) overturned strata in the footwall (Jurassic to Late Cretaceous formations with a northward 65° dip.). The Isona well-log shows horizontal strata in a Jurassic to Late Cretaceous concordant section. The Late Cretaceous sequences, which belong to the syn-tectonic Aren DSs, fill a foreland syncline and onlap the exposed external limb of the San Corneli anticline.

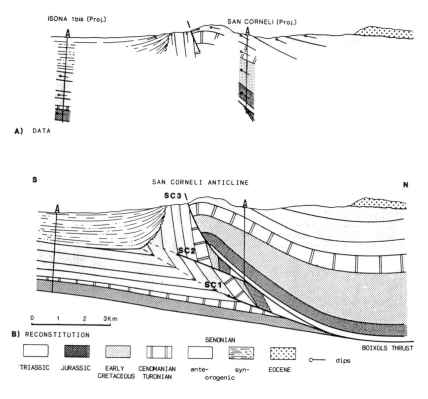

Fig. 9. San Corneli anticline interpreted from the data (**A**) as a fault propagation fold (**B**); see location on Fig. 3.

Tectonic interpretation of the structure: fault propagation anticline. The interpretation of the complete structure suggests the occurrence at depth of one or more thrust surfaces. The generally accepted hypothesis of only one thrust surface, with a weak displacement involves a large volume of Trias in the footwall; but, the occurrence of inverted strata is not explained and the observed displacement in drill-holes is not balanced by the measured displacement at surface. Thus, the interpretation of the San Corneli anticline as a simple décollement anticline on the Triassic evaporites or as a fault bend fold must be rejected. A better interpretation is that the structure is a fault propagation fold (Suppe 1983), characteristic of reducing thrust displacement.

The effect of displacement decrease is the rotation of the strata in the hangingwall of the blind thrust. When the rotation of the overturned limb becomes mechanically impossible, a new thrust surface develops in the hangingwall anticline. This surface is directed by the fold structure and it develops preferentially along the fold axial plane (Jamison 1987). Each new thrust surface develops in the hangingwall, resulting in overstep sequence of the thrust imbricate fan.

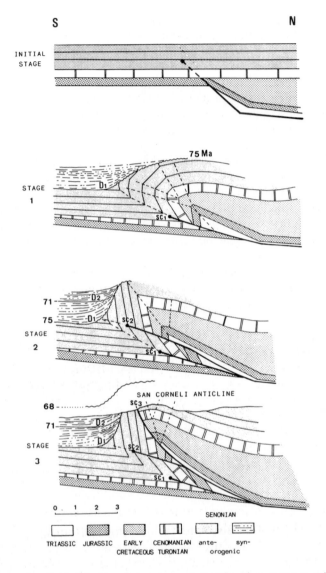

Fig. 10. Example of relationships between second-order thrust propagation, depositional sequences and tectonically enhanced unconformities in the San Corneli anticline.

Relationships between thrust propagation and sedimentation. The foreland syncline of the Boixols thrust is filled by the Aren DSs (75 to 63 Ma) which include (Figs 6 & 7) four depositional sequences (DS 75, Montesquiu; DS 71, Orcau-Vell; DS 68, Santa Engracia; DS 67, Orrit) characterized by type 1 basal unconformities. The relationship between this depositional sequence and the overstep thrust propagation is explained as follows (Fig. 10).

(1) Décollement propagation on the Triassic evaporites reactivates normal palaeofault. A fault propagation anticline grows and undergoes erosion

enhanced by a rapid eustatic fall (75 Ma). The lowstand systems tracts are preserved under aggrading strata; the erosional surface marking the boundary between the syn-tectonic and the pre-tectonic sequences. This contact (D1) is an onlap surface in the southern limb of the anticline. Southwards, the strata become concordant in the centre of the foreland syncline.

The fault propagation anticline continued to grow and the external limb became steeper generating the rotation of the D1 angular unconformity associated with erosional truncation of the underlying strata and correlative syn-orogenic deposits.

(2) When the displacement reached its maximum along the thrust surface, a new thrust branch initiated and propagated in the fold axial plane (Jamison 1987). This thrust is blind with a high propagation rate. This induced the formation of a new erosional surface at the top of the previous syn-tectonic sequence. This new erosional surface (D2) becomes basinward a disconformity which is dated at 71 Ma (Fig. 7) and is onlapped by the lowstand systems tracts of the depositional sequence DS 71, Orcau-Vell.

(3) A new thrust branch was initiated in the eastern culmination of the San Corneli anticline, where it was unconformably overlain by non-marine red beds attributable to DS 68, Santa Engracia.

The San Corneli anticline–Boixols thrust system illustrates how each of the first-order thrusts with a piggy-back motion developed into second-order overstep branches which controlled the uplift of the anticline. The first-order thrusting generated the basal foreland syncline unconformity (depositional sequence set scale) and the second-order thrusting controlled the tectonic enhancement of the internal foreland unconformities (depositional sequence scale). In the foredeep sequences the systems tract organization can be chronostratigraphically consistent with the global sea-level fluctuations although the thrust tectonics have the greatest influence on increasing or reducing accommodation space.

Interference pattern between two synsedimentary thrust-and-fold systems: the Turbón area. Some fold interference patterns are known in the western part of the south Pyrenean foredeep (Turbón area) due to the superimposition of a transverse thrust-and-fold system (N40 trend) on a N140-trending system (Papon 1969; Souquet & Déramond 1989). The Mesozoic series is deformed in 'domes and basins' (Ramsay 1967) by the superimposition of two syn-depositional fold-and-thrust systems. The first, contemporaneous with the Vallcarga II sequence set (85 to 80 Ma), fills the N40 foreland synclines (1, 2, 4 on Fig. 5) and the second, contemporaneous with the Vallcarga III sequence set (80 to 75 Ma), fills the N140 foreland synclines (10, 13, 15 on Fig. 5). 'Dome and basin' structures also occur in the central part of the basin due to the superimposition of NS and of EW fold-and-thrust systems but with the same chronological and geometrical relationships between deposition and deformation. The transverse structures are probably influenced by palaeoslopes and/or inherited faults.

Application to the Central Northern Pyrenees

The examples illustrated (Figs 2 & 11) are: the Late Cretaceous foredeep basin newly identified north of the Saint Barthélémy/Arize basement blocks, in the Nalzen

J. DERAMOND *ET AL.*

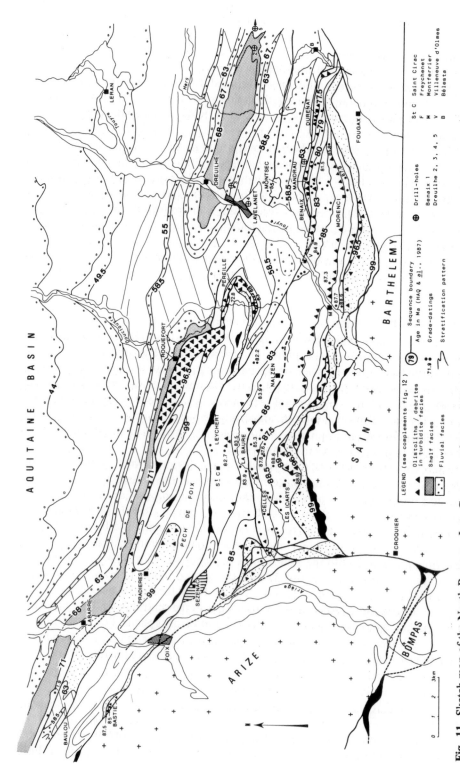

Fig. 11. Sketch map of the North Pyrenean Late Cretaceous foredeep (Nalzen basin south of the Pech de Foix pop-up) and Eocene foreland (north of the Pech de Foix pop-up) (France). See location on Fig. 2. This map shows thrust-and-fold structures, sequence stratigraphy surfaces, synorogenic facies and grade-dated points. The reconstructed blind structures are represented on the cross-sections of Fig. 12.

syncline and the Pech de Foix pop-up (North Pyrenean Zone); and the Eocene foreland basin known in the Dreuilhe and Roquefort anticlines (Sub-Pyrenean Zone) on the border of the Aquitaine Basin. In this region the sedimentary cover is detached on Triassic evaporites and the pre-foredeep series outcrop in the overturned south limb of the Nalzen syncline and in the core of the Pech de Foix pop-up (Fig. 11). These series include Jurassic carbonates (platform facies), Early Cretaceous bauxites, shelfal Urgonian limestones, open-shelf mudstones (syn-rift facies) and Albian to earliest Cenomanian turbidites (Flysch Noir: strike-slip trough facies).

The basal foredeep unconformity (89 Ma Coniacian) represents a significant time gap (Cenomanian–Turonian) indicated by the submarine erosion and reworking as olistoliths of hemipelagic mudstones from this time interval (sediment starvation of the early foredeep episode). The foredeep platform facies consists of pre-orogenic and thin carbonate–terrigenous assemblages which show a retrogradation to the north above the Hercynian basement (Benaix & Dreuilhe drill holes, Fig. 12). Syn-tectonic foredeep facies consist of terrigenous wedges, separated by tectonically enhanced unconformities. These outcropping syn-tectonic facies are the main topic of the following discussion which is based on new data in the Cretaceous series and on reinterpretation of published data in the Eocene series.

Late Cretaceous foredeep

Sequence stratigraphy (Fig. 13). **Nalzen depositional sequence sets**: Eight depositional sequences, which constitute the Nalzen DSs, have been identified in the Nalzen syncline and time-correlated with Corniacian to Campanian eustatic cycles (89 to 75 Ma, Haq *et al.* 1987). Sequence boundaries cross the rock units (Foix & Lavelanet, 1/50 000 maps) and are mapped (Fig. 11) below sandy turbidites (St) (DS 89, Les Icarts St; DS 88.5, Celles St; DS 85), below a carbonate key bed (DS 87.5, Morenci megaturbidite) or below units of lime olistoliths (Ol) previously interpreted (Bilotte 1985) as reefy platforms (DS 85; DS 83, Leychert Ol and Villeneuve d'Olmes Ol; DS 80, Benaix Ol; DS 79 Mandrau Ol; DS 77.5, Durenat Ol). The lowstand systems tracts show thick slope fans and evolve from fans to slope aprons in prograding suites. The highstand systems tracts are uniform hemipelagic mudstones.

Three major unconformities, dated 89, 85 and 80 Ma, subdivide the Nalzen unit into three sequence sets which are interpreted as tectonic in origin (Fig. 11): Nalzen I DSs (89 to 85 Ma) which exists throughout the southern limb of the syncline; Nalzen II DSs (85 to 80 Ma) which fills two main depocentres in this southern limb; Nalzen III DSs (80 to 75 Ma) which outcrops only at the eastern end of the syncline below the backthrust of the Pech de Foix pop-up.

Plagne depositional sequence sets: Four depositional sequences, which constitute the Plagne DSs, have been identified in the Sub-Pyrenean Zone (and in the Nalzen syncline: drill-hole Benaix 1, Fig. 12) and time-correlated (Fig. 13) with Latest Campanian to Danian eustatic cycles (75 to 63 Ma; Haq *et al.* 1987).

Their systems tract organization was reconstructed along a 120 km outcrop belt striking basinward in a NW direction parallel to the foredeep axis (Fig. 14). This section reveals that the stratigraphic surfaces cross cut the rock units and that the Plagne DSs fill several depo-axes obliquely cut by the Eocene fold trend. The lowstand systems tracts show proximal slope fan deposits in the oldest sequence (DS 75: Pereille olistoliths, unconformable wedges on the external side of Pech de Foix

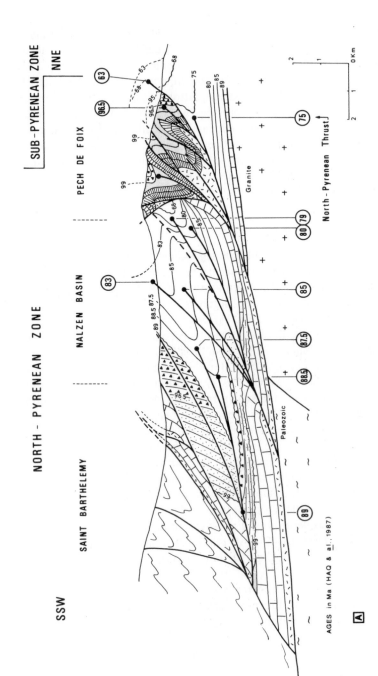

Fig. 12. Synthetic cross-sections through the Central Northern Pyrenees: (**A**) western part of the Nalzen basin and Pech de Foix pop-up; (**B**) eastern part of the Nalzen basin, Pech de Foix pop-up termination, sub-Pyrenean zone and southern border of the Aquitaine basin. These sections show the forward migration of thrust-and-fold systems (tip-lines in the synorogenic series in the Late Cretaceous foredeep and Eocene foreland; tip-line stepping along the main North Pyrenean Frontal Thrust branch). The date of the last motion, indicated by circled numbers, is deduced from the age of the outcropping unconformities (see map, Fig. 11).

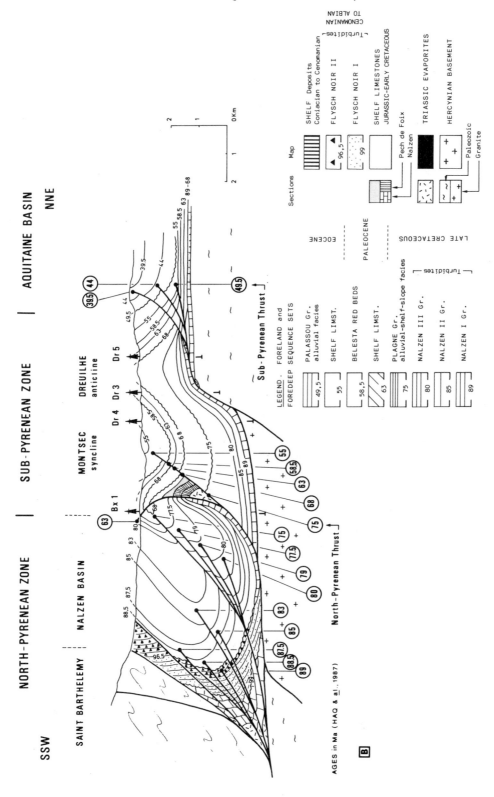

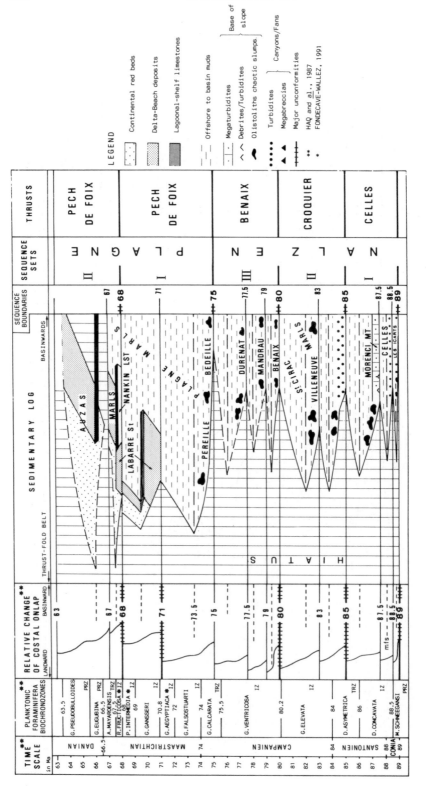

Fig. 13. Integrated tectono-stratigraphy records of the Late Cretaceous foredeep in the North Central Pyrenees (Nalzen syncline and Sub-Pyrenean Zone; Ariège & Haute-Garonne, France).

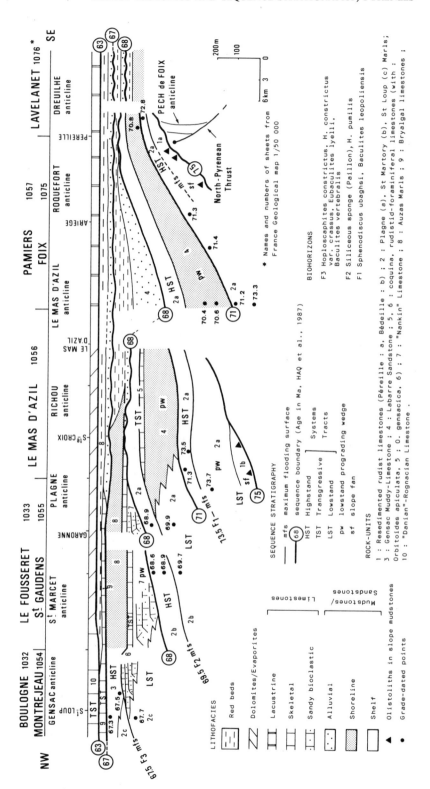

Fig. 14. Depositional sequence and systems tract organization in the North Pyrenean Campanian to Maastrichtian foredeep (Plagne DSs, 75–68 Ma). This section is parallel to the axis of the basin and allows dating of the unconformities from the eastern part mapped on Fig. 11.

anticlines, previously interpreted as a reefy platform) and thick prograding complexes in DS 71: Labarre sandstones and DS 68: 'Nankin' Limestones. The transgressive systems tracts are calcareous (Fig. 14) and consist of rudist-foraminiferal limestones, with specific orbitoids (DS 71, DS 68), or bryalgal limestones (DS 67). The condensed sections representing the maximum flooding events contain specific ammonoid faunas whose stratigraphic position can be determined by comparison with the ages given in the global chart (Haq *et al.* 1987) for the maximum flooding surfaces (mfs) of the correlative sequences (mfs 73.5 of the DS 75; mfs 69.5 of the DS 71; mfs 67.5 of the DS 68). The highstand systems tracts correspond to offshore mudstones, coastal deposits which are locally preserved (DS 68, lower part of the Auzas Marls) and alluvial deposits becoming younger basinward, to the west from the Dreuilhe anticline and from DS 71 (Garumnian red beds, upper part of the Auzas Marls). This sequential organization differs from the previously published interpretation (Bilotte and Segura 1991) because of the identification of slope fan gravity deposits, sandy-bioclastic lowstand prograding wedges, carbonate transgressive systems tracts (DS 71, DS 68) and ammonoid-bearing condensed sections.

Two main unconformities, dated 75 and 68 Ma, subdivide the Plagne unit into two tectonically controlled sequence sets: Plagne I DSs (75 to 68 Ma) which is present north of the North Pyrenean Frontal Thrust; Plagne II DSs (68 to 63 Ma) which extends farther onto the southern hinterland as the unconformity of Péreille at the eastern end of the Pech de Foix anticlinorium.

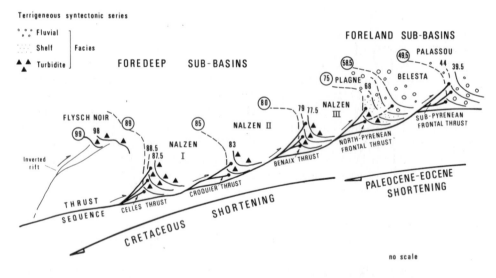

Fig. 15. Migration of the thrust-and-fold systems and of depositional sequence sets in the Northern Central Pyrenees. A significant Cretaceous shortening is deduced from the age of the different successive foredeep sub-basins. The circled numbers refer to the age of internal foredeep unconformities.

Synsedimentary tectonics. In the Nalzen syncline (Fig. 11) the strata are, in general, overturned with an increasing dip from the south to the north (Fig. 11). This relationship is apparent in the field (Foix & Lavelanet, 1/50 000 geological maps) and is known by drilling (Benaix). Progressive unconformities are also visible. The geometric restoration of the depositional sequences led us to reconstruct the thrust systems which have controlled the basin evolution. The southernmost thrusts are known as the St Barthélémy thrust system in which the Hercynian basement (north Pyrenean massif of St Barthélémy) overrides the Mesozoic pre-tectonic series of the basin. This thrust is now interpreted as the roof thrust of an overturned duplex. The intrabasinal thrust surfaces are often discrete but geometrical considerations give rise to an interpretation of the tectonic structures as fault propagation folds connected with thrust surfaces dying out in syn-tectonic deposits. Three main blind piggy-back thrust systems can be related to the three main unconformities identified as sequence set boundaries. The Celles thrust system, with a NS transport, deforms the syn-tectonic Nalzen I DSs (89–85 Ma) and is sealed by the next sequence set. The Croquier thrust system (Fig. 11), with a transcurrent component yields structures that trend mainly NNW–SSE, and these affect the syn-tectonic Nalzen II DSs (85–80 Ma). The Benaix thrust system, with a NS transport, affects the syn-tectonic Nalzen III DSs (80–75 Ma). In each thrust system, second-order thrust branches, with an overstep propagation sequence, are sealed by depositional sequences. One of the more important effects of the thrusting is the enhancement of all the sequence boundaries. The superposition of the three first-order thrust systems, propagating northwards, results in a migration of the basin axis connected with a decreasing basin depth (Fig. 15).

Eocene foreland

Sequence stratigraphy (Fig. 16).   Analysis of the neritic to continental foreland series in terms of sequence stratigraphy is given in Fig. 16. The main unconformities are dated by biostratigraphic zonations (foraminifera, ostracoda in shallow-marine facies (Tambareau 1977); molluscs, vertebrates in fluvial facies (Crochet 1989)). Their correlation with the global cycle chart (Haq *et al.* 1987) is inferred from a comparison with major unconformities in the same stratigraphic interval in the western deeper part of the basin (Bachiana 1989). All the depositional sequences are not recognized here due to the difficulty of analysis in shallow-marine to continental facies. The foreland series are subdivided into four sequence sets which are interpreted as tectonic in origin and related to thrust propagation.

Synsedimentary tectonics.   In this foreland basin, two main first-order thrust systems can be recognized (Fig. 12): (1) the older system, reduced to only two branches—the northern major branch (the well-known North Pyrenean Thrust) dips southward; the southern branch (the Pech de Foix backthrust) dips northward and limits the Pech de Foix pop-up. The main thrust surface was first sealed by the Plagne I DSs (65–63 Ma); it extends southward on the Pech de Foix hangingwall, then through the Boulou sequence (63–58.5 Ma), extending more southward, and finally through the Belesta red beds DSs (58.5–55 Ma). This northern thrust branch is post-dated by the Ilerdian complex (55–49.5 Ma) of the Montsec syncline. It does not yield data on the initiation and timing of the southern backthrust branch which cuts the Belesta red beds, suggesting only a post-58.5 Ma motion; (2) the younger thrust system (the Sub Pyrenean Frontal Thrust) controls the stratal pattern of the fluvial Palassou Conglomerates, characterized by southward onlap and northward decrease in dip, indicating three main unconformities (Crochet 1989). The application of our model leads us to the reconstruction of one first-order blind thrust system with two overstep branches.

Concerning the North Pyrenean Thrust (Figs 11 & 12), there is no reason to invoke second-order overstep thrusts except that the southern Pech de Foix backthrust acted only after 58.5 Ma. Sedimentary load and/or low subsidence rates in the foreland syncline explain deformation due to the tip-line stepping (Fig. 1B) between 75 Ma to 55 Ma. The location of deformation along only one surface explains the regional importance of the North Pyrenean Thrust.

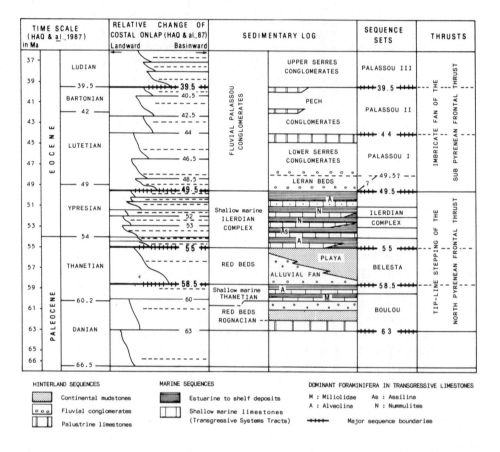

Fig. 16. Integrated tectono-stratigraphic records of the Tertiary foreland in the North Central Pyrenees (Sub-Pyrenean Zone, Ariège & Aude, France).

Conclusion

A link has been established between sequence stratigraphy and tectonics in foredeep or foreland basins where synchronous and dated surfaces are involved in synsedimentary compressive structures. The inferred model of syn-depositional thrust-and-fold systems is developed by an integration of surface and sub-surface data from the Cretaceous–Eocene series of the Pyrenees.

Table 1. Stratigraphic records of the interference of eustatic fluctuations and tectonism at different scales in the Pyrenean foredeep basins (The tectonic evolution, which seems continuous at the basin scale, is the result of changes in duration, rate and location of the tectonic events.)

Duration	Eustasy	Tectonism	Signatures in the stratigraphic record
≥ 50 Ma		Subsidence–flexure loading Imbricate stacking (*thrust-&-fold belt scale*)	Regional foredeep basin (*Tectonic belt scale*)
≥ 5 Ma	Supercycles (Second order[1]) (*Global scale*)	Fault-propagation anticline and foreland syncline (*Regional scale*)	Sub-basin filled by sequence sets[2] bounded by major enhanced unconformities (*Regional scale*)
5 to 0.5 Ma	Sequence cycles (Third order[1]) (*Global scale*)	Thrust overstep branches developing inside the fault-propagation anticline (*Local scale*)	Enhanced sequence boundaries Structural truncation and rotation; decreasing upward dips; sharp onlaps; thick lowstands Syn-tectonic facies (*Local scale*)
≤ 0.5 Ma	Paracycles (Fourth order[1]) (*Global scale*)	Normal listric faults[3] Minor folds lowstand deposits (*Local scale*)	Depositional systems—bed sets geometrically controlled by tectonism and bounded by unconformable bedding surfaces Maximum flooding surfaces superimposed on growth fault scarps Shelf-perched lowstand deposits (*Local scale*)

[1] See Haq *et al.* (1987).
[2] Similar to major transgressive–regressive facies cycles (Vail & Eisner 1989).
[3] Described in the Tremp basin (Fig. 6**B**, Fig. 7).

The model (Fig. 1) includes a fault propagation anticline and a foreland (or foredeep) syncline (plus a hinterland syncline not described here) both connected with basal and internal foredeep unconformities recording stratal folding and erosion. These unconformities are tectonically enhanced, but they time-correlate with the eustatic global chart when dated at the minimum hiatus as outlined by Vail's model.

This time-correlation does not express a relation of cause and effect but seems only due to the calibration of continual tectonism by comparison with eustatic fluctuations. The duration of the formation of tectonic structures is measured with respect to eustatic variations (Table 1): migration of the fault propagation anticline at sequence cycle scale; propagation of thrust branches at depositional sequence scale; growth faulting at paracycle scale. Finite deformation in thrust sheets may be quantified but the increments of deformation are not perceptible. Tectonic evolution of a fold-thrust complex appears to be continuous.

The forward propagation of a syn-depositional thrust-and-fold system in a basin (Fig. 8) is related to unconformable depositional sequence sets (Table 1), which fill foredeep sub-basins developed in a piggy-back mode. Basal unconformities mark the incipient compression in each sub-basin and age stepping indicates the complete growth of a thrust-and-fold system over a time span of several eustatic cycles (about 5 Ma in the studied case).

SOUTHERN PYRENEES		STRATIGRAPHY		NORTHERN PYRENEES	
THRUST SYSTEMS	TECTONIC DEPOSITIONAL SEQUENCE SETS	STAGES	EUSTATIC CYCLES HAQ & al.1987	TECTONIC DEPOSITIONAL SEQUENCE SETS	THRUST SYSTEMS
	II	DANIAN — 66,5	TA 1.2	67 II	PECH
	67		TA 1.1		DE FOIX
BOIXOLS (TAMURCIA)	68	MAASTRICHTIAN	UZA 4.5	68	PECH
	I 71		UZA 4.4	71 I	DE FOIX
		— 74 —			
— 75 —	75		UZA 4.3	75	
MIRALLES (PADARNIU)	III 77,5	CAMPANIAN	UZA 4.2	77,5 III	BENAIX
	79		UZA 4.1	79	
— 80 —	80		UZA 3.5	80	
TURBÓN	II 83		UZA 3.4	83 II	CROQUIER
		— 84 —			
— 85 —	85	SANTONIAN	UZA 3.3	85	
	87,5	— 88 —	UZA 3.2	87,5 I	CELLES
SAN GERVÁS	I 88,5	CONIACIAN	UZA 3.1	88,5	
— 89 —	89	— 89 —	UZA 2.7	89	
		TURONIAN	UZA 2.6		

(Southern sequence-set column vertical labels: ARÉN, ARGA, VALL C A. Northern sequence-set column vertical labels: PLAGNE, ALZEN. Northern thrust systems vertical label: NORTH PYRENEAN FRONTAL THRUST.)

Fig. 17. Time-correlation between depositional sequence sets and thrust systems in the two Late Cretaceous foredeeps of the Central Pyrenees (Spain and France).

The hindward imbrication in each thrust-and-fold system (Fig. 10) is related to unconformable depositional sequences (Table 1). Internal unconformities mark the syn-depositional uplift of anticlines, related to the propagation of thrust overstep branches. These unconformities indicate a time span sometimes as short as an eustatic cycle (about 0.5 to 5 Ma in the studied case).

Applied to the Central Pyrenees the model enables a reinterpretation of the structure and kinematic evolution of the two sides of the range (Fig. 17), in keeping with the concept of migrating foredeep basins from 89 Ma (Early Coniacian) and during the whole Senonian and Eocene times. Taking into account new observations on facies, stratigraphy and structure of Cretaceous series we have recognized two divergent Cretaceous thrust-and-fold belts, belonging to two piggy-back sequences: one, in the south-vergent Southern Pyrenees, detached on the Trias, and locally occurring like recumbent folds involved in an Eocene nappe; and the other in the north-vergent Northern Pyrenees, involving the basement (North Pyrenean massifs) and reactivated in an Eocene thrust fault zone. The north Pyrenean thrust-and-fold belt overlying the North Pyrenean Frontal Thrust, is related to the Cretaceous shortening (Fig. 15) and not to the Eocene shortening as previously suggested. Late Cretaceous Pyrenean Flysch represents turbidite series deposited in flexural basins linked to early stages of a piggy-back thrust-and-fold development.

It is now clear that the Pyrenean domain has undergone, during Senonian times, a significant shortening which generated north- and south-vergent compressive structures previously attributed to the Eocene (= 'Pyrenean') orogeny.

We thank an anonymous referee for constructive review of the manuscript. We are indebted to P. Eichene (CNRS) and A. Majesté-Menjoulas for their technical support.

References

BACHIANA, C. 1989. Etude séquentielle du Paléogène d'Aquitaine sud. *Strata*, **1** (5), 85–87.

BALLY, A. W. & SNELSON, S. 1980. Realms of subsidence. *Bulletin of Canadian Petroleum Geology*, **6**, 9–75.

BEN YAICH, A., DUEE, G., SOUQUET, P. & FONDECAVE-WALLEZ, M. J. 1989. Les grès de Zoumi: dépôt turbiditique d'une avant-fosse miocène (Burdigalien–Serravalien) dans le Rif occidental (Maroc). *Compte Rendus de l'Académie des Sciences, Paris, II*, **309**, 1819–1825.

BILOTTE, M. 1985. *Le Crétacé supérieur des plates-formes est-pyrénéennes*. Thesis Sc., University of Toulouse.

—— & SEGURA, F. 1991. Stratigraphie séquentielle des séries du Sénonien supérieur dans la zone sous-pyrénéenne (Petites Pyrénées et dômes annexes, SW France). *Compte Rendus de l'Académie des Sciences, Paris II*, **312**, 393–391.

BOYER, S. & ELLIOTT, D. 1982. Thrust systems. *American Association of Petroleum Geologists Bulletin*, **6**, 1196–1230.

CROCHET, B. 1989. *Molasses syntectoniques du versant nord des Pyrénées: la série de Palassou*. Thesis Sci., University of Toulouse, Doc. BRGM n° 199.

ECORS-TEAM. 1990. Ecors deep seismic data and balanced cross sections: geometric constraints on the evolution of the Pyrenees. *Tectonics*, **8**, 41–50.

FONDECAVE-WALLEZ, M. J. & SOUQUET, P. 1991. Signatures stratigraphiques de l'eustatisme et de la tectonique de chevauchement dans le Crétacé supérieur du versant nord des Pyrénées. Example de la Zone sous-pyrénéenne orientale (Corbières, France). *Compte Rendus de l'Académie des Sciences, Paris II*, **312**, 631–637.

——, —— & GOURINARD, Y. 1988. Synchronisme des séquences sédimentaires du comblement fini-crétacé avec les cycles eustatiques dans les Pyrénées centro-méridionales (Espagne). *Compte Rendus de l'Académie des Sciences, Paris, II*, **307**, 289–293.

——, —— & ——. 1989. Enregistrement sédimentaire de l'eustatisme et de la tectonique dans la série turbiditique du Crétacé des Pyrénées centro-Méridionales (Groupe de Vallcarga, n.gr., Espagne). *Compte Rendus de l'Académie des Sciences, Paris, II,* **309**, 137–144.

——, —— & ——. 1990. Sequence stratigraphy and grade-dating in the Senonian series from the South Pyrenees (Spain), the sedimentary record of eustasy and tectonics. *In*: GINS-BURG, P. N. & BEAUDOIN, B. (eds) *Cretaceous Resources, Events & Rhythms.* NATO ASI series, Serie C: Mathematical and Physical Sciences, **304**, 63–74, Kluwer Academic Publishers.

FRANCE GEOLOGICAL MAPS, 1/50 000: sheets: **1032**, Boulogne; **1054**, Montréjeau; **1033**, Le Fousseret; **1055**, St Gaudens; **1056**, Le Mas d'Azil; **1057**, Pamiers; **1075**, Foix; **1076**, Lavelanet. *Bureau de Recherches Géologiques et minières Ed.,* Orléans.

GARRIDO, A. 1973. *Estudio geological y relación entre tectónica y sedimentation del Secundario y Terciario de la vertiente meridional pirenaica en su zona central (provincias de Huesca y Lerida).* Tesis Doc. Fac. Cienc. Univ. Granada, Bibl. Geol. Univ. Barcelona.

GOURINARD, Y. 1983. Quelques vitesses d'évolution observées dans les lignées de foraminifères néogènes. Utilisations chronologiques. *Compte Rendus de l'Académie des Sciences, Paris, II,* **297**, 267–272.

HAQ, B. U., HARDENBOL, J. & VAIL, P. R. 1987. The chronology of fluctuating sea level since the Triassic. *Science,* **235**, 1156–1167.

JAMISON, W. R. 1987. Geometric analysis of fold development in overthrust terranes. *Journal of Structural Geology,* **9**, 207–219.

MEY, P. H. W., NAGTEGAAL, P. J. C., ROBERTI, K. H., HARTEVELT, J. J. P. 1968. Lithostrati-graphic subdivision of Post-Hercynian deposits in the South Central Pyrenees. *Leidse Geologische Meddelingen, Leiden,* **41**, 221–228.

MUTTI, E. & RICCHI LUCCHI, F. 1972. Le torbiditi dell'Apennino settentrionale: introduzione all'analisi di facies. *Mem. Soc. Geol. Italy,* **11**, 161–199 (1978, English translation by NILSEN, T. H., International Geology Review, **20**, 125–166).

PAPON, J. P. 1969. *Etude de la zone sud-pyrénéenne dans le massif du Turbón (Prov. de Huesca, Espagne)* Thesis 3° cycle, Université Toulouse.

PUIGDEFABREGAS, C. & SOUQUET, P. 1986. Tecto-sedimentary cycles and depositional se-quences of the Mesozoïc and Tertiary of the Pyrenees. *Tectonophysics,* **126**, 173–203.

RAMSAY, J. G. 1967. *Folding and Fracturing of Rocks.* McGraw-Hill, New York.

RIBA, O. 1976. Syntectonic unconformities of the Alto Cardener, Spanish Pyrenees: a genetic interpretation. *Sedimentary Geology,* **15**, 213–233.

SEGURET, M. 1972. *Etude tectonique des nappes et séries décollées de la partie centrale des Pyrénées.* Thesis Sci., Université Montpellier.

SIMO, A. 1985. *Secuencias depositionales del Cretácico superior de la Unidad del Montsec (Pirineo central).* Tesis Doct., University of Barcelona.

SOUQUET, P. & DERAMOND, J. 1989. Séquence de chevauchement et séquences de dépôt dans un bassin d'avant-fosse. Exemple du sillon crétacé du versant sud des Pyrénées (Espagne). *Compte Rendus de l'Académie des Sciences, Paris, II,* **309**, 137–144.

——, ESCHARD, R. & LODS, H. 1987. Facies sequences in large-volume debris-and-turbidity-flow deposits from the Pyrenees (Cretaceous; France, Spain). *Geomarine letters,* **7**, 83–90.

SPECHT, M. 1989. *Tectonique de chevauchement le long du profil ECORS-Pyrénées: un modèle d'évolution de prisme d'accrétion continental.* Thesis Univ. de Bretagne occidentale, Brest et Univ. de Toulouse.

——, DERAMOND, J. & SOUQUET, P. 1991. Relations tectonique-sédimentation dans les bassins d'avant-pays: utilisation des surfaces stratigraphiques isochrones comme marqueurs de la déformation. *Bulletin de la Société Géologique de France,* **162**, 553–562.

SUPPE, J. 1983. Geometry and kinematics of fault-bend folding. *American Journal of Science,* **283**, 684–721.

TAMBAREAU, Y. & VILLATTE, J. 1977. L'Eocène du domaine sous-pyrénées. *In*: JAFFREZO, M. (ed.) *Guide géologique régional: Pyrénées orientales–Corbières.* Masson Ed., Paris, 106–117.

VAIL, P. R. 1987. Seismic stratigraphy interpretation using sequence stratigraphy. Part I: Seismic stratigraphy interpretation procedure. *In*: BALLY, A. W. (ed.) *Atlas of Seismic Stratigraphy.* American Association of Petroleum Geologists, Studies in Geology, **27**, 1–10.

—— & EISNER, P. 1989. Stratigraphic signatures separating tectonic, eustatic and sedimentologic effects on sedimentary sections. Mesozoic eustacy record on western Tethyan margin. *2° Congrès français de Sédimentologie*, Lyon, abstracts, 62–64.

——, MITCHUM, R. M. Jr., TODD, R. G., WIDMIER, J. W., THOMPSON, S., SANGREE, J. B., BUBB, J. N. & HATELID, W. G. 1977. Seismic stratigraphy and global changes of sea level. *In*: CLAYTON, C. E. (ed.) *Seismic Stratigraphy. Application to Hydrocarbon Exploration.* American Association of Petroleum Geologists Memoir **26**, 49–212.

Index